Our Existence

Pt 2

The Nature and Origin of Life, Mind, and Soul

A straightforward and impartial guide to the science and philosophy of living things.

Christophe Finipolscie

Published by   Spontaneous Publications Ltd.,
                  Charter House, Marlborough Park, Southdown Road,
                  Harpenden, Herts., UK AL5 1NL
                  info@spontaneouspublications.com

First Edition January 2018
First published May 2018 – Imprint – Spontaneous Education

ISBN   978-0-9956491-5-6 standard Hardback full colour edition.

ISBN   978-0-9956491-6-3 standard Paperback full colour edition.

ISBN   978-0-9956491-9-4 primary electronic edition

A CIP catalogue record for this book is available from the British Library

CONTENTS

Foreword and Acknowledgements

We all come from a background which has given us abundant and direct experience of what life is, and perhaps even a basic understanding of how it operates. If the origin of Life can also be explained either by God or the Theory of Evolution, what more do ordinary people really need to know, (setting aside any particular needs for our jobs)?

Well of course, the fact that you've picked up this book shows that you have an additional level of interest in the nature of Life, because many unanswered questions remain on this vital & fundamental issue to us all.

The perceptions which we hold about Life influence the decisions that we take, so a better understanding of the facts & issues will hopefully lead us to better judgements on both a personal level and in the laws that our societies formulate. This goes well beyond the regulation of biological research and genetic engineering. The impacts are felt across the whole of our society: from our sense of morality, to everyday choices about what we buy, (eg. do we prefer experiences/holidays to goods?). In some countries this has even led to law suits that include passionate debates about the nature and origin of life.

Sadly these things can often be shrouded by issues of faith, (whether secular or religious). However some of us, who are not driven by such fervour, just want to know the facts plus an honest assessment of where the facts run out, in order to make up our own minds about what to believe.

I remember a series of newspaper and magazine articles, plus several TV programmes between the mid 1970s and early 1990s which effectively stated that the only explanations for life were to be found in the chemistry of our bodies plus evolution, and that anything which seemed to contradict that view in our daily lives was an illusion, (such as 'Free Will'; the mind; passion; randomness; control; or even love). Furthermore those aspects of our lives should be ignored as they weren't proper evidence.   Mmmm.

We are getting to the heart of why I began to write this book.

- Firstly, I was concerned by arguments and legal cases which seemed to be driven by popular misconceptions, and avoided some of the real underlying issues which are not being properly debated in public.
- Secondly, almost all of the books which I have read on this subject tend to promote a narrow interpretation of the facts in support of the author's favoured theory. I haven't come across any that attempted to present all of the viable alternatives in a balanced and fair way.
- Thirdly, I was annoyed by an increasing number of 'expert' claims that my experiences in life were not valid evidence, and that certain aspects of my existence should be dismissed out of hand as an illusion because it didn't suit their theory... yet I didn't know the alternatives.

There is clearly a balance to be struck between accepting the knowledge of experts, and being empowered to think for ourselves, yet we can't decide where that balance point is if we're not given the relevant facts within a framework that can allow us to interpret them. That is my objective.

I wanted to know all views, plus the key facts which they have to accommodate. If I then wrote them out I could also share those findings with you, because they are not always easy things to uncover, and take a lot of time to accumulate.

One of the big things I learned about this subject, and indeed the broader topic of 'our existence', is that *nobody* is an expert on all of it. Even top scientists can only claim expertise in fairly narrow areas. So whoever writes on this subject needs other people's help.

In this 'quest' I have been assisted by a number of people who have not only shared their expertise with me, but have also dedicated a significant amount of their time to read and sometimes re-read the text. In this respect I have to extend particular thanks to

  Dr. J.Francis, Dr. A.Punter, Mr. C.Huckle, and Mrs. S.Myers

I would particularly like to thank one other senior scientist from the world of biochemistry, who was also incredibly helpful but has preferred to remain anonymous. Again – I am very grateful for your help.

I also need to thank my wife who has had to put up with many lonely evenings and disturbed nights while I wrote this series of books. Without her tolerance these would still be an idea rather than a reality.

To everyone involved I can't thank you enough for all your efforts.

The people involved in this book represent a broad cross-section of opinion. Using their different perspectives I have therefore tried hard to be impartial, and if I seem to have wobbled slightly in places through a particular choice of words then I apologise, it wasn't my intention.

I would therefore like to make it clear that neither I, nor any of the reviewers, endorse any particular viewpoint, but we have tried to fairly reflect the different philosophies.

C.Finipolscie

November 2017

1 Setting the Scene

Welcome to this study of the most important factor in existence - Life.

We care about the physical environment because it sustains us, and it is a source of interest and amusement for us, but our lives as well as those of the ones we love are our prime focus.

We cherish the rich experiences that life brings, and whether they are good or bad it is those very experiences which set life apart from the purely physical side of our universe. Rocks and chemicals may exist and function, but they are not conscious of reality.

This is what will lead many people to believe that Life is fundamentally different to physical matter. Life is special.

This book will explore the full *range* of scientific and philosophical thinking about what Life is and where it may have come from. Along our journey we will also encounter the mysteries of the Mind which reveal some special characteristics that appear to defy physical explanation.

You may have also noticed from the title of the book that I will be asking you to consider one other possibility within Life – the Soul. I do not do this lightly, or out of any religious fervour. I do it because of the growing body of *scientific* evidence which is actually beginning to support the possibility that souls may exist, contrary to many people's expectations.

There isn't a vast amount of this evidence, and it cannot be regarded as proof, but it *is* both credible and remarkable, so it needs to be explained one way or another – which is still proving rather elusive by traditional scientific means.

Having said this, I want to be clear that I will *not* be conducting a religious debate, even if some of the issues will be of interest to both secular and religious beliefs. We will be looking at the evidence available and seeing where it might lead us both in terms of challenges as well as opportunities. You are then free to make your own informed decision.

Atheism is a faith as much as any religion as neither can prove their case. We should also be clear that Atheism denies God, but it is entirely possible for atheists to believe in the existence of souls – as in the case of Jainism. The world is a very diverse place that provides a full spectrum of opinion.

While the expertise of science is to determine facts, there are still many gaps in our knowledge which inevitably lead to speculation, especially from scientists who discover new things. This is where people enter the realm and the expertise of philosophy.

Philosophy isn't religion. It shows all of the different viewpoints from which facts can be interpreted, based on 'abstract' logic rather than doctrine.

For this reason, both scientific and religious perspectives can find their place within it. Philosophy places a framework around the unknown.

So to this extent, science and philosophy should work together to improve our understanding. From this I hope you will gather that I am not here to promote any cause or single view. I am genuinely interested in the full range of available ideas, and in having an honest debate, 'warts and all'.

My aim is to present the main facts in clear language so that everyone can understand the evidence and the issues, and how they all relate to each other, which you can then investigate further if you wish. Although I can only present you with a snapshot of what is known, it will at least enable you to observe and assess the changes in thinking going forwards.

I think it is reasonable to suppose that most ancient religions emerged from attempts to explain the unknown at a time when there was very little robust science available. It's therefore not surprising that when true facts about our physical existence were uncovered, many aspects of religious doctrine that concerned the nature of the physical world either had to be modified or be seen as metaphors. But that's not true of all religious beliefs. Other aspects have stood the test of time, and indeed scientists have poached many religious concepts over the years to explain new discoveries, such as:-

- the notion that our physical reality is made up of atoms, which first emerged 2,500 years ago in the religious philosophy of Atomism[1].
- terms such as awareness and consciousness which also emerged from religious debate, and are now prompting scientific analysis.

So science is not atheism. It's findings about the reality of our existence, (the reality of God's creation if you choose to think of it that way), point in both directions and after disproving a number of incorrect religious pronouncements it is now disproving some atheistic notions as well, (eg. we now know that the Universe/outer space is probably infinite after all, and the physical matter within it may, in more than one way, have had a true beginning, instead of an eternal existence – see Book 1 of this series).

There is no doubt that in many countries scientific thinking has come to dominate popular perceptions, and this is because its 'Laws of Physics, Chemistry, and Biology' have accurately **predicted** how the natural world operates and can be manipulated, allowing us to develop modern technology as well as many reliable medical treatments, etc.

Yet there are still many substantial grey areas in our understanding as some issues are hard to investigate, and other **facts** directly challenge some atheistic **principles**. Many of these can still be found in debates about Life. Science will continue to make progress in understanding our reality, but we should be cautious not to dismiss some valid philosophical ideas just because they seem more closely aligned with some religious thinking.

A good idea is a good idea, regardless of where it came from, and the ideas don't have to point to God as the only alternative. There are other options.

I suspect that the difficulty has been in seeing a need for these alternate possibilities, as well as turning them into a practical rationale that can fit in with scientific thinking and evidence. But the tide has been turning thanks to surprising discoveries over the past 30 years or so. We will look at some of these ideas shortly.

This is the 2nd book of my short series that will help you form an understanding of our existence. The first volume considered the nature of the sterile chemicals which make up both our environment and our bodies. It showed that there are numerous unresolved *scientific* findings which directly challenge our accepted perception of what physical reality may be.

These point to deeper capabilities and enigmas which may ultimately resolve the mystery of what our physical environment is... but will they also explain Life?

> Inevitably, these books share some common themes, because they are closely linked. To this extent the first couple of chapters in each book will introduce basic concepts that underpin all lines of enquiry even if they are presented with a slightly different slant.
> However later chapters will be quite distinct.

Let me also state a convention that I use throughout the book :
- I will refer to *mechanisms* with a capital letter, (eg. Thought, Time, Life), and
- their *effects* in lower case, (eg. our thoughts, the passage of time, or the presence of life and living things).

There is clearly a balance to be struck between accepting the knowledge of experts, and being empowered to think for ourselves, yet we can't decide where that balance point is if we're not given the relevant facts within a framework that can allow us to interpret them. That is my objective.

Yet I have also been concerned by some of the 'misconceptions' which have been advanced in popular culture, and even some of the media on occasions. We are often portrayed as being glorified robots or even worse, a rather incredible bag of chemicals which has somehow organised itself through the process of evolution. But essentially, it all boils down to chemistry and mechanics... doesn't it?

Well, maybe not. When the chemistry and mechanics don't explain what is happening in our bodies, and some of the mechanisms inside us leave us both astonished, and potentially beyond the abilities of Matter/Energy then there is pause for thought.

Those who then dig deeper find other surprises, because at a conceptual level too, there are a number of unresolved issues. For instance, when I first set-out on this path 30 years ago it became apparent that contrary to popular opinion, the current scientific mechanism of Evolution *cannot* explain the origin of life.

To quickly prove my point, a whole new branch of science (Abiogenesis) has since been opened- up to try to resolve the gaping chasm in theory that exists in this respect. I am not being antagonistic here; this is a scientific acknowledgment of the problems.

Evolution is a process of change, but it isn't really a process of 'start'

Of course, this is contrary to the popular belief that evolution <u>can</u> explain the origin of Life, but the original theory didn't claim that. The desire for an explanation of origin is an extension to the main theory, and while that may be based on logical assumptions, the single mechanism that we have for Evolution **cannot** work before the first cell – so there is no known way to achieve the first living cell – which was probably incredibly complex.

On this theme, I remember a TV programme where a well known British atheist went to the US in support of the Pro-Evolution debate, and was taken to meet a scientist who also held religious views. The celebrity opened-up by asking the guest how a man of science could possibly question the logic of evolution, as an explanation for the origin of Life? The reply was as surprising and devastating as it was simple: "The Ribosome" he said.

The look on the celebrity's face said it all, as he muttered something along the lines of "Oh, but I'm sure science will find an answer to that in due course." before there was a quick cut to another theme.

Ribosomes are miniscule factories within each living cell, (true programmable assembly lines with moving parts and all), which have tremendous complexity and importance. No living cell can work without them, (yet there is no known way for them to suddenly exist), and each of the three main branches in the tree of life have their own distinct version, with **no** apparent evolutionary path between them either, (see Ch. 5 - 7).

So there are people within science who raise valid questions about the story we are being given. They illustrate why some religious notions have not been disproven and why other scientific explanations may be needed.

However I must be fair to the celebrity and point out that **since** then there have been developments in research which now **hint** at an earlier type of evolutionary process for the ribosome, <u>before</u> the first living cells emerged - even if scientists have no idea what that other process may have been.

While there is no doubt that most scientists expect Abiogenetic research to succeed in producing an explanation of the origin of Life, based on the deeper principles of Evolution; that is not guaranteed within the confines of physical matter alone.

The debate is far from over, and new ideas are beginning to emerge.

We shouldn't underestimate the challenges involved because this is not a simple search for a few tantalizingly obscure chemical reactions. The issues go well beyond that. As you read the book you will come to realise the enormous barriers which had to be overcome to get life going, and yet we currently have no viable idea how that was done. The eventual explanation is expected to have several key elements from :

- a series of physical processes, to
- a number of conceptual and philosophical issues, which are still real none-the less.

Alternative answers to mainstream scientific theory **do not** have to involve God, but clearly, there are many people with religious views, about a divine creator, who will hold different hopes/expectations about the outcome of future scientific findings. That is equally fine. Yet the options do not stop there because Buddhism, Taoism, and others offer even more possibilities.

To avoid me getting embroiled in debates about whether God exists or not, I will adopt the position that to achieve certain things in nature, certain logical **capabilities** must exist. It is then your choice whether to attribute those capabilities to God or something more mundane.

Yet to all sides I will say that if something is shown to be a fact, it is wrong to dismiss it on the basis of dogma alone. All facts should be explained.

Facts by their nature are robust, (although they may be perceived and explained in different ways). Other statements will ultimately be shown **not** to be facts due to fraud or speculation, but genuine raw facts don't change – ever. Let me explain further.

> If you put something into a process and get a particular result, that is a fact which will not change, and must be explained even if we later find that there were errors or other things involved which we were originally unaware of. Yet if there are no errors, the facts become an absolute part of our reality which cannot be ignored.

I feel it's dishonest to ignore facts that don't fit your theory, and to present only part of the story simply because it suits your preferences.

An interpretation of experimental results can also lead us to a concept about what is going on, and we can be so familiar with an interpretation that people can often mistake it for a fact, *when it isn't*. For instance, something may be deemed impossible, (an opinion), but if later evidence then arises (facts) which shows that it **is** possible after all, then our ideas have to change, even if we don't yet know how that something is achieved. The new facts do not invalidate the old ones, they merely change the context in which we try to make sense of them. By way of example:

> It was once declared that no life could naturally exist in very high temperatures, without light, and in toxic chemicals... yet we now know that bacteria can live & thrive in the waste of nuclear reactors, (Deinococcus Radiophilus)[12], and there is life around deep sea volcanic vents in the midst of chemicals that are highly toxic to us, where temperatures are also several hundred degrees centigrade.

The earlier facts have not changed – only the interpretation of their context. It remains true that the types of life we were previously considering could not exist in those conditions, but the 'new' forms of life which we have identified, can.

So in any particular declaration we have to separate fact from interpretation. In these cases, only the raw experimental results would be a fact. We also have to be careful in the way that we phrase things, for instance :-

it would be wrong to claim that a fact has changed because (say) Pluto is no longer a planet, or that 'tomatoes are now a fruit rather than a vegetable'. Nothing has happened to Pluto or tomatoes. It is the way that we perceive them that has changed, and the earlier facts still stand; they <u>were</u> labelled that way on the earlier categorizations.

On the other hand, if there's any reasonable doubt about something it can't be a fact. So when something **is** correctly labelled as a fact it has particular significance, and should not be dismissed out of hand.

I say all this because life has a particular habit of not conforming to established rules – especially in relation to some key issues. The real science you will read about in this book is beginning to support old ideas about the nature of life which reflect more abstract philosophical thinking. There are facts which have to be explained.

I ask you to remember this when we consider contentious issues such as the Theory of Evolution, the origin of the first cell, or the scientifically gathered evidence suggestive of Souls.

While we each have different inclinations about our beliefs/preferences, an objective mind should recognise that if two theories both explain all of the facts then they are equally valid in principle, and neither should be dismissed, even if one is not 'flavour of the month'.

Put another way, there should be valid reasons for saying that one viewpoint is less credible than the other, and if you are honest with yourself about the factors which you feel are 'key points of difference' they will help you gauge your own bias as well as providing clarity about the broader points of relevance to the issue.

It is also important to consider the limits of certain arguments and how far they might reasonably be taken. For instance, it's very easy for people to assume that a description is an explanation and that formulae are proof rather than theory.

While I will try hard to give each perspective a fair hearing, we need to bear in mind that some philosophies have existed for a lot longer than others, and these will tend to have more arguments in their armoury. So if I spend longer discussing some subjects rather than others it will not reflect bias. Equally we can say that if, after many centuries, a philosophy **hasn't** been able to explain a particular issue very well, this may point to a real problem with that perspective.

New findings emerge on a regular basis, so I can only present you with a snapshot, however this book should enable everyone to place all evidence within a range of opinion, and thereby interpret its significance.

You will see from these opening paragraphs that this book is not particularly concerned about human politics or the actual choices that we make. Yet I will occasionally use those things to illustrate 'alternate mechanisms' or 'unknown capabilities' at work in the real world.

As we consider the tally of such points, including awkward facts and the enormous odds against life emerging from 'random processes', you will become truly awed by the question of how it could ever have begun.

By necessity our 'journey' will involve touching on beliefs that you may not agree with, and may even find fanciful, but I ask you to give each notion a fair hearing as you may well be surprised at the emerging evidence which lends support to some of those less familiar views.

I also ask that you do not fall for the smear campaigns of those who wish to discredit other beliefs rather than disprove them. A good idea is a good idea, regardless of where it came from.

In ancient times when comparatively little was known about the nature of the physical world, the blind were effectively leading the blind and some very inaccurate and discredited beliefs served to tarnish the reputations of both science and philosophy. For instance, the Earth is not flat, and the sun isn't pulled around it by the chariots of the Gods.

In modern times however, much more is known and proven about our physical environment, so the speculation is limited to quite discreet areas, and the justifications for our theories have to be much more robust.

The fact that many philosophies remain viable today means that they still offer reasonable explanations within the knowledge that we currently have... and this is true of ideas which may sound very strange at first hearing. The verdicts we all have to reach concern how well each of the arguments fits the facts, and whether we feel that the gaps could potentially be bridged by a particular theory's **principles** in future. That is a dynamic process as new facts and ideas are uncovered on a regular basis.

All of this seriousness may leave you feeling that the topic will be heavy and boring, but there are many remarkable findings within this subject so you will find many ideas interesting, engaging, and even entertaining.

In order to set us off in the right spirit let me end this chapter with an old joke to illustrate the point about different perspectives:

The First Law of Philosophy: For every philosopher, there exists an equal and opposite philosopher.

The Second Law of Philosophy: They're both wrong.

2 The Philosophical Range

When people try to imagine what has happened in the past either to establish a sequence of events, or even a cause/start point, they need a set of rules with which to do so. Those rules must provide a fixed pattern that we can extend backwards in time; because that is the only basis on which to speculate about earlier steps in a process.

It is therefore necessary to find out what something **is**, plus the rules by which it operates, **before** we can speculate about its origin.

The principle of strict 'Causality' has been very important in this respect because it says that **one** precise set of starting conditions can **only** result in **one** specific outcome. However as outcomes themselves may not be unique, (ie. they could have been achieved in different ways), the 'backwards view' is a little more complex to determine than working forwards. Yet if you know the factors at play when events occurred, you can have a pretty good guess at which starting circumstances could have led to the later situation.

So what can we 'reverse engineer' in our search for an origin of Life?

As already discussed, physical matter must be part of our story because all life on Earth is based on a physical body. That body is based on atoms, molecules, and energy, which should *always* operate within a fixed set of rules, called 'The Laws of Physics', (and for our level of reality, these are all based on causality). So, looking back into the *physical* past **is** theoretically possible, if we can be sure that we know all of the physical influences involved at each historical point in time... but that's still quite a challenge, due to the complexity and fluidity of events.

Yet some of the special aspects of Life, (which we will consider later), are so distinct, they suggest that **other** hidden factors may be at work, and operating by **different rules**. We will be considering the evidence for such claims, because if valid, they will make our view into the past more complex.

Whether we are thinking about 'other types of stuff' that underpin existence, or indeed the nature of God, people will set their own standards concerning what is 'reasonable' evidence, but it **is** fair to say that many more people will be persuaded by factors that are logical and go beyond wishful thinking.

Equally, we cannot sensibly argue that something is truly special if it merely represents a new combination of **known factors** that we haven't seen before. New combinations arise all the time; they're not *that* special.

We are only likely to demonstrate something distinct if the evidence for it challenges the *principles* by which physical reality is supposed to work.

By identifying the characteristics or abilities which seem to go beyond Matter/Energy, we not only develop a better awareness of what makes Life special, but can also focus our search for the source of those specific capabilities.   So let's begin.

2.1 <u>Awareness, Control, and Thought</u>

Consciousness: That annoying time between naps. (Anon.)

When people are asked to identify the main distinguishing factor about Life, many will say 'consciousness'. To me, this is a term which combines a number of more elementary factors – ie. awareness, control, and thought.

Yet these are terms that are generally applied to the 'higher' forms of life: creatures, rather than plants or bacteria. In seeking special characteristics that apply to all forms of Life we need to delve deeper: either looking for other factors; or more typically, looking at the three elements above to see if they can be applied more crudely than in full blown consciousness.

Awareness is our ability to sense and understand both ourselves and the broader environment in which we exist. Our bodies provide 5 senses to do this, (touch, taste, sight, smell, and hearing), and we also have a Mind with which to interpret what we sense. For the purposes of this book and in the absence of other suitable terms, I suggest that the 'understanding' behind awareness can have different levels of sophistication: as basic as 'do what?' or 'where next?' - evidenced by choices or maintaining a course.

If two rocks collide they will not sense each other, but if a living being comes into contact with a rock, only the being will be aware of that event. Yet modern cars have proximity sensors for parking, and if they collide, these metal objects will also be able to sense that the event has occurred, to deploy an air bag & potentially alert the emergency services automatically.

So physical matter *can* be structured to detect events but does this equate to awareness? Does this mean that modern cars have 'physical Minds', (in the shape of the computers that control their senses and actions)? That's a point of debate which we will explore later but it is safe to say that a computer chip is not the same as a Mind in the way that reality is ***experienced***. A computer may detect red light or the fumes given off by cooking but it won't have an emotional preference for the colour, or react in the same way to (say) the smell of frying bacon.

A computer chip will merely be acting out a fixed set of instructions based on its programming. It may 'detect' but it will not 'feel', and it will not understand. In contrast insects and even single celled organisms can recognise threats and opportunities: showing a degree of understanding even if only at a crude level. Individual cells also seem able to do this.

We don't know what plants experience, but they can detect which way is 'up' when sending up first shoots, and which way they need to face to gain sunlight. They can send out roots to find more nutrient, which can also avoid bad ground such as gravel; and they can compete with other plants for terrain. Even mosses and bacteria can adapt and evolve to match their environment. So awareness seems more than just a basic chemical reaction, but it also needs to be combined with other things to achieve consciousness.

Control is what we seek when trying to create favourable conditions to preserve life, or to generate effects that we find pleasing or desirable. Yet this is not a factor which is confined to the brain. We see control in the very smallest building blocks of physical life: living cells. Cells do not have brains or even Minds as far as we can tell, but the evidence for control and even purpose is very apparent in many aspects of their complex operations. Control is not generally regarded as something which acts like clockwork, (going off at regular intervals). Control adapts to different circumstances.

Thought is both a way to generate ideas/concepts, as well as a way to initiate actions that help us to survive in, and influence, the wider world.

Most people will instinctively feel that these three factors have a common theme linked to the special nature of consciousness, and for this reason it's an obvious possibility that they are all part of the same mechanism which allows these things to happen. The question is – what is that mechanism?

2.2 A Range of Thinking

In terms of gauging the significance of different events, the emergence of Life can be equated with the emergence of the physical Universe as one of the major 'start points' in existence. It is a massive step-change in activity.

If something 'starts' it only has two philosophical ways in which it might come about. It either represents:-

- a transformation of things which already existed,   or
- a moment of pure, spontaneous creation, (by divine or other means)

'True Beginnings' are very significant to our understanding of existence because if they move us away from an inevitable outcome, they directly challenge the principle of causality. Does Life represent such a change?

As already mentioned the physical element of both our reality and our bodies, Matter/Energy, is deemed to operate entirely within the principle of 'cause & effect', (Causality, and the philosophy of 'Determinism').

Those who have a deeper understanding of physics may say that the principles of causality **can** be broken by the behaviour of sub-atomic particles inside an atom, (a 'lower level of reality'), but we have to be careful when saying this.

There **are** results from experiments on sub-atomic particles that do not seem to conform to the principle of causality, **but** that is largely because we don't exactly know what is happening at that level of reality. We **can't** see it directly, and may not know everything that's involved because of that; so scientists are still formulating theories about what is happening. Science will extend its use of causality as far as it can, but in this deeper realm it has to live with uncertainty.

Just because we can't see & **predict** what a particle will do, it doesn't mean that it's operating 'outside the rules' that apply everywhere else.

It is vital to be clear about what causality means, so let me quickly restate the specifics: Scientists say that **one** very precise start point can only lead to **one** precise and inevitable outcome, and that everything must have a **prior cause**. The opposites of 'cause & effect' are therefore:-

- Spontaneity - something happens without a cause
- Randomness - a precise start point can have more than one outcome.

In those situations where we **do** naturally think of there being a *range* of possible outcomes, Determinism, says that there must in fact be something slightly different in each starting situation - such as an additional influence that we didn't fully appreciate or know about.

In other words, physical events can have outcomes which we *cannot yet predict* because we don't know all of the factors involved, but ultimately, if you did know all of the facts, you'd see that they are inevitable. Eg:-

> Lottery machines try to mimic random activity, but are actually just *unpredictable* in their outcomes. If we choose the example of stirring-up balls in a drum, it's very difficult to monitor what is happening exactly, but if we did, science could tell you precisely why we got each lottery result as each ball was pushed with different strengths from different angles.
>
> Truly *spontaneous* and *random* behaviour would be if the lottery balls were not stirred and one just jumped up and selected itself. Another example would be if one pool ball was struck by another at a specific angle, and it could potentially head towards any pocket instead of just being able to head for one pocket.

Of course we don't see random acts like this occurring in physical matter but we <u>can</u> see it occurring in Thought. If you put a ball in the middle of a circular room with ten identical doors it won't suddenly head for one of them, but a living being might. Their sudden decision to move 'now' rather than 'then' would be spontaneous, (without an external prompt), and the choice of door would be random – regardless of the knowledge they brought with them. (The 'straight ahead and then count along' option still begins with a random start point and requires the additional choice of a random number).

In contrast, even a motorised and computer-controlled ball could only follow pre-coded fixed instructions *immediately* and would have no basis on which to make a genuine random choice of door, (ie. its 'count along' option would be based on a number that could not be truly random).

So we begin to see how opinions may diverge about what is happening.

'**Materialism**' is a philosophy which believes that everything must come from Matter/Energy – a view that is largely justified on the basis of Einstein's equation $E=MC^2$, which tells us that mass and energy are interchangeable. Materialism accepts the principles of determinism, and it is a very good philosophy which underpins most scientific investigations –

as long as you accept that **everything** shares the same set of characteristics and principles, (an opportune moment to say that not all scientists are fully fledged determinist/materialists)!

Materialists generally argue that existence is part of a never ending process that has a strictly controlled level of change, which can only produce **one inevitable outcome** - a fixed eternal script that we are acting out.

The main alternative opinion is that true change and truly new beginnings are real within the physical realm, and that outcomes are **not** inevitable. Logically this would have to represent one of two things:-

- another hidden element of existence within or outside the Universe whose influence provides a cause that we simply cannot detect, **or**
- another type of stuff within the Universe which enables truly spontaneous start points, or multiple outcomes (randomness).

Experience tells us that the Materialist view is generally correct for the *physical* events that occur in our daily lives, but is it true of everything?

Book 1 pointed out some mainstream scientific findings from cosmology that appear to be either *true start points* or *moments of dramatic change* that are **not** obviously linked to the known capabilities of the Universe. These have forced traditional ideas about a Big Bang origin to change.

In seeking ways to explain these new findings some scientists have literally invented new aspects of 'reality' such as 'Dark Energy' or 'additional dimensions of existence' to provide hidden causes that might explain events, without breaking the current Laws of Physics. (Neither of these two conceptual things currently have any *direct* evidence to support them).

Yet, we don't have to travel to the far reaches of the cosmos or into the depths of academic research to find examples which are 'closer to home', (that touch our everyday lives), but which also seem to require more of these hidden factors... and again, not all scientists are Materialists...

A truly new idea that pops into your head would be a moment
of pure creation that science cannot explain
and which Materialists deny as ever really happening.

So one downside to Materialist thinking is that everything you do and everything you think must be part of their **inevitable** process: including the music of Mozart and the Beatles; the creativity of artists such as Picasso; the genius of Einstein; or even whether to scratch that itch now or later.

Materialism may ultimately be shown to be correct, but as things stand it seems to contradict some of our normal perceptions of life because our working assumption is: that we **are** able to make free choices between *different outcomes* that are possible from the *same* start point.

Society even structures its laws to make us responsible for our actions because it believes that we do have Free Will – ie. that life **does not** result in an inevitable outcome.

If we were to fully adopt Materialist thinking our laws might seem completely wrong, as punishing wrongdoers or praising geniuses might seem inappropriate if we were all acting out a fixed script and *people had no real choice in what they did*. This illustrates a core dilemma – and perhaps the split personality of our society. ☺

If you can demonstrate that either spontaneity or randomness are truly happening at our level of reality, then you must consider that something other than atoms, molecules, and 'electron exchanges' are responsible. Whatever that may be, (even if it is a hidden interaction with the 'Quantum' (ie. sub-atomic) level of existence), it would represent another core part of reality whose characteristics could manifest themselves in other circumstances.

The intangible processes of our thoughts have always provided the richest source of potential examples for spontaneity & randomness, which is why Materialists have previously claimed that these 'awkward' experiences are not really happening and are therefore **not** evidence - just an illusion. Again - they argue that there will always be a prior cause for every thought, and that the logical choices we make will always be inevitable.

We will test this thinking shortly. For the time being let me say this: if anyone suggests that we should simply dismiss all the experience of our everyday lives, from every person who has ever lived - that is a big ask. What level does the evidence have to reach before we can consider that the currently defined 'Laws of Physics' may only be part of the story?

As you can imagine, the debate is still very active, but those who believe in other factors beyond Matter/Energy have produced a range of ideas/ philosophies to re-interpret the facts that science has uncovered. These are **not** just wishful thinking because there are scientific findings which appear to support these concepts, which Materialism cannot yet explain.

It's important to understand this *range* of ideas because the facts & concepts we will encounter later are going to push your boundaries, and it is useful to know where other possibilities might lie.

Put another way, it's important to know the extremes in order to make sense of the middle ground.

So to give us a basic flavour of the range, let's begin with the polar opposite viewpoint to Materialism – ie. Idealism.

Idealism, (in its more extreme form - Metaphysical Solipsysm), suggests that our entire perception of physical existence is merely an illusion/image generated by our Minds. When Rene Descartes[4] asked what we can truly believe about the fundamentals of our reality, he took things back to first principles and began with the following base position:

I think, therefore I am.

We are all born into the middle of an existence which we then have to understand, and that begins in the way that our minds interpret the signals they receive. It **is** our true base point, as Rene Descartes pointed out.

If we judge everything by our mental impression/image of reality, the question then becomes – how can we **prove** that physical matter is real and has true substance? Extreme forms of Idealism basically suggest that we can't do so and that **all** reality is just an image within the 'stuff of Thought'.

The ever-present impact of our physical environment is so dominant in our lives that many people will roll their eyes at this point thinking how can anyone realistically believe that it isn't real? But entertaining films such as 'The Matrix' have shown how this could be achieved in practise, all-be-it with a fun twist that allowed both sides of the argument to co-exist... (neatly avoiding the potential for alienating one part of the target audience)!

In essence, this philosophy suggests that the ***illusion*** of structure & solidity is achieved through fixed rules in the way that our Minds manipulate ideas.

To be honest, this remains a very unpopular notion, however it **is** a logical possibility that still matches the evidence, so rather than junk the idea altogether it can be useful to accept it as one of the **outer markers** of the range of thinking. Let me clarify this a little more.

Both Materialism and Idealism are referred to as 'monist' philosophies – because they both advocate just one type of underlying stuff. It's just that they have very different ideas about what that stuff represents.

> Because constant references to 'underlying stuff' can seem very tedious, most commentators will adopt a convention that short-cuts the conversation by only referring to Matter/Energy or Thought rather than the underlying essence on which they are based – so please try to interpret me correctly if I slip into this terminology to keep the text flowing!

Dualism recognises all of the characteristics which justify these polarised philosophies: asking why make a choice? Why not have both Matter/Energy and Thought as a way of explaining all aspects of existence? Dualists can also illustrate why both influences may be necessary, with ideas such as:-

Thought is the only thing that can cause Matter/Energy to deviate from its inevitable chemical path.

Put another way, Dualists suggest that while Matter/Energy brings stability, Thought, (as a potential source of spontaneity or randomness, and perhaps the *only* source), is the stuff capable of bringing true change: altering the rules and thereby altering the inevitable script... evolution[2]?

Dualist thinking has been extended to form other '***Pluralist***' philosophies which argue that there may be *many other* types of fundamental stuff in existence – each with their own distinct characteristics, (eg. Time).

The evidence and ideas are explored in more detail within Book 1 but for our purposes it is sufficient to remain with the basic range of possibilities which can be illustrated in the following diagram:

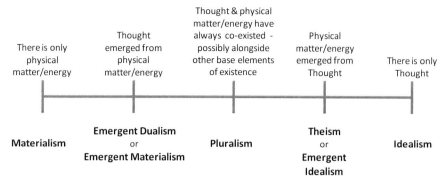

In effect, Dualism is a sub-set of Pluralism which argues that the different types of stuff may have *always co-existed*, however it is Dualism that most often features in debates, because it represents the most obvious middle ground between the polar extremes of Materialism and Idealism.

Yet we have to refine our thinking a little more as the range doesn't just represent a series of discreet options. There are graduations on the scale, and these are generally interpreted to suggest that one or other type of 'base' stuff may have *emerged/evolved* from one of the others, (which was more fundamental), before they became entirely distinct from each other.

On the diagram you will see that 'Emergent Materialism' suggests that Thought may have come from Matter/Energy; while it is in the realm of 'Emergent Idealism', (where Matter/Energy emerges from the stuff of Thought), that we find 'Theism' and ideas about God as the creator of physical existence.

I am not suggesting that any of these alternate perspectives are correct, but if the logic is sound, (and none of them have been disproven), then these alternate ideas all have validity because they all potentially fit the facts.

You should be able to position your own beliefs somewhere within the range, but as you progress through the book, the interesting thing will be to see if your perspectives change to slide further along the scale.

I find it significant that similar factors indicating that more than one type of substance may underpin existence, **do** seem to emerge across **all** fields of research. If they exist, such 'things' would indeed be more likely to exert their influence in all aspects of reality, not just one aspect of it.

This strengthens the credence of non-Materialist philosophies, but of course, that doesn't make them true! If nothing else, nobody can point to anything specific and say "There it is. This is the other type of substance we've been talking about". So I am just arguing for an open mind.

Strategically however, I find it remarkable that **all** of the different perspectives argue, in one respect or another, that **we are living in an illusion**. The illusions within Materialism and Dualism can be quite shallow because they accept that physical substance is real, but the illusions still exist, as demonstrated by scientific findings such as :

- objects are **not** solid in the way that we normally perceive them. Each atom is essentially a force field surrounding a lot of near empty space with a tiny dot of substance in the middle.

- objects may not have any colour because all of the colour is in the light that we detect bouncing off them.

I explore this a lot more in Book 1, but it is useful to liken our experience of physical reality to 'driving a car' rather than us having to focus on controlling every piston, pump, & spark. Illusion isn't necessarily a sinister thing, and in this case it can be quite helpful to our overall experience.

Alternately, Idealism suggests that by applying rules and structure to our thoughts we create the illusion of substance, stability, & order... instead of the chaos that our unrestricted imaginations would have on our sense of reality, (something we may indeed experience in dreams/nightmares).

The choice for you is to determine how deep the illusion might go, before you can then form an opinion about what our existence represents.

You will hopefully see why everyday experiences, as well as the latest scientific findings, may point to explanations that are 'further along the range' than you might expect.

The Theory of Evolution[2] has lots of evidence to support it, but it relies on things which are *assumed* to exist, yet are not necessarily explained or identified at this time. For instance, if you rely on a genetic mechanism to 'make a mistake' in order for the organism to evolve, how is such a mistake possible when there is only rigid cause & effect?

The most obvious answer is that external factors will interfere with the process, causing a change that wouldn't normally occur, and science has identified some possibilities. However we will see in Chapter 5 that various mechanisms within a cell **do** genuinely seem to make a mistake either in copying DNA code, or in undertaking a repair that is not correct.

Whether there are other more subtle influences that could explain these things, which scientists haven't yet identified, is unclear. The alternative is to say that Evolution requires a degree of spontaneity or randomness to occur... utilising something which is capable of such things.

Hopefully you can see why such issues have to reconcile potentially conflicting aspects of theory in order to bring credibility. That is why it is important to start with some of the basics before we consider the 'Higher' concepts of Life.

So is there any evidence for things/activities that go beyond the capabilities of Matter/Energy, which might explain the different nature of Life? The hunt is on!

(Those who have already read Book 1 may choose to skip to section 2.3 at this point).

2.2.1 Is there an Absence of Cause and Effect in Decision-Making?

You may have found the title of this section incredibly dull at first reading, but hopefully, from the previous section, you will understand why it is here and why it may in fact turn out to be quite interesting.

Those who believe in the Materialist philosophy of existence will see Life as a series of inevitable mechanical operations based in Matter/Energy. Others will believe that our day to day experiences of life demonstrate many wonderful and remarkable capabilities which Matter/Energy shouldn't be able to do, (according to Materialist thinking).

The base level question is whether those perceived 'special abilities' are real/genuine, because if they **can't** be truly demonstrated then why should we believe in them?

Materialism/Determinism says that a new idea must always have a prior cause, (you must always work up towards it), whereas spontaneity says that it can just pop into your head.

We can illustrate the differences through our use of computers which are programmed to operate in <u>fixed</u> ways, (even if they are set-up to identify different circumstances requiring different pre-determined responses).

If you imagine using your pc plus the fixed instructions that represent your word processing software, we can see that computers don't produce just one set text from this fixed routine. The range of written material coming off the printers is enormously varied. However the critical factor that changes the outcomes is the human user, who puts different things into that fixed process. Computers are not creative or spontaneous. People are... unless the principle of causality is true and we are all acting-out a script while living in an illusion.

Materialists have to prove strict cause & effect even in our thoughts, while Dualists/Idealists must prove that the principle of causality is being broken.

If even a single clear-cut example can be found to demonstrate that the true strict form of spontaneity or randomness exists, then it becomes very hard to deny that a second type of stuff, (or a separate aspect of existence), might also exist, together with its other special capabilities and influences.

As physical Matter/Energy, (especially in the form of atoms or bigger structures), is the primary way in which causality is demonstrated, it's not surprising that people look elsewhere for examples that 'break the mould'.

People familiar with physics may cite the decay of radioactive atoms as demonstrating truly random behaviour. In saying this they are arguing that we can never know which particular atom will decay at any particular moment, within a mass of radioactive material, and the pattern of decay is therefore an example of randomness.

Yet, 'knowing in advance' is a prediction and **unpredictability doesn't prove true randomness**.

Indeed, if there was true randomness, there shouldn't be a consistent rate of radioactive decay, (half-life), for each type of material – but there is, even if we can't predict when an individual atom will decay.

For this reason I find that Thought is often portrayed as the only *demonstrable* source of randomness and spontaneity in the Universe… assuming that those effects are indeed real and not an illusion.

We need some specific examples to prove a point one way or the other.

Yet that's not as easy as it may sound. In order to consider the arguments we first have to narrow the focus of the issues.

Let's assume for the moment that our Thoughts can indeed generate a new idea from scratch without a cause. In most cases we will be layering a new idea on top of an existing pool of background knowledge, a history of preferences, and some possible personal objectives to guide our choices. So it would be wrong to assume that any notion we might generate is *completely* original because we never start from a 'zero' position.

Let's say that I suddenly decide to go for a walk through the town. My pool of knowledge has allowed me to know that there is a town and that I have the ability to control my body sufficiently to move away from my present location. It has probably given me an outline of the possible routes I might take. I also know enough to interpret and navigate around the environment that I will encounter, even if it is unfamiliar.

If I was a highly sophisticated robot in a world entirely governed by cause and effect then everything would be pre-determined from the start. My decision to travel would be a response to a need for me to travel, and I would be pre-set to respond in an inevitable way to the circumstances that I would encounter en- route. To all intents and purposes the same journey might be undertaken whether or not I was a 'spontaneous' being. So where might the difference lie? What would make my thoughts different to such a robot?

If I am truly a spontaneous and free thinking being then I need to add or change something within the base position, and in this case the clearest demonstration of that ability would be in the original decision to undertake the journey in the first place. If there was no need for me to travel but I decided to do so anyway, where did that decision come from? Was it truly creative and spontaneous (ie. without cause), or was it an inevitable outcome from a complex series of circumstances that included my memories, the way I felt at that moment, and the things that I could sense from my surroundings?

Put another way, with 'strict cause and effect' the pot of circumstances doesn't change and events play out in an inevitable way against pre-set rules. The question of 'What set the rules' is open to debate later, but for the moment, if Dualists and Idealists are trying to demonstrate spontaneity, they have to distinguish the things that **change** or get **added** to either our knowledge or the background circumstances, in order to create a new scenario, no matter how small that may be.

In contrast, Materialists need to demonstrate that circumstances were following an inevitable pattern of cause & effect where pre-set causes would explain <u>every</u> situation, even if the people involved were not consciously aware of those factors.

A useful starting point is to consider how 'making a choice' from a range of similar options can lead to an <u>inevitable</u> outcome. Here the challenge for Materialists is to demonstrate that a free choice wasn't random. The standard argument used is that we will always rigorously apply a ***ranking*** to the options available and we will always choose the item at the top of the list, because it will reflect our best logical preference – making it an inevitable/unavoidable selection against the priorities of the moment.

> As an example, when faced with a range of drinks to choose from, we will assess how we feel, and then refer to our memories of what the different drinks tasted like to determine which is most likely to satisfy our preferences, needs, or desires of the moment – a ranking.

While this notion might seem perfectly reasonable we each have to decide whether it can be applied in every circumstance that we can think of, and whether the ***mechanism*** of prioritising things can be adequately supported by <u>identifiable</u> needs, preferences or desires that fit the moment.

Unfortunately, as you get deeper into this debate, you will see that examples arise where no obvious factors can be thought-of to rank the options, and it is often the case that in these circumstances Materialists will resort to comments such as 'a myriad of unknown influences' to explain a decision. You must ask yourself in each case whether that is a satisfactory explanation, or whether this points to an example of randomness or spontaneity.

In this battle-ground I think it's very hard to prove a case **unless you are able to strip away most, if not all, of the other potential influences on us**. To this end I have found that simple 'negative' examples are the most effective in demonstrating possible examples of spontaneity. That may not mean much to you now but a series of examples may illustrate what I'm getting at.

The challenge is on!

If you rank things, it would be fair to assume that you'd do so in 'order of preference' and therefore desirability. Yet it's an undisputed fact that we don't always choose the nicest options, (indeed, it's not unusual for people to select something which they actively dislike).

Such decisions can be done for logical reasons because something which we deem to be more important takes priority, as in the case of unblocking a drain. Yet in this case there's little alternative. We need to find examples where there are clear choices and yet people still take the counter-intuitive option – illustrating why there may be more than a simple ranking when we decide on something. Unfortunately the strongest examples are the starkest and they take us into uncomfortable territory. Apologies.

Let's start with the example of people choosing to have potentially painful or unpleasant forms of sex. I **am** talking about free choices here, not rape or other forced circumstances. So how could that be an inevitable free choice – top of the list?

Well there are many potential reasons, for instance :

- Wanting to please their partner whom they love.
- Curiosity.
- Wanting to prove that they can do it.
- They may like the idea, or even get something positive from it in some way.

As these examples show, in this and many similar circumstances Materialists can present numerous 'side issues/factors' that could take priority over the potential discomfort to justify the person's logical decision to accept an unpleasant experience. Only the individuals themselves will be able to judge whether those guessed reasons were correct, yet these factors do generally make random choices less believable.

Do 'ultimate choices' fare any better in demonstrating the ***potential*** for spontaneity or counter-intuitive decision-making?

> Deliberate self sacrifice on the battlefield is perhaps a stronger example. Such acts can be even more difficult to explain where the dead soldier has saved somebody he was known to actively dislike and whom he could have allowed to be killed instead.
>
> What about the sniper who sees the order to withdraw but decides to stay in an area being overrun by the enemy, from which there is no real prospect of escape later?
>
> We can speculate about: 'purely following routine'; or 'an overwhelming hatred of the enemy'; or standing up for a principle; simply making a mistake; or a desire to end it all. But we shouldn't dismiss the possibility that individuals may simply make a different choice which may be 'random'.

Even so, these examples still leave some room to doubt that the decision was spontaneous rather than inevitable. We need to look elsewhere.

The simplest examples can often be the strongest ones to establish evidence for an effect, and they may also show that if spontaneity or randomness are indeed possible then they may not be rare events at all. By way of example :-

> I may, for no reason, suddenly decide to move my arm:
> - raising it higher, or lowering it
> - waving it about,
> - touching my nose, etc.
>
> The choice that I make doesn't have to be driven by a reaction to external events, or a desire to prove a point. I may simply decide to do it in a particular way, for no particular reason.

Yet even these possibilities might have a secret cause – for instance a subtle ache that my body senses but my conscious mind doesn't really register, causing me to flex my arm in a certain way. We cannot prove that our precise movement wasn't driven by an inevitable factor, but equally the materialist explanation is now highly speculative.

We have to find examples which seem to purely originate within our minds and are not driven by a response to a cause. This is why I like negative decision-making. By this, I generally mean the decision to stop doing something rather than to start it. So...

> How long is a pause in conversation?
>
> Well, it's as long as you care to make it, because under neutral circumstances there's no rule that would make it an inevitable period of time. It is also a decision that's entirely under your control, so you could make it just that bit longer or shorter. Indeed you could potentially make it last for hours or even forever.
>
> So in a situation without external pressure, or moments of forgetfulness, the decision about when to end a pause either has to be random or spontaneous. A **deliberate** pause may even be the best example, because it comes from within your Mind. You decide how long it will be, but it cannot be an inevitable period.
>
> Try it with a friend, and see if your choice is inevitable or not.

What's more - *the natural world and chemistry are not capable of having a pause, but thinking beings can*, and if a simple basic choice shows clear signs of spontaneity or randomness, then it establishes a principle that can be applied through all of the other examples I presented earlier, and more.

> I regard a 'pause' as the stopping of a process for a while, and then a resumption of that process, as before. It is **not** the same as (say) the breaking of a picture cord after a period of time, as the string doesn't repair itself and then resumes holding the picture on the wall

If Materialists/Determinists talk about everything being an inevitable pre-determined outcome then here we may see an example which **does seem to break the mould** – making it a strong argument for the Dualist and Idealist positions – that Thought is fundamentally different to physical Matter/Energy because it doesn't have to strictly follow the rules, and can be random or spontaneous.

Chemical processes are based in 'cause & effect' and are **always** immediate. If our bodies are only driven by chemical activity then how do the pauses arise? Does this imply that mental abilities are not based in chemical activity? Quite possibly – and that is important for biology.

We can also say that if physical causality denies that true choices are possible, (because there is only one inevitable outcome), then the choices which are apparent within some biological processes, (and there **are** some as we will see), may indicate that the influences which allow Thought to break the mould are also, somehow present in cells too.

It remains a personal decision whether you accept these examples or not, however once you make your choice you have to follow the consequences/implications from that philosophy. So what are some of those implications?

Because of the two principles of

i)   'cause and effect', and

ii)   nothing ever disappears, it only gets transformed into something else

science is able to encode its laws and theories concerning the behaviour of atoms and larger assemblies, within mathematical equations: where a perfect balance has to be achieved, (for instance between prescribed inputs on one side and outputs from a process on the other side). At this level of existence it **is** considered that the entire physical environment works to balance such equations and cannot step outside the rules. That is why they are called the Laws of Physics.

So what could provide a new start point or write new equations, (new Laws of Physics) when this <u>is</u> a necessary part of almost all theories of origin based on an eternal existence? If Materialism is correct, inevitable processes should be put forward to explain **all** changes – **but they aren't**.

Whether we are considering the nature of Thought, the choices/errors that appear to be made in cell activities, or the process of evolution based on genetics, causality doesn't allow for 'mistakes' so again, there can only be:

- external interferences – outside normal processes.
- instability – which changes important elements within a process.
- faulty pre-programming – but we have to ask what wrote the program.

Beyond these there only seems to be spontaneous or random influences – from unknown aspects of our existence.

Please remember these possibilities when we consider some of the special activities that our bodies undertake, (in later chapters).

Yet, if people do consider the possibility of random or spontaneous influences to explain change and creativity, they should also consider how those influences could be prevented from turning everything into chaos. The way in which we use Thought may give us the most natural way to explore such possibilities.

An obvious argument in Dualism is that chaos is avoided by only having a narrow touch point between the stable material world and our random thoughts, **plus** that touch point would be structured to provide a strong level of assessment and control before any change is implemented. If Thought is indeed the only thing that can cause Matter/Energy to deviate from its inevitable chemical path, then this narrow touch point would probably be the brain.

Which of these descriptions do you feel most closely match your own experiences?

2.3 <u>Where does this leave us?</u>

Whether or not these exercises persuaded you that there is true spontaneity or randomness in the world, the examples should hopefully explain why there are different viewpoints, and as long as the other ideas remain viable no perspective can be considered conclusive, (even if you are not persuaded by the alternatives).

We have established a range of possibilities, but it's also true that many people will have their strong preferences.

There is no doubt that in recent centuries science has leant strongly towards Materialism, (possibly because we haven't been able to isolate and test Thought). What I and many scientists have found utterly surprising is that recent experiments which were intended to virtually kill off any opposition to Materialism have ended up supporting other views, (see Bk.1)

This isn't just a case of having to find a 'missing factor' to bridge a gap, these facts seem to fundamentally challenge the core *principles* on which Materialism and Determinism are based.

As examples from Book 1:-

- It has long been held that the speed of light is the maximum speed that could ever be reached by any form of physical Matter/Energy, and yet cosmology sees the need for faster than light 'inflation' of the Universe, and there is also strong evidence from different types of experiment to suggest that 'paired particles' of light moving **apart** at *twice the speed of light*, can still influence each other in a physical way, <u>instantly</u>.

  Significantly, this relates to **instant communications** not instant physical travel... but it <u>does</u> result in physical effects.

- The 'Dual Slit' experiment has been deemed to show that particles of light and electricity can **choose** to become a fluid spreading wave instead of a 'solid' particle, in ***anticipation*** of factors that they haven't yet encountered. (This concept is referred-to as wave/particle duality).

- Perhaps most importantly, there were numerous factors which seemed to challenge the fundamental principle of Causality.

  Some key examples lay in the Big Bang- Big Crunch theory which can no longer survive without a spontaneous cause or a spontaneous end to its cycle – due to new and proven evidence from cosmology.

For me, it is the number and consistent pattern of such findings that give credibility to some of the other viewpoints. They are no longer just wishful thinking. The case for Materialism is far from dead, however it now has to re-think its approach and come up with new answers.

By identifying the key findings which challenge our perceptions of reality we hopefully get to the core issues which will ultimately unravel the mystery of Life. These will also provide us with a practical tool, in the form of a checklist, with which to assess all ideas about origin and the nature of Life/existence.

You will then be able to re-shape your own opinions about our reality, and who knows, we may even start to bridge the gap between religious and scientific thinking.

Where such factors can be identified we are faced with a personal choice about whether we can reasonably expect a Materialist solution to arise in future. The reverse logic also poses an important strategic question – Is it realistic to expect that 'another type of stuff', or some other external factor will be revealed, given the level of knowledge that we currently have?

Although the biological sciences may identify circumstances that make us think about such things, the answers are only likely to come from the realms of physics, Quantum Mechanics, and cosmology.

In many ways, this question was part of the purpose of Book 1, because it demonstrated that unknown influences **do** seem to be necessary in explaining the very nature of our physical environment, both here on Earth and in the wider cosmos.

The clearest of these indicators is 'Dark Energy': an energy that we cannot detect but which is logically necessary to explain the accelerating expansion of the Universe. More importantly such stuff would need to be everywhere and in growing quantities – meaning that an unknown source is continuing to 'generate' it somewhere – perhaps everywhere.

Because we cannot detect this energy it has the potential to be different to the energies we *can* detect – which opens the possibility that it may have other capabilities beyond those of Matter/Energy that we *can* detect.

Could such things as Dark Energy represent the elusive 'life force'?

We will see later in the book that ideas about the 'life force' may be more subtle than people first imagined.

Many of the things that make life special are to do with Thought, choices, emotions, and control – new capabilities rather than new forces[3] as such.

This is because science has now identified where the vast majority of the energy/force comes from to power our bodies and cells, as we will see later in our considerations about *metabolism* (Chapter 5). Yet there **are** subtle aspects of energy that still remain unresolved as we shall see in Chapter 12 – particularly to do with the operations of the brain.

Dark Energy **is** part of mainstream scientific thinking, but it was instituted to explain cosmic movements – not to fulfil a different function as a life force. We honestly have no way to say what else it might be capable of - whether as a source of new capabilities, or of energy. Yet if additional capabilities are shown to be needed, then this is sort of factor which will warrant investigation, in the absence of an ability to test God.

However in support of the idea, it can be pointed out that Dark Energy does seem to have 'emerged' some 5 billion years ago – *just before* the formation of our solar system & our planet, Earth. Coincidence?

There **is** a lot of speculation in such ideas, but such concepts have driven us to many remarkable discoveries in the past. Who knows what the future holds? So a more balanced interpretation would probably be to say that

> *if we acknowledge one type of 'other stuff' then either its influence, or those of others cannot be ruled out.*

Part of the reason why Dark Energy has gained acceptance as a concept is that the subject matter itself helped to simplify our considerations and narrow the possibilities – ie. there seemed to be nowhere else to turn.

For instance, when dealing with movements of the Universe the only viable influences had to be both massive and strategic. Similarly in the 'Dual Slit' and 'Faster than Light' experiments there were very specific things being tested, in isolated conditions, which have left scientists having to face up to some very unusual properties.

Unfortunately we will not have the same luxury in our considerations about Life, which have to deal with the proven intricacy of living things and many real factors that could influence outcomes which are difficult to isolate or trace.

Inevitably as we pursue some of these issues we will need to delve into a reasonable amount of detail, but that doesn't mean that it has to be boring or leave us overwhelmed. If you have any interest in this subject you are likely to be fascinated by the processes of Life and we will explore them in ways that keep our eyes on the big picture and minimise jargon.

3   The Definition, Scope, and Timeline of Life

If somebody stopped you in the street and asked you how you would describe 'Life', what would you say? Would you...

- talk about the rich variety of plants, and creatures in our environment?
- ❖ say that life is for living: to be enjoyed or suffered depending on the twists of fate and love.
- be more mechanical and define it in terms of metabolism and reproduction?
- ❖ say that life is a construct of the mind, or maybe a gift from God.
- talk about cycles of birth, life, death and evolution?
- ❖ say that life is merely what you make of it.

In the modern age, as across history, there are many ways to perceive life.

The successes of scientific advances in medicine & biology have inevitably led some people to define life purely in physical/mechanical/chemical terms, yet the fact that **there's no consensus about a definition** shows that academics are not satisfied by this, let alone the general public.

In browsing the web I have come across over 280 definitions and none seem to cover all of the circumstances, even though I find some of them to be really ingenious. In part, this is because the scientific analysis is incomplete, yet at a more fundamental level, many people find that functional descriptions don't account for what we **experience**, even physically.

Physical factors such as *metabolism*, (ie. a means to generate and use energy), plus *reproduction*, are universal characteristics of living cells/bodies but they cannot define:

> **what life is;** *when it begins;* **whether it has particular meaning;** *or how it relates to consciousness.*

Such questions are very old and have tested thinkers throughout the ages with only partial success. We all start by realising that life is special, and many will feel that it is also fundamentally different from the rocks and base chemicals of our environment because of what life does.

We tend to instinctively recognise Life in its different forms such as plants, fungi, bacteria, insects, animals, birds, fish, & the more bizarre creatures of the sea. Yet we do struggle to define it, both in terms of its nature and its boundaries. As we'll see, there always seem to be **exceptions** to every rule due to the diversity that life achieves. But should one size have to fit all?

Despite the physical differences between species, and even individuals, we know that all life on Earth has a common building block: the living cell.

Its different forms all use the same **single** but **complex** core mechanism based in DNA for reproduction & perhaps evolution. This is very significant and it's partly because of these facts that people have sought a single common definition of life which distils the universal factors that set it apart.

This is also one of the strongest reasons which suggest that life has only originated *once* on this planet.

It also means that a section of genetic code from one species can be introduced into another, and it will be understood and processed in the same way as the original DNA.

While it's likely that there **are** universal factors, those troublesome exceptions also imply that at some deeper level there are *fundamental* things which set the alternate forms of Life apart – and that these may need to add to the overall definition in some way.

As you may imagine, there are many web sites which 'define' life as a series of capabilities but these are really lists of common functions. They are therefore more like *descriptions* rather than getting to the essence of Life. Those functional terms often incorporate some of the other trickier perceptions which people generally share about life, that imply something beyond pure chemical processes but remain unexplained, for instance:

Organization of structures and processes; **Homeostasis** – the maintenance & control of stable conditions; **Adaptation** to changing circumstances, etc.

These processes are not random acts, (which would be expected to take Life both forwards & backwards), because they seem to display purpose and direction. They also seem to go beyond simple cause & effect.

[*As a reference for later* – these are also processes which seem to go in the opposite direction of 'entropy' – which is the ever increasing state of *disorder* that is implied by the 2nd Law of Thermodynamics].

Yet I personally think that those other aspects can be taken too far when people try to define life through some sort of *meaning*. Don't get me wrong, meaning is very important, but it blurs the purpose of a definition.

Something can exist without it necessarily having meaning, because that is a consideration we apply to it in retrospect, and 'meaning' doesn't stop the organism from being what it is. It is also something that lies 'in the eye of the beholder' and can therefore be so varied as to break all boundaries. There is a balance to be struck.

The philosophy of 'Vitalism' emerged in the 17th Century and it argues that there is effectively a life-force which must be involved in all aspects of Life that are not purely chemical, (ie. turning sterile particles into living things). Life would effectively be using the stuff of physical matter to give it a physical presence. Aside from being **unable** to identify this mysterious force, the core trouble with this type of thinking is that it is very difficult to know where to draw the line on what is living or not. There is no definition.

Yet Vitalism lost its general appeal when scientists began to form some biological products from raw chemicals. For instance, Friedrich Wöhler synthetically produced urea in 1828. While I suspect that many people now regard urea as a mere chemical by-product, other scientists have artificially generated more complex organic compounds such as nucleotides & amino acids which definitely get close to the essence of life, as we'll see later.

One of the more remarkable developments of recent years has been the ability of laboratories to actually create proteins from scratch. Proteins are the chemical workhorses of physical bodies. There are potentially a million different types across all species, each being highly tailored to specific circumstances in the body. The laboratory manufacturing techniques are highly intricate and can require such things as resins to act as a type of scaffolding while creating a protein's structure. Yet it is essentially do-able.

While it may be a lot simpler to continue using cells to manufacture proteins for day-to-day research, these specialist techniques can give scientists high precision when required, and can even allow scientists to experiment with new forms of protein that they construct using 'non-standard' chemical elements.

Does that mean that Life can be defined in purely chemical terms? Not yet.

As we look into the mechanisms of life in later chapters we will see that there are some significant aspects that appear to go beyond pure chemistry. The other significant aspect of proteins is that they are more than just a string of molecular components. They have to have a useful purpose, and we are still not in a position to predict what any protein might achieve from its composition – at best we can tinker with something that is known to work, somewhere, and then see if the changes offer any beneficial or catastrophic consequence.

So where does this leave us in terms of definition? Somebody with religious leanings might take the approach that

" **Life is the union of body and soul**."

I have been surprised at how many young people do not understand the term 'Soul' which is now used in various ways within popular culture to denote passion and emotion, particularly within music. Traditionally, a soul is regarded as the means by which the essence of a person can be preserved and transferred, allowing them to continue life beyond death.

It is therefore something which holds the essential characteristics of an individual, from the instinctive preferences and desires we are all born with, to the knowledge and personality we develop in life. However even without a desire to capture those characteristics, those non-physical aspects of life might still pose challenges to any definition.

Equally, to fulfil the 'transfer function', souls would **have** to be separate things from the physical bodies that they occupy... if they exist.

The above definition, (in bold), is neat in terms of its simplicity but it will inevitably be highly contentious because it doesn't define very much and relies on concepts which are not yet proven, such as the soul – although it is based in a rationale that is supported by some evidence, (see Ch 9-10).

It also fails to bridge the gap between faith and science.

It took a giant of science, Erwin Schrödinger[5], to begin the process of that translation when he started to point out functional aspects of life that appeared to go against the Laws of Physics. His definition of Life is:

" That which avoids the decay into equilibrium."

This phrase may not mean much to you now but its huge significance was explored in Book 1, and I will also explore it more in section 3.2 below.

However, I cannot leave this part of the dialogue without mentioning another working definition used by NASA in the 1990s:-

" Life is a self-sustaining system capable of Darwinian Evolution[6]."

NASA has funded a lot of research into the nature and origins of Life to assist its search for extra terrestrial life and the ways in which it might be recognised. That said, I find it to be a rather cold definition especially in its alternate form which specifies that life can only be a *chemical system*[7].

As a direct challenge to this definition, we might consider that within the vastness of space there could be other forms of life that are not based on chemicals or which cannot evolve. We need to look at the variables a bit more closely to understand some of the deeper source factors.

Evolution will be covered in some depth in Chapter 6 but at this stage in our thinking it is interesting to simply note that the full title of Darwin's theory (first published on 24 November 1859) is:

"On the Origin of Species by Means of Natural Selection, or the Preservation of Favoured Races in the Struggle for Life"

We should all have a general perception of what this means through our basic schooling, but there are also hidden messages within it. For instance the evolutionary process potentially gains part of its 'sense of direction' through the application of Thought, or at least crude consciousness.

The process of 'natural selection' that determines whether changes/ mutations are successful, (ie. that a new species will survive longer), might simply reflect the improved/worsened capabilities which any new physical features provide. This would apply to plants. But the theory goes a lot further in respect to changes in creatures.

In circumstances such as a bigger arm or better eye, Darwin and others clearly extend this to include *how* those new capabilities are used, plus the *perceived desirability* of those attributes when individuals select a mate. Both of these aspects may make the process partly dependent on the *thoughts* of the creatures.

The *physical/mechanical* differences between life forms on Earth seem to arise from two main types of issue: structural aspects, and more dynamic variables, both of which we will look at in the coming chapters. In this context it's interesting to see that the vague factor we call 'consciousness' also seems to increase as organisms become more physically complex.

Bacteria just seem to drift, and use whatever they come across as best they can, but plants *seek out* better opportunities. Time lapse photography shows some of them turning to face the sun, while others can send out roots or creepers to invade the space of other plants if the environment offers opportunities. There are even suggestions that plants can sense and slowly respond to positive or negative human emotions - which is an *interesting* concept even if the theory can't be demonstrated scientifically.

Across the realms of all creatures, from animals, to birds, and fish, the size of the brain is a broad indication of the level of consciousness that we suspect. (In saying this people are saying that consciousness is not just the human form that we experience, and that it can exist with different levels of sophistication in other creatures). Yet if we then compare jelly fish to whales, and then to dolphins etc. we can deduce that brain size seems more closely associated with the *complexity* of the body, rather than overall size.

To some, this indicates a strong association between physical factors and consciousness, but such theories don't seem to offer explanations when we look at the repair and control mechanisms **within** living cells, which are all tiny and without a brain, (see Chapter 5 and the Appendices).

This is why people who say that 'other types of stuff' are responsible for consciousness can argue that *their* ideas can apply to all levels of life as it wouldn't depend on a brain and could therefore exist at all levels.

Whichever way this points you, to God, Vitalism, or elsewhere, *we are all left with a sense of awe about Life*. Even the most hardened materialists recognize that life is an extraordinary step-change in physical complexity.

It's amidst these notions that people try to derive insight into a meaning or purpose for Life, however as I stated before, we cannot attribute meaning without first determining some facts about what Life is. So let's begin with the broad groupings and timeframes for the emergence of Life.

3.1   The Tree of Life & its Timeline

In order to pursue a sensible discussion about Life we need to form an overview of the types of life that have emerged, plus the latest scientific thinking about how long each broad category has existed.

I won't be taking this to the level of individual species, but forming a broader strategic perspective - which requires me to use a small number of technical names to be in line with a lot of scientific shorthand. You will find them useful so please don't let their strangeness put you off.

Analysis of both living and 'recently dead' creatures has shown that there are three main forms of life: **Archaea**; **Bacteria**; and **Eukarya**

All living species on Earth fall into one of these 3 branches in the 'Tree of Life' which means that we need to get a basic understanding of the 'strategic' differences between these *branches/categories*, as well as the variable factors which differentiate the individual *species*.

Achaea and Bacteria are miniscule **single celled organisms** which are structurally quite close, and are therefore categorized under a common grouping of '**Prokaryotes**'. Most of us will have heard of Bacteria - being some of the essential microscopic work-cells of life, which either help our bodies to perform useful functions such as digestion, or act as a source of infection & disease. Both exist in vast numbers, and as groupings they have incredible variety in terms of the materials they can digest and use.

Archaea seem to occupy more obscure corners of our environment – allowing life to exist in some of the most extreme circumstances imaginable, (eg. super-hot undersea volcanic vents). This may partly reflect their origins in the toxic environment of the early Earth – without oxygen.

Eukaryotes/Eukarya are typically **multi-celled organisms** that account for all of the forms of life that we consciously recognise and encounter from fungi, to plants, fish, animals, birds, and humans. There *are* a small number of single celled Eukarya, however all Eukaryote cells are much larger than those of Archaea & Bacteria – being much more sophisticated.

Having emphasised their differences, it is worth saying that all forms of life also have a lot in common because many of their **core** processes are the same for all living cells, even if they are implemented in different ways. The instruction manual to build any type of cell is contained in its DNA, and it is such a universal mechanism, that DNA from another species can be read and reproduced if it is inserted into the DNA of another organism.

In broad terms these wonders of nature all have to generate energy and chemical components, which are then used to replicate themselves, and also produce some useful by-products. It has been suggested that Eukaryote cells emerged through a series of chance encounters where, (for instance), one form of Bacteria that could digest one type of nutrient, was captured or merged with another bacterium that was able to digest a different type of mineral, and they found that they were helpful to each other, not only in terms of process but also because their genetic templates (DNA) combined - allowing them to be reproduced as a combined entity.

While that narrative is pure speculation it is potentially viable and it does help to illustrate the basic differences in complexity between the different types of cell. Eukaryotes do tend to organise their activities in more than one way, by separating different chemical processes into separate compartments called 'organelles'. One of these compartments is the cell nucleus – which holds the DNA, and it is from here that they also reproduce themselves as a combined entity.

Eukaryote means 'truly nucleated' while Prokaryote means 'pre-nucleated'.

The structures and chemical flows within Prokaryotes are therefore a lot simpler – typically dealing with just one digestive process and one set of chemical by-products. So even if some of the core mechanisms are the same there are structural differences between the 3 types of cell which distinguish the 3 main forms of life.

As mentioned, the single celled Prokaryotes do **not** have a cell nucleus or any of the other organelles. Within this we can distinguish Bacteria from Archaea in a small number of ways, but I will focus on two main ones:

1. while Bacteria do **not** have *membranes* which create organelles, they **do** have protein-based micro-compartments which are often regarded as primitive organelles. Archaea have no such compartments.
2. all 3 branches of life (Bacteria, Archaea, and Eukarya) have their own distinct forms of 'Ribosome', (components which are vital in the process of reproduction - which I will explain later).

These are some of the key strategic factors which keep the branches in the Tree of Life separate, however it is the DNA which differentiates between the species & individuals along each branch - the twigs of the tree.

Even if you believe that God directly created each species, these facts are beyond dispute because scientists have manipulated the DNA of cells and proven that different creatures emerge as a result, in predictable ways. So if God was the designer, He would have been elaborating on 3 main themes for physical life, (at least on this planet).

Yet those who exclusively believe in the Theory of Evolution will consider that nature itself found ways to manipulate genetic code so as to produce life and all of its subsequent diversity. *How* it might have done this is open to debate, but when we consider the extensive chain of interwoven processes that assemble, check, and then correct the detailed mechanisms of life within cells, (which is where evolution happens), we have to question the philosophical basis on which this overall cohesion in the functionality could have arisen without any specific need for life in an environment composed of unthinking chemicals.

There is also a need to explain how a succession of such evolutionary changes could occur naturally in the time available; since the Earth formed.

For those who believe in the Theory of Evolution, the fact that there are 3 core types of cell, (one for each of the 3 main branches in the Tree of Life), might lead some to believe that physical life had 3 start points, however the general consensus is that life began with one or other of the different **single-celled organisms,** or possibly a common ancestor for them. This belief is driven by two key facts:-

i) The most ancient rocks on the planet only ever contain the residues or fossils of single celled organisms.

ii) All forms of life share the same core method of reproduction.

It might be argued that multi-celled creatures (Eukaryotes) were another pure start point which happened to take place a lot later, but the Theory of Evolution also drives most scientists to look for a continuing process of change rather than acknowledging new beginnings without explanation.

This reasoning still leaves us with two of the branches of life as a potential start point and the evidence which has been discovered suggests that both forms of life existed from very early dates in the lifetime of our planet.

One line of thinking suggests that the slightly more sophisticated/advanced structure of Bacteria may indicate that they evolved from Archaea, but again, scientific opinion is divided on this. In short, with the evidence currently available, we cannot be sure whether

a) there were separate pure start points for the 2 Prokaryotes, or

b) an evolutionary path from one to the other, or

c) an evolutionary path from an undiscovered common ancestor, (sometimes referred to as the 'Last Universal Common Ancestor').

Yet without God, at least one of these forms of cell must have emerged from a mixture of sterile chemicals, either as a 'happy coincidence of factors', or as part of specific process that we have **not yet fully identified**.

Mainstream thinking lies firmly with option 'c' which I believe is mainly for 3 main reasons:

i) The **extreme** difficulty in finding any explanation for the origin of the first cell – which we will consider later, in Chapter 7.

ii) The fact that strategically, all three types of cell use **the same** complex mechanism for reproduction.

iii) There is no apparent 'evolutionary path' from one type of Ribosome to any of the other types.

The shape of our 'Tree of Life' therefore becomes a little clearer, but how can we tell how old it is? Once again our initial thoughts must be guided by strategic factors.

Firstly, it is logical to believe that physical life **couldn't survive** before the right environment existed to sustain it - which must also mean that the first cells appeared on Earth after the rocks had cooled to bearable temperatures.

Both rocks and fossils can be dated using 'Radiometric' techniques (equivalent to 'carbon dating'), which effectively measure the decay in radioactive substances that are present in all things.

We also find that the different *layers* of rock plus the fossils or chemical residues which they contain give us an outline of the main sequence of events, because they are of different ages that also follow in sequence from each other. The fact that specific types of fossilised bones only exist in certain layers of rock shows us

- the periods when these creatures existed, and also
- which ones co-existed and which ones didn't.

All of this information gives us a *consistent* picture of what seems to have happened across the globe. For these reasons we believe that the dinosaurs died out 65 million years ago, while the earliest example of modern man arose only half a million years ago. The bones of men **never** appear in the same layers of rock as the large dinosaurs, and radiometric dating also shows the two were separated by millions of years. So contrary to the myths of various movies the two could not have lived at the same time.

While it is true that: the presence of certain trace chemicals in rocks is *assumed* to be a fingerprint for the earliest forms of single celled life; and radiometric techniques make *presumptions* about how radioactive substances decay over millions of years, (which nobody has been around long enough to prove), I don't know of anybody with an understanding of the science who disputes the logic of the techniques. It **is** widely accepted that the techniques are accurate enough for these purposes.

Those who retain faith in the accuracy of timelines described by their Holy Scriptures could perhaps remember that time can be measured in different ways and that, for instance, a day in the life of God could equate to billions of years for us. At some point science and faith have to be reconciled.

From these types of analysis scientists have produced an approximate timeline[8] for the development of life on Earth, which helps us to gain a sense of perspective :-

Event	Distance in the Past (Millions Yrs)
• Big Bang – Universe and measurable Time began	13,700
• Earth created	4,600
• Oldest known rocks	4,200
• **Origin of basic life** (single cells)	**4,000**
• Development of Oxygen atmosphere	1,900
• **Multi-cellular life begins**	**800**
• 1st Homo Sapiens (modern man)	0.5

This is the best evidence we have gleaned from physical reality, so let me briefly talk through these stages to make them clear.

This timeline suggests that the chemical evidence for Bacteria and Archaea points to life emerging within a 200 million year 'window of opportunity', approximately 4 billion years ago. (Finds in Australia in 2015 indicate that the oldest rocks containing certain carbon isotopes plus a phosphate mineral called 'apatite' may even date back 4.1 billion years ago, narrowing the 'window' to 100 million years)[9,10].

The Earth's crust also indicates that it suffered a number of major hits from very large meteorites and if any of these were on the same scale as 65 million years ago, (when the dinosaurs died out), the timescales for the emergence of life from sterile chemicals could be reduced even more.

However, once the first single celled organisms appeared it took a further 3.2 *thousand million* years for the first multi-cellular creatures to emerge.

Within this timeframe the first step that's assumed for the process of evolution was that the earliest forms of Archaea and Bacteria multiplied in enormous quantities, within a very dark and oxygen-free environment, and also diversified by mutation to exist in a wide variety of circumstances.

Through this, particular strains of bacteria, (believed to relate to blue-green algae/cyanobacteria), learned how to feed off the hydrogen in water molecules, and release the waste oxygen that was poisonous to them, into the emerging atmosphere.

In this way, over the course of approximately 2 thousand million years, oxygen built up in the atmosphere to levels that are similar to today, forcing most forms of the Archaea and Bacteria to either die or retreat to areas of the planet where the oxygen couldn't reach. Some of the bacteria that *was* able to survive in oxygen also learned how to 'photosynthesise' (using sunlight to power their metabolisms), as a very dark atmosphere increasingly cleared and eventually became transparent.

One of the puzzles from this period is that the early atmosphere would **not** have stopped ultraviolet light from reaching the surface of the earth in quantities that would be expected to destroy the chemical bonds in the molecules of life – and yet Life did emerge at the Earth's surface, as well as below it.

It is the ability to use oxygen that gave modern bacteria the extra energy to develop more complex forms of life, (the Eukaryotes), over the next one billion years or so; eventually resulting in multi-celled organisms.

As mentioned earlier, the more popular theory for the emergence of Eukaryotes is that different types of Bacteria started working together to form new 'combined cells', however it is possible that these new cells emerged from a major genetic mutation, or a spontaneous event - (ie. another entirely fresh start).

One of the factors that supports the notion of mutually beneficial (symbiotic) bacterial relationships, is that two basic forms of Eukaryote cells emerged, (reflecting the abilities of earlier Bacteria):

- those that require/use oxygen, (animals); and
- those that produce and release oxygen, (plants)

From those very basic forms of multi-celled life, it took almost the whole of the subsequent 800 million years (to the present day) for evolution to produce modern human beings... per scientific theory.

The following diagram summarises the different factors giving a rough indication of when the different forms of life began to emerge according to the scientific evidence available.

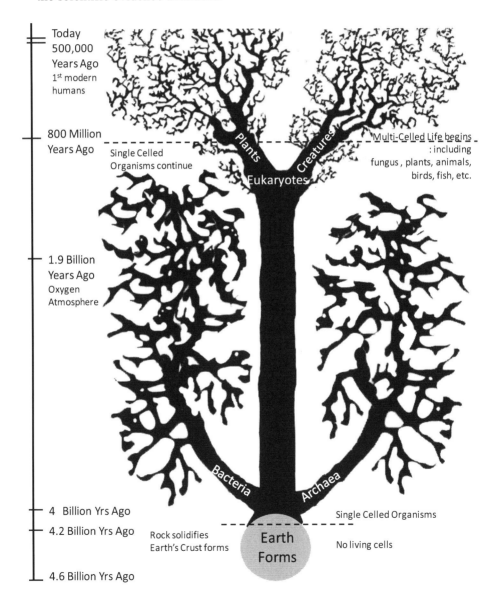

3.2 <u>Other Factors that May Help to Define Life</u>

Having spent a bit of time looking at a series of scientific findings I'd like to begin this section in more philosophical terms.

To a clear majority of people, (religious believers and beyond), Life is more than a bunch of sterile chemicals. If that is correct, the distinguishing factors must represent the boundary points with the living world.

So what are they? We need to look for clues. Those of you who have read Book 1 will appreciate that physical matter is characterised by a constant process of degradation, ("increasing entropy"), which is stated in the 2nd Law of Thermodynamics – one of the pivotal Laws of Physics.

In support of this we can point to mountains and buildings which erode & crumble through chemical reactions and friction: ultimately flattening out to the background level of the ground. Alternatively, heat moves from hot areas to cold until they reach the same temperature. Suns eventually burn out and then explode, spreading their contents across the universe.

So for many scientists the 2nd Law of Thermodynamics is an absolute rule, and yet it ignores the fact that you cannot disassemble something before it has first been assembled.

It can be argued that Life is one of only two 'forces' in nature that flow in the opposite direction by broadly **assembling** things rather than degrading them: the other force being Gravity. Science doesn't recognise Life as a true force[3] but we see that bodies *grow,* (from seed, or in eggs, or the womb), and beyond that life *multiplies*, spreads, and even *constructs* things such as buildings from less structured forms of matter.

> The typical counter-arguments that seek to preserve the 2nd Law of Thermodynamics even for Life, are that: 1) many living things obtain & use energy by destroying/consuming other things to release the energy contained within them; 2) that energy is then spread into the background environment; 3) Life itself is also temporary as all living things die and return to their base chemical components.

But as with all of these arguments it's a case of where do you draw the line in terms of defining 'assembly'? If ultimately all energy is distributed into the background environment then assembly must represent a gathering of that stuff to either create something from it, or to use its power for specific purposes. Human beings **have** learned how to gather free floating energy and use it, (eg. capturing the sun's radiated heat): a truly assembling influence? Of course, plants have already been doing this for billions of years, using the power of the sun's rays to grow and to produce oxygen as a by-product. We can even say that the cells in our bodies gather & store energy as they build their chemical structures.

Electromagnetism, (one of the other 3 recognised forces in nature[3]), powers chemical reactions, and superficially could be seen as an assembling force because (say) it is the force that builds mountains. However most scientists will argue that this is not the same as an assembling force, because (say) the formation of mountains is really no more that a large scale flow of rocky liquid which happens to settle in a bunched-up form. It is not a gathering of material in the true sense that is displayed by Gravity and Life.

As briefly mentioned earlier, Erwin Schrödinger[5], (a giant in the scientific community, who made his name as a leading light in the development of Quantum Theory), was fascinated by this reverse flow, and his book "What is Life" (1944) is seen by many to mark the beginning of the search for a definition of Life. He even defined living matter as

" that which avoids the decay into equilibrium."

Technically this doesn't require Life to assemble anything: just to maintain what exists; and it could also (falsely) imply that gravity was 'alive' because it is also an assembling force, thereby 'avoiding decay'. These considerations may help to explain why it *hasn't* been adopted more widely, but the key significance for me in this definition is that it began to draw philosophy and science together.

We have therefore seen that *physical life potentially goes against two core principles* that would otherwise govern the behaviour of matter/energy: ie.

causality and decay/entropy.

Once again the underlying question must therefore be 'What factors allow it to do these things'? What makes it special?

If we consider that Life 'assembles' through its **controlled** physical processes of metabolism and reproduction, plus the instructions & concepts generated in the Mind (which cause us to design and build complex objects/tools), we are inexorably drawn to the distinguishing characteristics of Thought and Consciousness.

In this sense it is interesting to draw parallels with thoughts themselves. While physical matter can be broken down into ever smaller components, Thought cannot. A concept may be assembled from several individual ideas but people don't believe that you can have $^1/_3$ of a thought, or half an emotion. The base notions **don't** seem to be reducible – perhaps another defining characteristic?

Equally, a single idea can rapidly lead to a huge number of consequential thoughts: multiplying and spreading into other associated areas of interest as our Minds seek out potential connections.

If you are persuaded that these special characteristics are real then there is a strong argument for suggesting that another type of stuff may be responsible for generating the associated capabilities.

However the materialist counter-argument is either to say that :

a) the supposed special effects are actually an illusion, or

b) that the effects are real but are generated by properties of Matter/Energy which only exist within the realm of Quantum Mechanics where different 'Laws of Physics' seem to apply.

While arguments along the lines of option 'b' aim to preserve the notion of Matter/Energy as the only stuff of existence, they have 2 main difficulties.

Firstly, as we have seen, we cannot prove that the observations emerging from Quantum Mechanics do actually represent true spontaneity or randomness, (because we cannot actually observe what is happening).

Secondly, and perhaps more importantly, whichever side of the fence you position yourself, it is acknowledged that examples of spontaneity or randomness only occur in very specific circumstances. Put another way, there appears to be a separation between the factors that can generate change and those that maintain stability.

It therefore makes little difference whether spontaneity and randomness arise from other types of stuff or different layers of reality. In terms of capability, the main arguments presented in relation to Thought, Dualism, or Idealism would largely hold true either way.

For this reason I will maintain the analogy of 'Other types of Stuff' as I feel it is clearer in explaining later arguments.

3.2.1   Consciousness and Experience

As consciousness is such a fundamental aspect of life it is perhaps unsurprising that it has also been very hard to define. While we all have first-hand knowledge of it, people are again driven to *describe* the abilities of consciousness rather than necessarily being able to *define/explain* its essence. We don't even have a real measure of consciousness.

The characteristics we normally attribute to it include :-

experience, *purpose*, **principles**, *desires,* **control**, and *awareness*

These are not properties that we attribute to sterile chemicals, and in many ways they do **not** instinctively relate to logic or the causality that reason implies, because they are not precise factors and they are **proactive**, not reactive. To explain this a little more, Causality requires a response *after* the cause, and Logic works forward from a start point, even if it tries to anticipate an outcome. In contrast: purpose, principle, awareness, & control all have to **proactively** monitor and adjust an emerging situation.

Experience is essentially a blend of feelings which reflect how we perceive a circumstance - an **emotional** reaction to events; while Awareness in particular is an **interpretation** and **rationalisation** of what is happening in the broader context, not just the immediate factors causing an effect; and going well beyond a simple recognition that one or other fact has occurred.

This is all very different to the mechanical systems that we engineer in cars, computers, etc. While it is true that these devices have sensors which loosely equate to our touch, taste etc., we believe that *our* reactions to such signals go well beyond even the most sophisticated computers that mankind has designed, and there is no apparent way to bridge the gap.

Of course a way may reveal itself in future, but as things stand that way seems to require properties which Matter/Energy is not deemed to possess.

> A sophisticated robot may detect the need for a new source of energy as it uses up its power pack or fuel store, and it may even be programmed to see the urgency of this need, but that doesn't equate to **feeling** hungry or **enjoying** the taste of food.

> Put another way, we can find nourishment in very bland food, so there is no need for us to enjoy it... yet the experience exists.

> Now it might be argued that taste is important in identifying desirable or undesirable foods, but *enjoyment* seems to be a complex addition to the process without a clear need. If our bodies have to identify the desirable nutrients **before** they can generate a sense of pleasure, why not simply let us know – 'good' or 'bad'.

> Equally, with optical character recognition there is a conceivable way in which machinery could gain information from written texts, but they won't respond emotionally to a novel. Could a robot truly enjoy music or could it only ever hear sound?

> To me, it is interesting that some of our strongest experiences are attached to some of the most fundamental aspects of life such as love, friendship, and empathy. By forming much stronger bonds than (say) the cold logic of an alliance, these emotions help families and the broader community to survive in hard times. Yet we still don't know how they are generated

These special distinguishing factors are known as **Qualia** and they begin to indicate that even if we succeed in creating artificial intelligence, it doesn't follow that we have created **artificial experience**.

Qualia do seem to point to the special nature of Life and Consciousness, and we will see some reinforcement of this in experimental results about the way that we make decisions in Chapter 4.

However a key test of whether such things can be replicated by purely physical means will emerge with the results of the Blue Brain Project[11] in 2023 – which is based on the 'Computational Hypothesis' of the brain. The research team is hoping to create a digital model of a brain by exactly replicating the activities of all the nerves, cells, neural networks, chemical agents, etc. which can be gleaned from real brain tissues.

Clearly a lot will depend on the realism of the simulation in how the different elements work and interact, even if the structural models of the brain are accurate. However if the simulation does generate true Thought in the same way as a real brain then it will change our perceptions of consciousness... and presumably offer the possibility of immortality through digital modelling of the individual, and capturing his/her knowledge at a given point in time!

Beyond matters of the brain, in the 'higher' animal species, there are issues relating to the nature of Life which suggest that Life is dependent on an active Mind. Consider this :-

> Thought is dynamic and needs stimulus because without
> something to think about, Thought will cease. To this extent
> Thought may be seeking-out experience or generating it where
> it cannot easily be found, in order to continue.

These interesting notions reinforce the fact that our very survival depends on us perpetuating our mind - not just our physical bodies. Admittedly this can't be applied to plants which don't think, (although we saw earlier that plants can be argued to have a basic form of awareness). Yet where Thought does exist, there does seem to be a need to get satisfaction from life in order for us to derive meaning from it. It has been argued that many people, (particularly the elderly), have given up on life because they no longer see the point of it. Their bodies shut down because their minds don't have the will power to sustain them.

If we are purely mechanical constructs would this still be true?
Could a robot 'want to live' if it wasn't specifically programmed to do so?
Are these additional pointers to the distinct nature of life?

Across all of this thinking you may begin to see where new ways of defining Life are emerging beyond the 3 main 'traditional' themes of:-

- Perceiving it as the source of 'vigour and control',
- Life as a mechanism, (whether physical or in the mind) – per modern scientific thinking & some philosophies of Descartes.
- Life as 'complex organisation' - per Kant, as modified by Darwin.

As an example of the new approaches being considered – life might be defined as the factor which enables things not to be dead. *You may well groan on reading that*, but the more interesting side to this notion comes from the challenges that are thrown out when we consider things such as:-

- life-support machines which can keep people 'alive' in a comatose state for years, when those people would otherwise not be viable living entities in their own right, or
- people who have donated their living cells to science, and science has continued to grow those cells for research - so while the cells might still be alive, the donor may not be.

Extending such concepts even further, I believe that some people have even asserted that dead bodies could be deemed to be alive as long as their

DNA was able to offer the potential for them to be re-grown. I suspect that ordinary people would generally disagree with this logic for some obvious reasons... such as :-

- a lack of participation in life ! and
- the fact that there's more to a person than their DNA
  eg. knowledge and personality.

If we use a dead person's DNA to generate a new being, society will still regard the cloned individual as a different entity, in much the same way as a child is a different being to a parent; or 'identical' twins are distinct from each other. Our unique set of knowledge and experiences makes each of us very different people, even if we were to have identical DNA.

There are also different forms in which consciousness can appear.

We can see that termites can organise themselves to build their mounds with cooling fins, gardens, and other 'big picture' structures. Their 'society' will designate certain parts of the mound for particular uses such as a nursery which is a nurturing and feeding ground, not just a dumping ground for eggs. They also compost their rubbish to grow their specific types of food. How can this *collective consciousness* be achieved in such tiny creatures with pin-prick sized brains? There is often talk of 'scent trails' acting as a chemical form of neural network, but that hardly explains how they can design and build a large cavern with cooling fins, or work out farming techniques.

The notion of collective consciousness underpins several other ideas such as the notion, based in Idealism, that if everything is a mental construct, the stability that we perceive in our reality may come from sharing our perceptions across the whole of humanity, which forces us to operate on a common standard of perception which then becomes the expected stable norm. On this basis if enough people were to perceive that something might happen, they might bring it about. We look at experiments to test this in 8.1.1.

Having said this I must, out of fairness, also mention another strand of human perception - that perhaps all consciousness is shared through God. Sadly, there is no known way to test this as we cannot distinguish God from other potential influences. Yet it is equally true that experiments like the Global Consciousness Project (8.1.1) might reinforce ideas about God as long as they don't disprove God, (which they are not in a position to do).

Science is only just beginning to test ideas of collective consciousness as **it would seem to require a mechanism that goes beyond each physical body**. Inevitably the evidence is very slim at this stage and cannot lead to any firm conclusions, but we will consider it later.

So you will hopefully begin to see the challenges to definitions that are thrown up by well-known circumstances. If we can accommodate those challenging factors we may get closer to a true understanding of Life.

3.3   <u>Positioning & Sample Definitions</u>

With exceptions to almost every rule more people begin to question why a definition is necessary at all, when we have to deal with what's there, regardless of how we label it.

As we have seen, definitions of Life can be useful to mark boundary points and help us to distinguish the elements that make it special, but the uncomfortable truth is that they largely serve to justify the varying levels of respect & care that we extend to other living things.

Put another way, definitions are often deployed to segregate and to treat things/beings differently, (for instance as a way to justify different levels of expenditure in medicine; or why slaves or animals have less rights; or to kill weeds as opposed to other plants).

If robots could replicate human levels of thought and could look after themselves, renew their energy sources, reproduce and evolve without our intervention, etc. then some might see them as a new life form. Yet others would still see them as machines which we could abuse in any way we wanted. The film 'I Robot' posed this question when it showed 'humanoid robots' being shot 'execution-style', or being put through gladiatorial challenges, for the entertainment of a human audience which saw no moral issues when the expendables were machines.

If computer generated intelligence based on human programming, without an ability to have 'feelings', are the factors that distinguish a machine from a living being, then if more sophisticated devices could bridge these gaps would they count as true life rather than elaborate machinery? After all, according to Materialism – that's what we are; elaborate machines.

Take the issue of reproduction as an example. What's the underlying difference between humanoid robots that could only reproduce through a separate manufacturing unit, and a mule that is essentially the product of separate manufacturing units (because they can't reproduce themselves)?

If we say that the test of life is just based on living cells, then we exclude the possibility of acknowledging life in other forms even though we begin to see the possibilities for such life. There is no right or wrong answer here other than to acknowledge that we use definitions for our own purposes and agendas.

As things stand we **don't** know how to generate *experiences*, or *growth*, or *self reproduction* in small machines, so these are theoretical arguments... but they do help us to focus on the issues of what Life may be.

Would there be a moral dilemma if we did manage to re-create such mechanical capabilities in a proven way? The robots would be there, either way, and labels wouldn't stop them becoming another competitor or friend in life.

In short, are we are being inconsistent when applying our assessments about life, and are we trying to do this without having any clear purpose? Are we simply making judgements on the basis of what is more familiar to us? I think that many people will need more time to ponder these issues.

If you don't believe that Life is anything more than sophisticated mechanics which we will one day learn to mimic using other materials, then you will lean towards mechanical definitions. Those who feel that life is special will try to articulate the special factors.

With these considerations in mind I offer some alternate definitions with which to assess the nature of Life from the vast array that are out there :

Life	is a source of randomness and spontaneity in the universe, that can change the inevitable path which physical things would otherwise follow, and which has the capacity to sense an environment and interact with it in order to 'create, assemble, and achieve', instead of succumbing to decay.
Life	is an assembling influence which is able to adapt to its environment and control its own functions in order to metabolise, grow, reproduce, and otherwise function.
A Physical Being	is the physical manifestation of the underlying stuff of life which may include: a life-force; a soul; a mind; and knowledge.
Spiritual Life	is the active deployment of Thought alone.
Conscious Life	is an assembling influence which is aware of its circumstances through experience and logical analysis, allowing it to anticipate and control its circumstances to improve and prolong its chances of survival, while allowing it to grow, reproduce, and achieve objectives.
Physical Life	is a self-sustaining mechanism that can seek out and use sources of energy to perform activities and achieve things such as growth, reproduction, and manipulating its environment.
A Social Group	is an assembly of living entities that can act together as one unit with an overarching co-ordination that may also provide self-generated thoughts to guide its actions.

Food for thought at least.

4 Some Key Aspects of Physical Life

After looking at definitions, we should now be much more aware of the factors which have relevance to the nature and origin of Life and Mind.

As a general rule our understanding of Life tends to work from big picture issues that people have identified, down into the detail which might explain them. When we find the nub of those details we can uncover some remarkable facts, but we often have to understand that detail in order to appreciate the wonder that is hidden in the depths.

In this chapter we will try to understand some of the bedrock facts on which we can build the 'castle' of our understanding, and these relate to some basic questions from each of the 3 main aspects of our enquiries: the workings of our bodies; the workings of our Minds, and our origin.

- Why is **water** always a **vital part of Life on Earth**? Does it have special properties? Could it even be the mythical 'Life Force'?

- Is it true that a bunch of scattered spare parts can *assemble* **themselves** into complex biological machines, and even entire cells?

- Building on Chapter 2, is there anything else in the workings of our brain to suggest that *hard logic* **is not enough** to explain our Minds?

- Is there anything in the beginning of a life that could give us clues to its special nature? **At what point do we judge Life to begin**?

In considering these things we will begin to uncover more of the core factors that make physical Life work, but also more of the challenges that Life had to overcome in order to get going. Yet we also need to develop a sense which can, like a good detective story, probe for answers to a number of questions, such as:-

- **What** is happening strategically – ie. the conceptual position that each activity fills within each process, and the overall workings of a cell?

- **How** does it happen - ie. the mechanics and chemistry that seem to be in operation through the known chain of events?

- **Why** does it happen – what triggers it, (setting the objective), or what makes a choice between different options that could be followed?

- What is the **source of energy** that powers each activity?

- How can the **effectiveness** of physical functions within a living cell be far more successful than we might normally expect outside it?

- How do cells ensure the **purity** of their outputs, seemingly by applying **control** over the quality of each process which might otherwise be disrupted by contaminants or other factors?

Armed with all of these we will then take a close look, (in Chapter 5), at the physical mechanics of how life works, uncovering some of its amazing abilities; after which we can then consider the nature of Evolution and the Origin of Life in Chapters 6 & 7.

However before we get going it's worth setting a context.

As we saw in Chapter 3 there are vast numbers of *single* celled organisms that exist on our planet in the form of Bacteria and Archaea. Such is the diversity of life that an estimated 99% of these 'Prokaryote' organisms have yet to be documented and characterised[12].

They sustain themselves; they replicate; and they can produce chemical by-products – but that's about it. The cells which have a greater 'sense of purpose' tend to be Eukaryotes which make multi-celled organisms like us.

The abundance of Prokaryotes and their relative simplicity compared to Eukaryote cells may make them seem like prime candidates for analysis, but we have discovered that most of the ones which **have** been tested and categorised **cannot** be cultivated/cultured using standard laboratory techniques[12], so they can be tricky to work with. Given the vast number of prokaryotes that we haven't even looked-at, we should also recognise that anything we have learned so far is only likely to be part of the overall story, and that other species may well reveal more mysteries.

Eukaryote cells are generally many times larger than Prokaryotes, (approx. 10 times in linear dimensions, and 1000 times by volume[12]), and are far more complex in their structure and activities. Yet studies into Eukaryote cells have been far better funded because they help us to understand our own bodies, where some ten trillion cells, (10^{13} - ie. 10,000,000,000,000), co-exist, with their different specialisms, to make up the average human.

Eukaryotes are primarily defined by their internal operations and compartments, *not* because of any ability to work together as a group. So the domain of 'Eukaryotes' also includes *single celled organisms*, (such as Amoeba), which go much further than simple reproduction - displaying many characteristics of competitive life, even though they don't have a brain. Some of these single celled creatures are passive, while others are aggressive, such as Didinium which swim around looking for prey, then fire paralysing darts at those other cells before literally eating them![12]

All of this activity strongly indicates that control and purpose is being exercised by these miniscule creatures, and yet none of the individual cells I have mentioned are thought to have a brain. Put another way, if cells are just bags of chemicals they shouldn't have any sense of purpose or intent, especially when *starting* activities or making *choices*.

This has been recognised by scientists and they have therefore suggested[12] that unthinking 'Signalling' mechanisms inside cells, (similar to a series of 'on-off' switches), could equate in some way to a pseudo brain. As things stand, that is merely an expression of hope, as nothing like this has been demonstrated. A pseudo brain of this nature is **not** impossible, but equally it is **not** something we can take for granted.

Even if it were correct, such a 'biological computer chip' would seem to require a lot of pre-programming by something. I say this because all chips work by flicking micro-switches; it's not a silly point to be dismissed. Sterile chemicals are not expected to understand information or programming – they should only be able to react in a fixed way.

4.1 <u>Philosophical Considerations</u>

Richard Dawkins[19] and others have described living creatures as the most **complex** objects in existence anywhere in the universe. As a concept that is both fascinating and believable, (even though we say so ourselves)! Suns, rocks, oceans, and air all appear simple in comparison, even if their important secrets are buried deep within the working of atoms.

However it's the amazing **variety** of living things that gives an extra dimension to that complexity. Living things manage to survive in some of the most hostile and remarkable environments on the planet – pretty well everywhere you can imagine – which shows huge adaptability.

There is also a third dimension to this subject, which is to consider **how these organisms emerged**.

For much of human existence the wondrous intricacy and sophistication of physical bodies, (whether plant or animal), plus the things they achieved, made it seem that they couldn't have been the product of sterile chemicals acting in unthinking ways. So people turned to God for an explanation.

Philosophically, this explanation has been challenged by the Theory of Evolution[20] which was originally proposed jointly by Wallace and Darwin in 1858, (as explained in the notes). Each man had separately formed his opinion after making a series of observations which showed that species living in different locations, had developed distinct & unique characteristics.

They suggested that a continual series of small changes in each group of animals occurred as they reproduced, explaining how they gradually adapted to their environments, & accounting for all forms of life that we see today.

The acceptance and encouragement of scientific analysis has led to many other discoveries which have added support for this evolutionary view; showing that the physical operations of life do indeed have large elements which **could** be explained by physical Matter/Energy alone, (Chapter 6).

It remains a separate question whether Matter/Energy was the sole **origin** of Life. The evidence doesn't rule out the possibility of direct creation by God; or that God used His earlier physical creations as tools to achieve His later ambitions for Life. Neither does it rule out other possibilities: such as the influence of 'other types of stuff' that underpin reality, which might also bring other useful capabilities beyond those of Matter/Energy.

I leave you to judge which of these is more likely to be correct based on what scientists have observed about the mechanisms of Life, as outlined in this and the next 3 chapters. Yet this is far from being a complete picture, even if the analysis has been taken to an impressive level of detail so far.

When you look at these mechanisms in overview, there are still many basic questions relating to the special nature of Life that remain unanswered, as well as some scientific findings which seem to challenge the *principles* by which Matter/Energy is believed to operate.

In Book 1 we saw that mainstream science **does** now accept that there *may* be hidden factors at work in the Universe and some of these, such as Dark Energy are considered to be all around us, even if we can't detect them.

So the possibility of 'other types of stuff' casting an influence on Life is not one to be dismissed out of hand; especially when we see in section 4.3 that 'cause & effect' factors are not sufficient to enable us to live normally.

We will find another remarkable pointer to the essence of Life in the ability of some complex cell components to **assemble themselves** – they're not made/'born'! Although this might seem to be out of the pages of some wild science fiction fantasy, this does actually happen[12], suggesting that there might be knowledge and purpose being exercised by unthinking chemicals.

While Materialists may find such suggestions 'emotive' they cannot deny that these are eye-catching capabilities: and they do not have an answer of their own. A purely chemical solution may yet emerge but as things stand observations of what is happening do not fully explain why & how specific molecules are selected, drawn together, and then assembled **in a particular sequence**, using 'tools' such as scaffolding to assist them[12]!

I mention these things as a lead-in to one other important factor in our analysis. As we go through the mechanisms of Life you are likely to be struck by the remarkable intricacy and control of the processes operating inside a cell, which will leave you wondering how unthinking chemicals could possibly manage to avoid the chaos of random reactions, to only produce desirable outputs, at speeds which are 'way above' what we would normally expect in the wider world, (from which they had to emerge).

Part of the answer is that the **structures** & **mechanisms** inside a cell ensure that only the right things happen, so the chemicals 'flowing through the system' have no choice in what they do: but this just accepts that they exist.

Beyond such structural controls we will see that a number of processes within cells actually seem to make *choices* & *decisions* that seem much more than inevitable chemical reactions, which again suggests that other factors may be at work than unthinking atoms & molecules. Examples of such activities are sophisticated *quality checking* & *repair* mechanisms; or elaborate transport & route planning... *all without the influence of a brain*!

Again, this doesn't rule out the possibility of purely Materialist solutions emerging at some point, but in terms of making a judgement *today* about where solutions might be found, there are a number of reasons why people are prepared to consider other possibilities beyond strict Materialism:-

- There are quite a few unusual factors, not just isolated exceptions.
- The actions being undertaken by the components of Life seem to indicate a **pro-active** purpose that goes beyond the *reactive* abilities we might expect from any mechanism based in 'cause & effect'.
- The deeper that we investigate the core mechanisms of life, the more intricate and complex they become - throwing out new challenges.

A 'starter list' of factors which are posing some of the biggest challenges to an explanation of Life is presented in section 5.3 - showing why the observed activity of these functions can suggest the presence of crude 'awareness'– whether that is actually the case or not. As a lead into that we have to begin separating processes and their explanations into 2 categories:

- **'Structural factors'** which have been set-up in advance to manipulate chemicals in fixed ways. *But what put these things in place?* This is where we turn to the traditional explanations of Evolution and/or God.

- **'Dynamic factors'** which are 'of the moment', either appearing to arise spontaneously or somehow 'to order', as the need arises. *But what detects those needs and raises 'an order'*; or *allows unthinking chemicals to* adapt *to circumstances and appear to make decisions?*

It is easy to see why the 'dynamic factors' could point to other types of stuff with different capabilities, if the activities seem to go well beyond the abilities of Matter/Energy. You will have to make up your own mind about those examples as we pursue them in Chapter 8; however prior to that, we have to consider the implications of the structural arrangements, (in Ch 7).

In principle, all of the critical functions/mechanisms needed to be in place before the first cell could come into existence – that means **all** of the core components, structures, chemical processes, and perhaps some basic controls as well. Admittedly the first cell could be more simple than the ones we see today, but because many of the core mechanisms are universal, (across all known cells), it is fair to assume that most if not all of those, at least, would have been present for the first cell too.

There is a general inclination for people to believe that Evolution can explain the origin of pretty well everything in the emergence of life. Yet we have to distinguish the general notion of evolution from the single core mechanism available to perform the task. As mentioned before, the *only process* for Evolution that we know of cannot have existed before the first cell, therefore **it is logically impossible for it to explain the origin of life.**

This is acknowledged by science. So the best which scientists can hope-for is that we find an alternative mechanism of evolution, applying similar principles that could operate before the first cell existed: but as yet even the detailed *concepts* for such a mechanism have a fair way to go.

Research into this is being conducted within the new scientific field of Abiogenesis. It will not be an easy task. The challenges are not simply to demonstrate an outline chemical/mechanical process, (which no longer exists), but to realistically explain how this could bring us to our present position within the **timescales** that are available.

No proposed solution can be '*down to chance*'; potentially taking us '*as far backwards as it could forwards*'. Mechanisms must be slick enough & with enough '**sense of direction**' to make steady progress in the time available.

It will be fascinating to see what emerges from this research, and I will indicate some lines of enquiry as we progress through various descriptions of what currently happens within living things.

So what *can* the existing Theory of Evolution[20] contribute?

If the theory is correct, and there's a lot of evidence to suggest that it is, then it provides a compelling way to explain how the huge **diversity** of life which we see today could emerge from very simple beginnings: its original purpose. As things stand, *how* those simple beginnings came to exist, (the complete story of our origin), remains a matter of faith - whether that's a belief in scientific materialism, or religion, as neither can prove their case.

Put another way, if Evolution is to be the answer, it must not only explain how the **stable profile** of each individual species **is forced to change** within a process of steady improvement, but must also show how sterile chemicals came alive. I will consider this in detail within Ch. 6 & 7. While one aspect of Evolution Theory does seem to be universally present across the globe, we have to find out how it is justified in the context of origin.

If Materialists are to avoid suggestions of divine influence they must also explain any 'Direction of Travel' that was achieved *before* the first cell existed, as well as afterwards. That will be tricky when survival wouldn't be an issue for anything that's not alive, because chemicals won't care.

It's interesting that part of the explanation for such a sense of direction within the process of evolution today seems to rely on the influence of thought, (as we will also see in Ch. 6). Is this another indication that not all influences are entirely based in mechanical or chemical activity?

I make the point now because of the findings that will emerge in section 4.3 below, which also seem to indicate that our every-day mental abilities cannot be achieved by the logical parts of our brain alone. They are dependent on more nebulous factors which may ultimately point to other influences than Matter/Energy.

If that is true, it may open-up the possibility that those other 'more nebulous factors' might be an influence at 'lower' levels of life without a brain, giving them the appearance of 'awareness'.

You will need to make up your own mind, based on the findings.

4.2   <u>Two Important Physical Factors</u>

In this section we will initially take a brief look at the properties which seem to make water so vital for all life. They relate to subtle factors in the way that water interacts with other things, and although that may not leave you breathless with excitement, I hope you'll find a lot of interest in there.

From those few pages, you will learn a lot that will help you to understand some of the more detailed processes described later; because here I start to look at the other crucial molecules for life – polymers.

The second area of interest will be the ability of certain molecules to get together and ***assemble themselves*** into complex structures. It's a remarkable thing to even consider, but it's real, and may ultimately help to explain the origins of life.

In trying to understand these things I will outline some of the techniques used by cells to achieve particular shapes, because shape is almost as important as the ability to perform specific reactions, for many of the components inside a cell.

4.2.1   <u>Polarity & the Special Properties of Water Necessary for Life</u>

Life, as we know it, cannot exist without water. This basic fact implies that there's something special about water which helps life to emerge.

Is it because water is a conduit for the elusive 'Life Force'? Those who argue in favour of this can point out that within the tissues of our bodies the highest percentages of water content are found in the parts that do most of the work - ie. the brain, other organs, and muscles.

Human bodies are made up of around 60% water, with the brain being composed of some 73%, (growing with use), and lungs 83%.[13]

Without identifying such a life force, we cannot say if this association is correct, however it seems *unlikely*. The higher percentages are probably just related to the delivery of much higher levels of oxygen and nutrient to those active areas which use it, via the blood stream.

What scientists do recognise is that water has a number of special features which help life in a variety of ways. Many of these, as we shall see, relate to the **polarity** of its molecules, (ie. a slightly negative electric charge on one side, and a slightly positive electric charge on the other side).

Without forming any firm chemical bonds, these charges can cause the water molecules to stick together to a degree; and can aid other types of reaction; plus, in other circumstances, might also assist the transmission of electric currents, as we will see.

These are all very 'physical' effects and nothing to do with any hidden life force, yet by exploring these properties a little further we can gain more insight into the 'boundary lines' for normal functions. There are persistent rumours that living things are able to perform reactions that **shouldn't** normally occur in water. We will see if that is really correct.

As a reminder to those who've forgotten their school chemistry, water is a combination of two gasses: hydrogen and oxygen. In fact, in a water molecule, two hydrogen atoms will attach to one much larger oxygen atom – hence the chemical formula H_2O. The different atoms bind with each other because they are each quite reactive substances, but in combination they stabilise each other by forming strong bonds and sharing electrons.

From one perspective, the simple fluidity of water can be thought of as helpful: **enabling** reactions to occur by bringing together chemicals that are dissolved/mixed with it, allowing them to react. However in many other ways water can be seen as an insulator – *hindering* or *preventing* reactions from occurring, and therefore acting as a stabilising influence.

These contrasting aspects of water effectively compete against each other, and it depends on particular circumstances which of those effects will win out. However these symptoms actually arise for three main reasons.

Firstly, in most circumstances **pure** water is chemically neutral, so it will not easily react with many other chemicals that may be 'dissolved' within it, (although it can react violently with some metals like sodium & potassium). Secondly, liquid water molecules are densely packed, so they'll completely surround anything that enters the pool thereby acting as a barrier to other chemical reactants that may be around, (unlike gasses where the molecules have lots of spaces between them). These are the factors that stabilise.

The third aspect, which generally aids reactions, relates to the polarity of the water molecules, which arises because the negatively charged electrons in the molecule are not shared equally between the hydrogen and oxygen atoms – making one side slightly negative and the other slightly positive.

As with all other substances, if different sections of a molecule are pulled apart, they will also **not** share the electrons evenly. The separate parts, become known as 'ions', because some will always become positively charged while the others will have an equivalent negative charge.

In water molecules the strength of the polarity is pitched at just the right level to make it do a number of extraordinary things, such as:-

a) dissolving many chemical compounds, by separating *their* active elements - turning each into ions, but not fundamentally changing them.

It does this by severing the chemical bonds which hold these active elements together and then surrounding each part in water molecules – making them less concentrated. For instance, salt is a combination of sodium and chlorine, but water splits these two elements apart and holds them as separate 'ions' waiting to be used. This makes them more accessible and usable to the bodies of living organisms.

In this way it can also trap free oxygen within it, allowing water-based creatures to breathe through their gills.

b)   allowing liquid water molecules at the surface of a droplet or even a pool to form weak bonds between each other, that acts like a thin skin with a certain tension across it. This tension is important because it allows water to be drawn up thin tubes, as we see in the stems of plants and the trunks of trees.

In combination with the solvent properties of water, this ability allows the liquid to distribute chemical nutrients to all parts of a plant.

c)   enabling water to structure itself in a crystalline form (ice) at lower temperatures, making it far less dense than liquid water – which means that ice floats instead of sinking to the bottom of a lake or sea.

This allows aquatic life to live a lot longer in extreme conditions, because the ice protects/insulates the underlying water from further heat loss to a colder atmosphere – keeping it liquid.

It also means that when water freezes the ice takes up more space, which can help to break down rocks into soil.

d)   absorbing proportionately more heat than other chemicals before its temperature rises. For instance, if you pump a specific amount of heat into an empty metal pan its temperature would rise by a greater amount than would be achieved by an equal mass of water receiving the same amount of heat.

This is because some of the energy that's put into water will be used to break its hydrogen bonds creating water ions that effectively store the energy for use rather than raising pure temperature.

This means that water helps to regulate the temperature of the environment by generally being cooler than the background in hot conditions, but warmer in cold weather, and in the process it makes some of that stored energy available to the creatures within it.

Water itself only becomes more chemically active when it is 'ionised'. This could occur through the influence of other chemicals mixed within it, (which have pulled some of the hydrogen atoms away from their oxygen atom); and/or raised temperatures.

Ionisation exaggerates the polarity of the different water components, but **not** generally to the extent that it makes them react permanently with the other chemicals mixed in it, (which would change both). For the most part water ions will form a loose connection to the other chemical, helping both sets of ions to become more stable, in a manner reminiscent of 'holding hands' rather than merging. It is this state of affairs that is often referred to as chemical hydration.

If the temperature of water is raised, the energy available encourages ions to react with each other, whereas if temperatures fall reactions are less likely to occur - generally stabilising the environment. So in any particular set of circumstances there are a variety of factors that will influence outcomes.

Aside from these specific properties which relate to polarity and ionisation, water has a very mixed relationship with electricity.

Pure water is a very poor conductor of electricity because it contains very few ions, (and ions are the things that allow electricity to flow). Yet if water has dissolved chemicals within it, the ions from those elements can allow water to become a very good conductor of electricity indeed.

The ability to conduct electricity is enhanced by two additional features. Firstly, it can increase dramatically in the presence of a strong electric field, allowing the current to flow with even greater power. Secondly, water, (being a fluid), can work its way into all the nooks and crannies of an object, increasing the exposure to any electric current. In practical terms, this means that your wet skin might receive a larger shock than it would otherwise get if touched by the same thing when dry.

Given the high water content of the brain, and a recognition that there is a delicate chemical mix within it, this may be one reason why electrical activity could be so efficient there, and might also provide opportunities for subtle but unproven electromagnetic effects to help memory and thought.

In the 'real world' pure water is a very difficult thing to find, so most chemical activity will depend on which chemical elements are dissolved within it. Living cells maintain a very specific mix of chemicals in their water-based environment that are suited to their activities, whereas outside that 'closed world' the chemical soup could be very undesirable.

On this basis is there any truth to the suggestion that living cells enable reactions to occur that shouldn't normally take place?

This turned out to be a lot harder question to answer than I was expecting.

Let me say clearly that none of the chemical reactions which occur in a cell break the Laws of Physics. To that degree they are all normal.

Yet there **are** special things occurring in cells, and we have to dig a little deeper to understand some of the suggested issues.

The working components of living cells are '**polymers**', and a lot of cellular activity is dedicated to making them as well as using them. Polymers are chains of 'monomer' building blocks, (smaller types of chemical molecule), yet in broad terms polymers do not easily occur in the wider environment outside a living cell, if at all.

This is for a number of reasons. Firstly, a useful polymer should only be assembled from monomers, and yet in an **un**controlled environment there will be many other chemicals that would want to react with the monomers. Those could also be more reactive than the monomers are with each other – making contamination more likely if a choice of reactions was available.

It is likely that an unwanted reaction like this would also end any emerging polymer chain, (ie. stop it growing further).

However there are two other factors which demonstrate special circumstances. The first is that the type of chemical bond which holds monomers together within a polymer chain, are enabled because of a 'dehydration reaction' – which essentially means 'removing water'.

As a general indication of something special we can instinctively appreciate why this will be a lot more difficult, and highly unlikely, if you try to perform a dehydration reaction while immersed in a pool of water without special apparatus... but cells do have special apparatus, known as 'Enzymes' and 'Ribozymes'. These also work according to the Laws of Physics, but they are, none-the-less, remarkable evolutionary developments.

Before going on to explain a little more about these processes, let me tell you the other 'special factor'.

The processes which assemble polymers seem to be much more efficient/effective than even the controlled cellular conditions would suggest. Put another way, if the same concentrations of monomers and Enzymes that occur in a cell, are placed in a test tube, the resulting reactions will be nothing like as efficient as a cell. Why? Is it because we are seeing the 'life force' in operation? No - that doesn't seem to the case.

In layman's terms, active components such as Enzymes are not evenly distributed across the volume of a cell, as they are in a test tube. They are concentrated in certain positions and often in areas which can channel the monomers past them. As the various reactants are concentrated into a tighter space they seem to generate additional effects on each other making them more efficient. This effect is known as 'Macromolecular Crowding' which is thought to explain the efficiency difference. However while scientists generally seem confident that this will be the full answer, more work is needed to prove how specific circumstances improve effectiveness.

So returning to the earlier point about dehydration reactions - these do **not** remove water molecules as you might expect from the name.

The reactions remove hydrogen and oxygen ions from different 'host' molecules, (in this case, monomers), and then assemble those removed ions into a pure, stable water molecule which is chemically neutral. In the meantime, the host monomers effectively become more active as a result, causing them to react with each other, forming the polymers.

With the right conditions it is quite possible to achieve these reactions outside a cell, so once again there is no mysterious 'life force' at play – but that doesn't quite remove the mystery. Dehydration reactions are not an automatic first choice for a bunch of chemicals that are 'floating around'. These reactions would be a rare occurrence without the Enzyme molecules which engineer them – and they do not generally occur in the natural environment outside a cell.

Therefore the key point is not that the reactions are occurring, but how the first cell could ever arise to generate the conditions and the enzymes. As Bill Bryson pointed out in his book, "A Short History of Nearly Everything"[14] most headline theories about the origin of the first cell say that it emerged from a water-based environment, but they skip over the absence of Enzymes and controlled conditions. The challenges are clear.

Those challenges grow bigger when we realise that a lot of these reactions occur in circumstances where the chemical bonds which have been formed between the monomers **could be reversed** or undone by other reactants. A long polymer chain could therefore be quite a rare event in an uncontrolled environment. So to get life going, there would need to be a way to preserve polymers long enough to be used. Enzymes and Ribozymes also play a key role in that stabilising effect within cells, as we shall see later, so in many ways they are very necessary to life, but their origin is a mystery.

We will see in Chapter 7 why a pre-cell evolutionary process is so difficult to envisage. However to briefly cover-off some other suggestions, the possibility that clay or crystal surfaces could encourage the development of polymers, and might give them stability, hasn't been fully demonstrated. Nor do they provide the 'direction' that evolution needs, as neither clay or crystals have any need for life, and nor do the polymers themselves.

So creating the right environment for many polymers to emerge outside a living cell, **is**, and would always have been, very very hard to envisage without a process or mechanism to guide it – which we don't have.

4.2.2 Self Assembly and the Importance of Molecular Shape

As mentioned earlier, there's a real dilemma over the origin of the first cell including some of the remarkable internal devices within it, such as Ribosomes. In simple terms the only natural way to produce more cells & more Ribosomes is by getting them to reproduce themselves, but before the first cell there was nothing to do this – so how did they come about?

A clue may arise from another astonishing feature in life: that a number of complex 'structures' seem able to **assemble themselves** from their many necessary components.... we just don't know how they do it!

Some Ribosomes do this and also many viruses[12], but of course, in these cases the final object, (Ribosome or virus), doesn't exist before it is created, so it is perhaps more accurate to say that the individual components seem to know what they want to build... and these **aren't** just processes where things happen to be drawn together as if to a magnet.

The procedures are highly complex, requiring a very precise sequence of steps, (even using proteins as a scaffold, etc[12]!). It seems like the stuff of sci-fi fantasy but we see it happening[97], so it has led to a lot of analysis.

Viruses have many similarities with cells but they are not generally considered to be alive because they don't have their own reproductive capabilities. They invade all types of cell and then cause *their host* to manufacture copies of both the virus DNA and other necessary components, after which those 'alien' parts will then spontaneously **self-assemble**. For instance one type of virus can form a ball with an outer shell that is made from a lot of regular shapes, in a similar manner to a geodesic dome.

As a demonstration of this outside a cell, the necessary components of a virus , (such as specific types of RNA and proteins), can be mixed in a test tube, (which is obviously much larger than a cell), yet they somehow manage to come together, arrange themselves, bind, and then fold into distinct shapes, before becoming fully functioning copies of the virus[12].

To gain some clues on how this might be done, let's look at the normal 'duplication' mechanisms within a living cell.

The working machinery of cells, (plus some walls/membranes), are all made from thin strands of organic chemicals, (typically **protein** and **RNA** *polymers*), which bend themselves into elaborate shapes.

It is that shape which is so important because each distinct form, positions the active components on that strand in the precise 3D locations necessary to perform very specific tasks. For instance, 'enzymes' fit around the molecules they are trying to manipulate, and they therefore have to mould themselves into a 'negative' form of that shape, while also precisely positioning their active elements opposite the specific atoms on the target molecule which they are designed to manipulate.

To be clear, unlike viruses, these very long polymer chains *don't* create the simple outline of a shape we might recognise like a ball. They allow a filled-in 3D shape to emerge from the tangle of spaghetti that they resemble. Yet these shapes are actually very precise. Each type of protein has a distinct form, which each copy of that protein must achieve.

In terms of explaining the complex folding process, the study of protein polymers has shown that these specific shapes are achieved by both

- the position of each **type** of monomer molecule along the chain, plus

- the different energies that each of these different monomers contain, which exert forces on each other that can either attract or repel other monomers as they come close, positioning each other in 3D.

Yet this is only part of the story because, as I mentioned earlier, some proteins must use *scaffolding* structures or *containers*, plus 'assistants' known as '*Chaperones*', to check and correct a shape. This is because the chemicals can fold and stabilise in very unhelpful ways. The tools and chaperones have to be used in a specific sequence at specific times – not immediately when they happen to be near each other. This seems to smack of purpose, if not 'intent'. But of course a chaperone may be shaped so that it can only chemically attach to one protein with a particular type of error, without intent. In many cases these perfectly matched components exist for just one task amongst many, so there are vast numbers of these 'tailored' parts. If so, we have to ask if these are really just lucky evolutionary developments that happen to work seamlessly together in a long process?

The situation becomes even more intriguing when we realise that *some* of the Enzymes can flex their shape to achieve different things, or to assist more than one type of target molecule.

We can speculate that viruses may fold themselves into precise geometric shapes, (such as helixes, spheres, cylinders, and flat sided objects), using similar techniques... however the virus components will be alien to the cell, as will its need for any specialised shape or support structures. In this respect it may be significant that viruses bring their own genetic code with them, (their own instruction manual), but it is also surprising that the components assemble themselves in a particular sequence without pre-established structures in their host to guide them.

Neither is this like a crystal where the shapes and internal energies of the **same** chemical molecule line up to form a solid shape with a fixed geometric lattice. These things have very diverse components which could theoretically be assembled in very different sequences, even with the chemical attractions involved, (eg. the virus DNA is always on the inside of a shell; and the outer shell needs 'external assistance' to form its shape).

These are all indicators of dynamic influences that are 'of the moment' rather than being structural. The difficulty for mechanical self-assembly processes is that the molecular energies only have a very short range, and their distinct signatures would become very blurred well before they could find their way across a test tube, so it's very hard to rationalise how self-assembly could work in a precise sequence? In short, we just don't know.

4.3 Elements of Decision-Making

This section deals with properties that are only applicable to thinking beings although they could point to deeper factors that operate in life as a whole. As mentioned in Chapter 3, the characteristics we normally attribute to consciousness include :-

experience, *purpose*, **principles**, *desires,* **control**, and *awareness*

These are not properties that we attribute to sterile chemicals, which leads many people to suspect that some other fundamental factor may be at play, and it's very interesting to see that such ideas have been reinforced by findings from recent research.

As I hopefully demonstrated in Ch. 2 our capabilities for experience/ awareness/etc. go beyond even the most sophisticated computers that mankind has designed, and there is currently no way to bridge the gap.

In concept, the best Materialist hope of a way forward in understanding the mechanical elements of Thought & experience seems to be to accurately model all of the neural networks, nerve fibres, sub-cell mechanisms and chemicals in a brain, and then see if something like emotions and control can emerge from them. This is being attempted in the Blue Brain Project[11].

Based on the 'Computational Hypothesis' of the brain, this project hopes to deliver an accurate digital model of a human brain in 2023, by replicating all of the neural networks and even neurons, at cellular, sub-cellular, & chemical levels based on what we can glean from real brain tissues. Part of the declared purpose in this project is to shed light on some diseases of the brain, but it will inevitably be seen as a test of whether we are anything more than glorified computers, so any outcome is likely to be faced with a barrage of criticism from one side or the other.

If this model generates anything that resembles true emotion and awareness then the implications will fundamentally shape our perceptions of consciousness. However, the difficulty will be in persuading the world about its authenticity, by having to prove that the programmed mimicking of biological processes hasn't introduced artificial logic or changed/bolstered circumstances in the model.

Yet, even before this project, modern brain scanners **have** shown that there are a myriad of separate neural networks in the brain: some seemingly dedicated to logic while others are dedicated to emotion, and that **both** are normally **always** used when we make **any** decision. If the two conflict then these networks will battle it out to determine a conclusion. Sometimes logic will win; sometimes emotion.

The research[15] goes further to suggest that if the logical and emotional areas of the brain become disassociated from each other, (eg. due to brain damage), even if they are both still active, the individuals concerned find it very difficult to make a decision despite them being aware of the available facts and being able to apply their full logical reasoning.

The symptoms have suggested to doctors that these patients may be lacking the ability to *generate a sense of purpose/direction* without the emotional assessment – our way of focussing-in on relevant facts. In one example the afflicted person was shown to be overwhelmed when asked to choose from a small range of potatoes at a supermarket while doing her weekly shop.

There were approximately half a dozen varieties of potato, but they came in different bag sizes, prices, etc, and she **was** overwhelmed because there were too many possibilities within the uncertainties of the situation.

That inability to prioritise the options perhaps illustrates that logical 'cause & effect' brain networks don't work when there is vagueness rather than precision; or there's a need to generate objectives; or in situations where there could be multiple outcomes – ie. true randomness.

It is the **need** for emotion that is so striking here, because it seems that it's *those* networks which handle vagueness, randomness, & creativity in order to set objectives. Causal logic is not enough for us to function effectively.

While it's easy to imagine that physical computer chips might be able to generate the equivalent of a 'logical neural network' based in cause & effect, it is very difficult to imagine how similar networks and components could produce something that's not logical or precise, like an emotion.

So do these findings imply that thought and reasoning tap into something beyond Matter/Energy? Given the above, it's a possibility. Please try to bear this in mind as we progress through the chapters.

4.4 <u>When does a Life Begin?</u>

Despite the many known facts surrounding the biology of fertilisation for eggs or seeds, plus our knowledge of early cell development; the subject of *when* a new life begins is shrouded in personal judgements.

The question has potentially great significance if we relate it to matters of government policy on such things as pregnancy terminations and contraception; or even the morality of research into the use of stem cells etc., but these matters are only part of the issue.

If you believe in the concept of a 'life force' then it must exist *before* it can animate a seed or a body. Equally, if you believe in the soul as a necessary factor in human life then it must either :-

- exist before being 'injected' into a body, or
- the process of creating a new life on Earth must also mark the creation of a new soul.

There may be equivalent factors that you could imagine for plants and other forms of life, but the point I am trying to get at is, that the moment of conception may **not** be the start of life. A new life may only exist after **all** of the necessary ingredients are added, or perhaps once a foetus has developed sufficiently to become viable on its own.

On a broader philosophical point, as mentioned before, Materialist thinking says that nothing since the Big Bang has been a true start point, just the next step in an inevitable process. The associated principle of Causality also means that true start points are very hard to explain, so if new life is a true beginning it would be very significant in many ways.

Yet we know that the physical aspects of life <u>are</u> part of a continuing process, as parents generate the genetic material for the next generation... **except** that of course, the 'life process' does seem to have had a true beginning on Earth with the origin of the first living cell... in whatever way that occurred. Again, we will look at this vexed question in Chapter 7.

Suffice it to say that while some people will look for chemical processes to explain the origin of life, others will look for sources of spontaneity, and still more will turn to God. However in terms of guiding our assessment of Life we need to consider whether there is anything in the beginning of a new individual that can help identify critical factors about what life is.

As we should all know by now, all physical life on Earth is based on cells, yet some of these cells are active from the moment of their creation, while others start-out dormant and become active under certain circumstances.

In plants, the dormant seeds are **presumed** to become active through a chemical reaction when they interact with water plus a cultivating medium such as soil or compost. Those seeds will already have been fertilised, and although the pollen itself was transported to the seed plant, pollen is not generally seen to be alive.

The key question with plants is therefore what turns an inactive container of chemicals into a living organism? We don't know, but as we can store sacks/boxes of seed for a long time without them growing, if there is such a thing as the life force it doesn't seem to enter the seed or do anything to it without water, and generally soil as well. Because water is active/dynamic, (while soil isn't), it draws the eye as a triggering factor.

The follow-up question is whether water is purely a chemical trigger; or a neutral fluid that can help **facilitate** other chemical reactions; or whether it might act as a conduit for other influences – such as the 'life force'?

For animals, birds, and fish, the fertilising elements that come together are more dynamic than plants, and are also enabled through water-based fluids. Unlike seeds, eggs will start to develop as soon as they have been fertilised. Through the microscope we see sperm moving under their own power via a wriggling tail, and they also seem to seek out an egg.

As we do not see eggs developing before they have been fertilised, then in terms of identifying the source of life, some people have concluded that the dynamic sperm carries the life force, not the egg.

Of course it may be that this is also a purely chemical process, with the wriggling sperm being nothing more than an energised motor which carries a chemical trigger to activate the egg. I'm not aware of specific sensors in the sperm, or of any other chemical attractions that might draw the sperm to the egg, but that doesn't mean they don't exist to help them seek each other out.

The chromosomes in a sperm are also known to determine the eventual sex of a foetus, (at least in mammals), although there have been suggestions that each egg may only permit one type of sperm to enter, (yet to be proven). While it is clear that DNA is normally required from both parents, and that the mother's protective development of the foetus in the womb is vital to life, it is also true that cloning is achieved with the DNA of just one living being, and that reproductive development **can** be triggered by specific chemicals not necessarily a sperm.

This reinforces the perception that it **is** chemical reactions which activate the processes of life, and yet those processes go well beyond the normal boundaries of chemical activity, becoming self-sustaining, controlling, repeatable, and leading to growth not decay. So if there is something more, such as a life force, it may be that the egg and/or sperm may transfer enough of it to begin a new life, or allow the cell to tap into that force.

There is a lot of speculation here. We don't have a complete story, and yet we have to be fair: the only philosophy which can be expected to produce more direct evidence of its case in the foreseeable future is Materialism.

Sperm are not self-sustaining, cannot reproduce themselves, and outside a perfect environment they cannot survive for longer than a few moments. Even within a perfect environment (the male testes) they can only survive for a few weeks at most, and inside a womb, perhaps 5 days to one week.

Is a sperm alive? Only a few would say so, and the egg also has to be active in order to allow conception. Once again science observes a number of key processes such as 'Spermatogenesis'[16] and 'Meiosis' that bring sperm and egg to readiness, but we don't know what drives these processes or how chemicals become alive.

Within the reproductive process there are various moments that could mark the starting point of life. The early foetus becomes much more stable around day 14 when a number of basic factors are firmly established - a critical stage in early development known as 'gastrulation'. This is the point which many scientists regard as the start of the 'individual', which is why it has been used to determine a boundary for stem cell research.

However, the individual cells will certainly be alive almost immediately after fertilisation, even if we may not classify them as an 'individual' or being. There is an implication from this, that life at this stage may simply be mechanical, and yet there are single celled creatures which seem to go well beyond simple mechanics, (such as Didinium[12] mentioned earlier), whose identification of prey, targeting them, and firing of darts, all seem to display control & a crude but **proactive** awareness. Perhaps you disagree?

Although the fertilised cells of humans will be active and reproducing themselves over many weeks to create a body, western society generally only recognises new human life when the foetus becomes self-sustaining, (scientifically considered to be at 23 weeks gestation). However at this early stage, very few foetuses (20%) will survive birth without intense medical care, and survival rates only really become meaningful in the traditional sense around 26 weeks. Other forms of life will have very different periods before the new life becomes self-sustaining.

From another perspective, if you believe that life ends when brain activity stops, then its presence must mark a beginning and it's interesting to note that recognizable patterns of EEG activity in the foetus also begin around 24-26 weeks[17].

Yet if you translate the notion of a life force into a crude level of awareness and control, we might speculate that all cells contain very primitive forms of 'consciousness', meaning that life is marked by the activation of each cell. All these ideas have degrees of validity, and have their own interest factors, yet Life will just do its thing and carry on regardless, (until matters of policy intervene to stop it).

If we consider all of the unused eggs, wasted sperm, and the many foetuses that are rejected in nature prior to them becoming viable, there are differences of opinion about whether all living cells have to be protected from experimentation on moral grounds. Yet there's a risk that 'the earlier we set the start point of life, the less valuable life may appear to become', so the politicians have to balance this against the value of research.

If you believe that life only has true significance when a soul enters the body, (a moment known as 'ensoulment'), would it really occur at the moment of conception when we know that some 65- 90% of human fertilised eggs are thought to be **rejected**[18]? If so there would be a lot of discarded souls.

> Such studies have shown that the **success** rate for other creatures can be as high as 90% while it is only 30-35% for humans. This higher level of human failure has been attributed to various early processes becoming out of sync with each other, or not starting at all, plus the surprisingly high rate of chromosomal abnormalities in human embryos. The reasons are not clear, (although there may be links between these factors).
>
> I should also say that the term 'chromosomal abnormalities' doesn't have to mean mutations. It can include incompatibilities between a specific mix of chromosomes in the random selection we inherit from our parents, which we do not yet understand.

The level of 'wastage' after fertilisation, has prompted some religions to suggest that ensoulment may not happen at conception. While some may follow the guidance of science, saying that a soul may only enter a body at (say) 26 weeks, others may take a more traditional view.

A more challenging question concerning the timing of ensoulment may arise when we consider the case of twins. If a soul enters at fertilisation what happens when the cells separate at a later stage to form two foetuses? You can hopefully appreciate why there isn't a consensus on timing or the nature of souls.

5 How Cells Work – The Basis of Life

While most books about life will look at the amazing way in which bodies are assembled and operate, (with their complex and intricate bone structures, fluids, nerve system & organs), these all represent things which have grown from a single cell that was fertilised, and then reproduced itself ten trillion times, (in the case of humans), as we saw in the last chapter.

As the very first cells in an 'embryo' were duplicated and began working together as a unit, they started to produce chemicals of their own, and these in turn slightly changed the nature of the new cells that were produced later. Through this development period, (of the foetus in animals, and seedlings in plants), cells became ever more specialised to produce the specific components that mature organisms require to live.

So for our purposes, as amazing as bodies might be, the real secrets of Life will be found in the activity of cells.

This is a moderately technical chapter, but please don't let that put you off. It contains lots of interesting things in two main sections, revealing:

- The astonishing processes of reproduction and new life, including the purposes and uses of DNA, plus the manufacture of proteins.

- A description of the amazing cell metabolism – and the mechanisms which keep you alive on a day to day basis.

Compared to the processes of reproduction which deal with the magic of new life, day to day body functions don't have the same WOW factor, especially when they delve into the muck and grime of chemical processes.

Yet within these mechanisms are true nuggets of unbelievable amazement that make the operations of Metabolism *equally astonishing* features in the core processes of life.

So although this subject may not sound like the most exciting topic on earth you are likely to find a lot of fascinating things in the coming pages.

Individual cells have been described as living *cities* of activity for good reason, because they have:

- '**Power stations**' which distribute their energy for use when needed.

- true '**Programmable Assembly Line Machines**', with elaborate supporting mechanisms for quality control and 'on the fly' repairs.

- elaborate mechanisms for the **Repair** of intricate components.

- an astonishing range of transport **vehicles** which left scientists 'gobsmacked' when they were first discovered. Honestly you won't believe what these things do!

- intricate '**Road**' and '**Telecoms**' *networks* for transport and signalling, which do not have access to a brain, and yet somehow manage to work out routes to a myriad of end destinations.
- 'Buildings' with **security systems that control what goes in and out** of the workspace they create.
- **Storage** and **Retrieval** facilities.
- **Recycling** and **Waste Disposal** units.

As you can imagine, I will be identifying these factors as we run through an overview of the way that cells operate.

To people who are not particularly 'attuned' to the intricate details of science, I have deliberately kept the chapter at a high enough level to retain your interest, while still probing the factors that pose challenging questions. Please don't be deterred, I aim to make it easy to follow.

However it may require a small amount of determination on your part to get through these core details.

The rewards will be that you get to fully appreciate the **truly** amazing cell components that enable physical Life to exist, which will then allow you to discover why the mysteries of life remain so elusive.

For those who are interested in a more complete picture of how cells work, to better appreciate the underlying issues, I have placed more extensive descriptions in the Appendices.

5.1 DNA and its Remarkable Contribution to Life

In relation to our 'quest' to identify the nature of Life, those unresolved issues which should gain most of our attention will *not* be the ones where we might simply look for a new mix of chemicals to explain a certain phenomenon. They are the factors which appear to breach the **principles** behind Matter/Energy: that may seem to break the known Laws of Physics.

In this respect the typical things being looked for are:

- Points of true beginning, as an indication of *spontaneity* or *randomness*
- Strong indications of <u>dynamic</u> *control* and *purpose*, which arise 'in the moment', (not part of a structured & inevitable process) – so beyond the abilities of atoms & molecules, which can only react chemically.
- Strategic factors which indicate a '*sense of direction*', having *objectives*, or the application of *concepts*.
- In terms of our brains and our minds, an explanation for *consciousness*.

This is not just theory. Here are some examples which illustrate real activities by living cells which are kept in a 'test tube' and therefore isolated from any brain. It is taken as a fact that :-

- DNA holds **information** which is utilised through a series of **codes**.
- We see enzymes **controlling** processes to only allow certain types of reaction to occur: even making **choices** and getting them wrong.
- We see cells **repairing** DNA and other internal structures in different ways – showing **adaptation** to circumstances.
- Evolution needs a way to establish a **sense of direction** in order to work

Scientific text books are littered with such descriptions, because that **is** what we observe to be happening. Yet atoms and molecules do not think; they do not see purpose or objective; and they do not make decisions. They only act in an inevitable chemical way.

Could it be that such perceived behaviour is just an illusion which reflects how our Minds work? We **do** seem to instinctively look for patterns & concepts as a way to rationalise things and impose meaning on them, but do these notions really reflect the underlying reality?

While the challenges for Dualism and Idealism are to demonstrate the presence of another type of stuff that can provide additional capabilities, the challenge for Materialism is to find explanations for the activities above, which can only use unthinking chemical processes.

From the examples later you will start to appreciate why so many processes within cells have appeared to display a level of 'awareness'. They go beyond the 'simple' detection of light or another chemical, (the normal 'mechanical' sensory functions), to seemingly display an understanding of the meaning behind those detections in relation to a situation.

Awareness doesn't *have* to be a high-end function of our brain in this respect, the nub of it is the understanding, even if that is very basic – and we each have to judge whether the individual circumstances could indeed be achieved in an inevitable chemical way, without understanding.

In this respect, scientific analysis has pushed ever deeper and found mechanisms of incredible intricacy which provide a description of what is happening, but not necessarily an explanation. **Often these details simply push the core mystery to even deeper levels of existence**.

This is where Materialists will typically argue that science hasn't yet delved deeply enough to reveal how the observed realities are achieved.

The great difficulty in this subject is that, whether you are Dualist, Idealist, or Materialist, it's very hard to **prove** that something doesn't exist. There will always be the suggestion that we simply haven't found 'it' yet, but on the other hand, humanity could waste many generations of effort looking for something that doesn't exist. There has to be a reasonable justification to continue any search.

I do not pre-judge where this will lead. I simply feel that it **is** important to acknowledge what is known, and what issues remain, because such facts are necessary to shape our beliefs against the reality of our situation.

5.1.1 The Stunning Structure and Purpose of DNA

From basic schooling you're likely to remember many of the core operations I am about to describe, but for accuracy I will give you some of the technical names for a number of the chemicals & components involved.

They are not difficult, but they are not obvious, and there are quite a few of them, so lack of familiarity may make them seem overwhelming if you try to remember them all at once. That isn't necessary. The most important thing is to get the gist of what is happening, so 'go with the flow' on your first read-through.

For those who have more appetite for the mechanics of how things work, again - I have placed fuller explanations within Appendix A, which may provide a more complete explanation of why some of the unresolved issues are relevant to our theme.

Once you have a general sense of how things work you can always go back and refresh your mind on the names if needs be. Only some of those names will recur later and, long-term, those will be the ones to try and remember, if at all.

So let's crack-on.

The 'nucleus' of every cell contains a full 'instruction manual' on how to build an entire body. In broad terms it does so by :-

1. providing a 'design template' for every cell component, **and**
2. providing the sequence in which they should be produced, in order to assemble them into a full working copy of that cell; **before**
3. 'saying' how each subsequent generation of cell should be adapted and linked together to create an entire body.

That manual is known as DNA.

Deoxyribo Nucleic Acid (DNA) is a polymer, and as we know from earlier chapters, such things are made by stringing together a long chain of standard building blocks known as Monomers. There are different types of monomer, and in the case of DNA, there are just 4 versions of one monomer 'family' being used, (the type known as **Nucleotides**). It is the *sequence* of those 4 nucleotides copied many times along that enormous chain which acts as the coded language of the manual.

The DNA inside a cell is split into sections known as 'Chromosomes', which provide separate sets of templates for things that need to be constructed, or describe different activities . There are 23 pairs, (46 strands of twisted ladder 'double helix' DNA), in the human genome. Each of the 23 pairs of chromosomes has one DNA strand from the mother and one from the father. These pairs are matched because their code basically describes the same sorts of instructions, but there will be slight differences between the two as each person is different. Across the 23 pairs we each have a complete set of DNA from **both** parents.

Like other multi-celled organisms, (Eukaryotes), our chromosomes are all linear, **_unlike_** the 1 or 2 chromosomes which exist in Bacteria & Archaea, (the single celled Prokaryote species), that are circular[21]. This fact has indicated that Mitochondria, (one type of compartment in our cells), may have originated as a bacterium which was absorbed by our larger cell.

Other Eukaryote species have different numbers of chromosomes. For instance, fruit flies have 4 pairs, while a rice plant has 12 pairs, and a dog has 39 pairs. So the size or complexity of the organism doesn't determine the number of chromosomes, and in a bragging contest for who's 'top dog' it would be a bad example! The size of each chromosome will also vary.

How the DNA code is divided between chromosomes is not yet understood. Although the human genome has been mapped it has not been fully analysed, so we cannot say whether there is a logical grouping of code inside each section. Having said that, we do know that just one of the 23 pairs is dedicated to sexual reproduction.

We also know that each chromosome is sub-divided into a number of '**genes**'. Each gene is an instruction that either describes how to build a cell component, (a '**_coding gene_**'), or a molecule that will help to regulate cell activities, (**_non-coding genes_**). There are 21,000 coding genes in a human genome, representing just $1\frac{1}{2}$% of DNA's length, plus 9,000 **non-coding** genes which help to configure and regulate the reproductive processes – so approx. 30,000 genes in total[12]. There is also a lot of duplication within the DNA code, making up the percentage differences.

Even with this in mind, at a more basic level, with two full sets of DNA inside each of your cells, the question arises as to which genes will be used to make you into a distinct individual? We all know that we display some traits from our mother and some from our father, but how is the selection made: of that gene from her, and this one from him?

Despite intensive research, this remains unclear, yet there are indications that it may relate to *many* factors such as: how genes are positioned along the DNA strand; the presence of regulatory chemicals; the nature of some code modifications; and the way they are stored in the nucleus.

Returning to the main processes, gene codes are flagged at the beginning with a 'start marker', and at the end with a 'stop' marker, which are used when the gene is copied. Those markers also help scientists to identify them, even though we don't always know what they do.

For the chromosomes as a whole there are also 'end stops' which are known as Telomeres. In normal cells, a bit of the Telomere coding seems to be lost each time the cell reproduces, until there is insufficient to reproduce again and the cell dies. It is tempting to think that this mechanism helps to prevent errors through 'wearing out' and excessive reproduction, yet some cancers are very aggressive because their Telomeres do not degrade[21].

Each of the paired chromosomes is wound around a spindle and this tight packaging helps them to fit into the nucleus in an orderly way. However it also means that the incredibly long and tightly wrapped DNA strand has to be uncurled before specific instructions inside it can be used/copied.

This is **not** simply a case of something working its way along that long strand, reading the code from beginning to end on a continuous sequence. New components can often be made in isolation. We need to ask how the triggering/copying molecules know which bit of code they are interested in, as well as *where to find* that particular set of instructions in a wound-up chromosome? There is no index and no Thought process to ask the question.

Many of these probing issues remain unanswered. So we can see *what* is happening but don't know everything about **why & how** they are achieved.

As indicated above, the key function of DNA is to act as a preserved instruction manual for every cell that is produced. To achieve this it is made from very stable molecules however the very need to make copies for the purposes of reproduction means that the DNA has to interact with other things – but carefully! This is achieved using the relationships that exist between the 4 nucleotide components.

The core of every nucleo**tide** is a nucleo**base**. The 4 nucleobases generally operate in 2 distinct pairs. Thymine always matches with Adenine (T-A); while Guanine always matches with Cytosine (G-C).

These base pairings **never change**, and when they are attached to each other the molecules gain a degree of stability, (become less reactive).

One of each pair can also be considered as the '**negative**' of the other.

Nucleobases are quite reactive compounds but they can also be stabilised, or made to react in specific ways, using one or more other 'bolt-on' molecules. The least reactive form is DNA but when it is copied as part of the reproductive process, the copy is set into a more reactive form – RNA.

DNA is a very long chain of nucleotide pairs set side by side in a line, taking the shape of a twisted ladder, (double Helix). The **rungs** are made

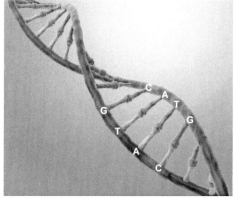

by the individual pairs which form a bond between them, (in the middle of the rung), while the sides of the ladder are made by stringing together the nucleotides at the ends of the rungs, (which are not pairs). As mentioned before, it's the **sequence** created by the **4 types** of nucleotide running along either *side* of the ladder which acts as the critical information store/code/ instruction manual

Orig. Image courtesy of FreeImages.com

Due to the pairings, **each side of the ladder represents a full copy of that manual**, but they are 'negatives' of each other. Copying, (or 'transcription'), of the DNA sequence to form RNA will normally be undertaken on just one side of the ladder, beginning at the start marker for a gene. It **always** results in a *single* strand of RNA nucleotides, (not a twisted ladder pairing).

Different types of RNA are used for different purposes. Some have specific functions in their own right, (such as rRNA and tRNA), but a large proportion will be used as working templates, (mRNA), copied from 'coding genes'. This type of RNA is used to produce the main working components of our bodies: another type of polymer known as a protein.

Proteins are long chains as well, but they are assembled from a different family of monomers known as Amino Acids. Unlike nucleobases, there are 20 amino acids that are available for use in a cell.

It is here that we see more clearly why DNA and RNA are regarded as codes. Particular combinations of nucleotide are used to signify different Amino Acids. More specifically, when 'devices' in a cell read an mRNA strand, every **three** nucleotides in the mRNA sequence, (a '**codon**'), will represent an identifier for <u>one</u> specific type of Amino Acid.

However, due to the pairing of nucleotides, an Amino Acid can be described in two ways – a positive and a negative. The matching description of a codon is therefore known as an **anticodon**.

5.1.2 An Overview of How Cells Make the Building Blocks of Life

The DNA in the nucleus of a Eukaryote cell, (like ours), is used to produce RNA (directly) and proteins (indirectly). Once manufactured, messenger RNA (mRNA) and transfer RNA (tRNA) move out of the nucleus to enter a manufacturing process, outlined in the following diagram.

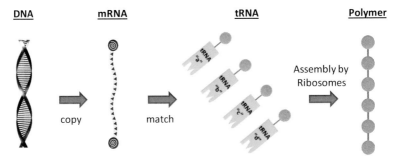

The short tRNA molecule, (shown in green above), is used as a label which attaches a corresponding Amino Acid, (shown as orange), based on the anticodon code, (at the bottom of the label). The thing which matches the two, and links them, (literally by a thin label 'string'), is a particular sort of enzyme. This is actually the translation mechanism for the code.

The long strand of mRNA, (yellow strand above, dark green below), is a precise description of the **sequence** of Amino Acids that have to be assembled in order to make a single viable protein. A mistake in the sequence or the use of an incorrect Amino Acid at any point could render the chain either useless or very destructive, (if it does the wrong thing).

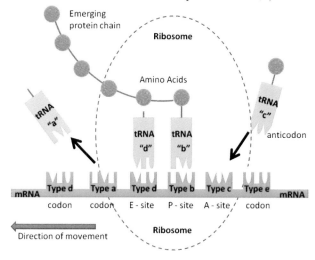

The complex assembly line machine which assembles a protein is called a Ribosome. This takes a strand of mRNA by its 'start end', and feeds it through its mechanisms like a conveyor belt. Each codon on the mRNA strand is read and a corresponding tRNA is matched-up to it using its anticodon. This matching mechanism is used because the positive and negative pairings are naturally drawn to each other.

However mistakes can arise, and these seem to affect the ribosome, causing it to flex slightly. This causes more errors, and before long this will lead to a rejection of the emerging protein, which will then be recycled for its components.

Despite this, some errors will still slip through, but there are other controls later in the cell's processes that try to pick up errors which are not rejected at this point. Cells are truly remarkable in this respect - because those checks are done in very different areas of the cell that don't have access to a template. How is this done, and why unthinking chemicals would 'see the need' to develop such checks, is unknown.

While a very small number of incorrect proteins could slip through these various safety nets, this type of error is **not** generally thought to be a source of cell mutation, even if they were to happen in the early stages of foetal development. This is because the error **wouldn't** affect the genetic code and would almost certainly be a 'one-off'. Given the millions of proteins each cell needs, a tiny number of incorrect proteins would be unlikely to kill a cell, but even if it did, it wouldn't affect the entire body.

So the prime areas of interest in the process of Evolution must lie in the mechanisms of the Nucleus. Ribosomes also pose a real dilemma for Evolution theory, because they are partly made of proteins, and yet they are also the **only** things capable of manufacturing those proteins. So **how could the first ribosome come to exist**?

This is one of the many questions that has to be answered by Abiogenesis research. It is made even more significant by the fact that there is no apparent way for the different types of ribosome to have evolved from each other, (ie. between bacteria, archaea, and eukaryotes). They all seem to be discreet developments. We might speculate about an earlier 'common ancestor' in the distant past, but if so **all** trace of it has disappeared.

As you might imagine, Ribosomes have drawn a lot of interest from scientists but we are still far from an answer. There is a similar mystery surrounding Enzymes, but these are conceptually less complex.

They are vital to ensuring that only specific types of reaction occur, and they are also (typically) proteins. So if cell activity is dependent on the different forms of enzyme, (which they are), the proteins would have to emerge before any process required them.

From a 'cold start' something would have to make the proteins and allow them to experiment with each other before they somehow managed to find a useful purpose for each other, when working together. Yet sterile chemicals have no interest in creating life, or even finding purpose, so what drove them to do it? As you get to appreciate the complexity of a cell this becomes an ever more important question.

5.1.3 DNA Repair

Although I have emphasised the stability of DNA as a mechanism for preserving the genetic 'instruction manual', it is a fact that every piece of DNA in our bodies suffers **tens of thousands** of damaging effects each day.

This damage is caused by a variety of things such as: heat; mistakes in the mechanisms of the cell; and exposure to environmental factors such as radiation, (sunlight or nuclear), or undesirable chemicals, (from excess alcohol to cigarette smoke, diesel fumes, and other toxins).

The integrity of DNA would quickly be lost if a series of mechanisms didn't correct such damage almost immediately, and with remarkable efficiency. Collectively these are known as 'DNA Repair'. I will give you some detail about how these seem to work because they are so remarkable and do *seem* to imply some hidden awareness, whether that's correct or not.

The different types of damage to the ladder can be rationalised in the following ways, (which may seem dull at first glance, but the interest factor comes later by imagining how *you* might repair each of the bullets):-

a) In many places along its enormous length, **one side** of the DNA ladder **can be broken**. At each of these points, mechanisms have to *decide* if this is a simple break that can just be re-connected, or whether an entire section of the ladder has been knocked out and needs rebuilding.

If one side of the ladder remains complete then the other side can be rebuilt because the one-for-one pairing of nucleotides will clearly indicate which nucleotide has to sit on the opposite side of each rung.

b) **Both sides** of the DNA double helix ladder **may be broken** causing the ladder to split completely & separate. In this case the mechanisms have to *determine* whether the ladder has any missing sections, or can again be simply re-connected. A rebuild will use the complex process of Homologous Recombination, described below.

c) Individual **nucleotides can potentially be knocked-out,** even if the sides of the ladder remain intact. These 'missing teeth' are generally the result of chemical activity rather than a collision with something. For instance there are an estimated 18,000 instances each day, within every cell, of 'depurination' – where the bonds holding Adenine or Guanine nucleotides to the ladder are broken & they float away. Rare gaps on both sides of the ladder would leave the mechanism *guessing*.

d) **Nucleotides** in the rungs of the ladder **can be chemically changed** so that they no longer represent a valid pairing. Some changes put a nucleotide beyond all recognition but others are more sinister, changing one nucleotide into another. In that circumstance, any later check has to *guess* which of the nucleotides on either side of the ladder was the correct original. They don't always get it right.

e) Ultraviolet radiation can lead to **a Thymine nucleotide changing into a form that will no longer replicate**, even though it is still in place in the ladder. This will cause one or more of the nucleotide rungs to be missed, (effectively deleted), every time it was replicated.

Because the start and ends of codons are not marked, and the nucleotide sequence is just read in groups of three, this could be catastrophic as every subsequent codon from that point on would be misread as something else – eg. a different type of Amino Acid.

f) **Other chemical changes** can also occur, each of which would change the purpose or effectiveness of that part of the DNA.

Each cell appears to use a significant proportion of its DNA coding plus an equally large amount of its resources to build repair mechanisms. An array of protein enzymes constantly **scan** for different types of damage, and theory suggests that each enzyme is dedicated to just one type of problem, enabling it to recognise which solution to apply. They constantly test every section of DNA, and act when they find an error that matches their profile.

There is an obvious logic to repairing double helix DNA. If one side of the ladder still exists, any missing parts must have been the negatives of the nucleotides that remain. This is indeed the logic which seems to be applied by many repair mechanisms – except of course that chemicals don't think. So were these methods of repair just a mechanical inevitability set up by an unknown evolutionary process? Let's look at some details.

Where single nucleotides are either shown to be damaged or missing, and the sides of the ladder still remain, processes can surgically cut a hole in the side, remove the nucleotide, and replace it. That's still quite an impressive series of steps for unthinking chemicals. (How did it arise?)

Yet where **one side** of the ladder is actually broken, a more complex set of processes is able to cut out a section of 30 nucleotides around the break, and rebuild that side again!

The problem becomes a lot harder still if **both sides** of the ladder are broken and the two parts separate. Here the difficulty is in detecting whether any of the code is missing because neither side can act as a completeness check. Of course, this may not be a clean break either with additional torn sections on either side of a split.

When an inspecting molecule finds a break there are many permutations, each with different potential solutions.

A crude repair would be to simply join the available ends together, assuming, (consciously or otherwise), that there was nothing missing in the gap. Yet the technique which does this sort of repair isn't perfect and always results in one of the remaining rungs being deleted at the join[12]! This mistake in its logic means that a ***mutation is inevitable***.

However if there are complete sections of code missing as well, the situation could become very severe if the gaps were formalised and then used to produce radically incorrect components. As we are talking about broken DNA here, any change of this magnitude would be instituted as a norm on every copy of that code thereafter – which could easily be very destructive to the cell and possibly the wider body if the chemical produced was distributed elsewhere.

Raising the level of complexity, cells can combine different repair mechanisms to not only rejoin the broken ends of a ladder but also fill-in a **single** side of missing code if there has been an uneven break, but this still doesn't guarantee that no code has been missed in the gap.

Sometimes the *way* in which a DNA strand is broken can point to a solution.

Quite a number of double breaks can occur when the entire chromosome is being copied, and in these situations the code which has already been duplicated, (sister chromosome), can act as a template to rebuild the original DNA strand. This technique, referred-to as **Homologous Recombination,** can be very accurate even if it is highly complex. There are indications that the mere presence of the sister chromosome can somehow be detected, leading to this procedure.

Yet in the absence of a fresh copy of the code, a final option comes from a risky twist on Homologous Recombination.

This uses the paired chromosome from the other parent to rebuild the DNA: however we should remember that this will **not** be the chosen form of gene that is being used by the body, so this technique could end up forcing different versions of components into existing structures.

At first glance the following section may seem complicated but it isn't, and it will show you the incredible lengths to which repair mechanisms can go.

To give you an idea of the complexity of such processes, (which is not fully understood by scientists), let me share these outline steps:-

1. A preliminary step in the process seems to check that there is a good alignment between the two paired chromosomes – ie. that significant sections of the code seem to match on either side of the break.

2. If necessary, carefully positioned extra breaks can be engineered in the broken DNA, by introducing DNA damaging agents[22] or the Spo11 protein[23]. This <u>does</u> happen during the deliberate process of Meiosis where sections of code are to be exchanged; but in repair situations it might be used to establish 'clean' places where the codes match.

3. The ends of the strands are partly 'digested' by various types of enzyme, to provide a good join point for the rebuilding of the ladder.

4. Specialist proteins such as Rad51 coat the ends of the DNA strands with a nucleoprotein to form filaments, (thin strands), which are used to pull **one** end of **one** side of the damaged DNA, over to the complete chromosome at a position where the codes match.

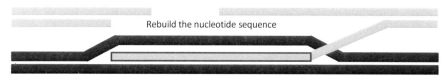

5. The damaged section is then rebuilt using other special enzymes which replicate the code from the undamaged DNA: (normal copying processes would require enzymes to attach to the same strand).

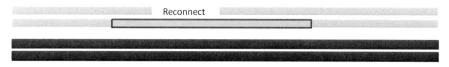

6. Once the missing sections are reconstructed, (and somehow these processes seem to know where to stop), the repaired strand is dragged back to its broken counterpart and the two ends are reconnected, to form one complete side of the ladder on the damaged DNA.

7. The final process is then to duplicate the code on the other side of the damaged DNA to complete the double helix, (ie. twisted ladder).

Replicate

You have to admit, that's not bad for a bunch of unthinking molecules... but the precise chemistry of how they do it is not yet understood.

I asked you to invest your time in considering Homologous Recombination because to me at least, this procedure is one of the most complex and far reaching set of steps in all cell activities. It seems to illustrate the strongest potential for a crude level of awareness in cells rather than just mechanical 'sensing' – ie. it seems to indicate some basic level of understanding.

You might argue that it's quite possible to sense another strand of DNA nearby, but something has to distinguish that strand as something useful – whether that's a partly formed copy, or the other parental chromosome in a pair, (requiring different treatments), as opposed to say any other chromosome in the nucleus which would not be useful.

As part of that process, the complete genes directly opposite the break in the chromosome, (ie. in another strand), may **not** be the same gene, or it may be out of line to some degree. So the checking process also has to go looking for matching code on **both** sides of the break. Is that just a mechanical and inevitable process?

Usefulness is normally determined by an understanding of purpose and objective, which you wouldn't expect an unthinking chemical to have. If the logic of that process is built into the structural components then we have to establish a reasonable means by which they could be deployed, using information from a number of sensory devices which allow all aspects of the situation to be monitored and an assessment made.

While it is only a matter of time before we find all of the necessary sensors to cover the different aspects of these operations, we do not know what **utilises** the logic, to (say) cut 'here' as opposed to 'there'; or to pull a strand across to the right place where a section can be copied, (which matches both sides of the break), and then pulled back afterwards to be re-connected... etc. Sensors are not computer chips.

So some aspects of this intricate process are structural, (ie. the enzymes and other chemicals deployed), but other aspects seem dynamic and 'of the moment'. Until a purely inevitable chemical process is demonstrated to cover all of these observed activities then questions will remain about whether there is indeed crude 'awareness' in operation.

This ***doesn't*** mean that materialist solutions ***can't*** be found. We will just have to see what emerges from future research. Yet, one thing which might be worth thinking about is; that such repair mechanisms may not have been part of the original, simplest, form of cell, and therefore may not have been required to exist from the very start. Going against this is the fact that core elements of this procedure are used in other more fundamental processes.

As a final consideration, we should ask whether the original principle of one enzyme performing one discreet function is correct. This principle was incorporated into early theory to reinforce the point that chemicals can't make decisions and can only act in inevitable ways based on circumstances in their immediate locality, (things they can directly react with).

Yet some of these processes are more versatile: seemingly able to look for different types of damage, and also exercising a broader and more proactive overview of what is happening – including the identification of other suitable strands of DNA that may be similar to the one they are working on. Finding similar code sequences in other parts of the matching chromosome, (while rejecting the other 22 paired chromosomes), is not straightforward in terms of logic. For chemicals that don't normally operate beyond the strand they are working on, that's a surprising move.

It is clear that with direct physical contact there is potential for chemicals to do a comparison with things that are directly linked, such as each side of a ladder, but it's hard to see how the detection of relevant things can occur when the chromosomes are not linked; the strands of DNA may not be sitting directly alongside each other; and genes may be held in a different sequence/position in chromosome strand. If there is some sort of chemical 'odour' being released into the fluid nearby, scientists haven't detected it.

5.2   Life's Amazing Metabolism

Despite the huge and impressive advances that scientists have made in understanding how our bodies work, (as well as those of many other living organisms), the *essence* of Life remains elusive.

What we have discovered is that our bodies are far more intricate than we ever imagined, and probably do represent the most complex objects in existence, anywhere in the universe, (distant alien beings aside).

In earlier sections of the book I made statements about the remarkable complexity and sophistication of the **metabolic** processes inside living cells. It is now time to see what some of those are.

To keep things manageable for the average reader, I will pick out some key facts which help to illustrate why the mysteries of life are being pushed ever deeper, while demonstrating some of the astonishing features that scientists have already discovered.

In terms of headlines, watch out for vesicles, transport trucks, and roads!

As before, a more detailed and extensive description of cell metabolism is contained in Appendix B for those who wish to gain a fuller knowledge of the facts that science has determined.

5.2.1 An Overview of Remarkable Structures and Capability

At the start of this chapter I described cells as a veritable city of activity, encompassing a remarkable array of functions that we can easily recognise. The aspects commonly known as cell metabolism, have two main groupings:

- A circular flow of functions which

  – **break down** food molecules - to release energy from them, and/or to salvage spare parts, (a process known as *Catabolism*),

  – **construct** larger molecules & cellular components such as proteins and nucleic acids, (a process known as *Anabolism*),

  – **recycle** used or spoilt components, and **dispose** of waste.

- An ever-changing and intricate transport network whose 'roads' also act as a structure that supports the shape of the cell

(Across all of these, there exist a vast number of signalling and communication mechanisms that are largely based on chemical messengers although they may be supplemented by electrical signals in some areas).

Both energy and raw materials are gained from the wider environment, as food or nutrient. These have to match the needs of each cell in terms of what it aims to construct, which is why each '**metabolic pathway**' represents a *fixed pairing* of catabolic and anabolic processes. This is illustrated in the following diagram.

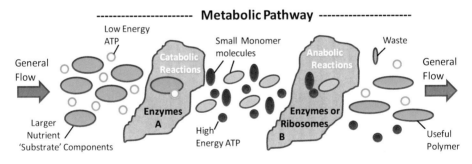

Put more simply, food is broken down to salvage both usable components and energy in the earlier 'catabolic process', after which those components and energy are used to assemble things in the later 'anabolic processes'.

Interestingly, the paired reactants are so perfectly tailored that *any* species which either uses the same food or requires the same outputs will deploy the same chemical combinations[12], (ie. same form of metabolic pathway).

Chemicals that enter a metabolic pathway are transformed through a series of chemical reactions which use **enzymes** to assist and also regulate those processes. The pathways can be likened to a general flow of material that passes around those near-stationary enzymes, positioned at different sections along the path. They enable specific reactions to take place.

The simpler Prokaryote cells will generally operate just one main pathway, while the separate internal compartment in Eukaryote cells will operate different metabolic pathways that use different nutrients/components[12].

These paired activities, and indeed all other functions in the body, require energy to fulfil their tasks, and the generation of that power within Eukaryote cells is done by compartments known as Mitochondria. These extract energy from nutrients and store it in tiny batteries known as ATP molecules. These get distributed across a cell and also into the wider body as a 'universal energy currency'.

In order to obtain the different materials and energy that they need for their particular types of protein, some organisms (Organotrophic) will feed off organic material such as fats and proteins, while others (Lithotrophic) feed off rocks & inorganic chemicals.

However not all catabolic processes digest nutrients to gain energy. 'Phototrophic' organisms, (typically plants), obtain their energy from sunlight using a process known as photosynthesis. They do this by using a specific ring of molecules in their key chemical, chlorophyll. Its shape helps to position the collective energy of those molecules at a tipping point.

Even a small amount of sunlight is enough for the ring of molecules to absorb enough energy to take them to the next energy level. The extra energy causes an electron to be lost, which is used to bind carbon dioxide to water, creating sugars that grow the plant. Yet the missing electron in the chlorophyll then has to be replaced from a lower energy source, which is taken from other water in the plant's system. The end result is the production of free oxygen from the water - which is how the oxygen in the atmosphere is believed to have originated, and is still replenished today.

We should first realise that in larger animals, digestion begins in the stomach which delivers partly processed nutrients to each cell via the bloodstream. This is what is used by the **catabolic** mechanisms.

It's interesting to note that while bacteria and plants can generate all of the 20 Amino Acids they require to make proteins, mammals can only make 11 **non**-essential Amino Acids. The other 9 essential ones can only be obtained/salvaged from the food they eat[12].

Anything that enters the cell has to pass through its outer membrane which is quite selective about what it allows in.

Behind this barrier is a watery fluid known as the 'cytosol' which fills the interior of the cell and its compartments. Yet within those different compartments the mix of chemicals in the cytosol will be different, allowing a variety of reactions to occur at different points.

Down the middle of the cell, (although shown on the left hand side of the diagram, for convenience), are a series of main compartments (organelles) which perform the main functions of Metabolism. In terms of the general flow of activity, the first of these is the **Nucleus**, followed by a 'huge' and strangely shaped organelle known as the **Endoplasmic Reticulum** (or ER), and finally there's the **Golgi Apparatus**.

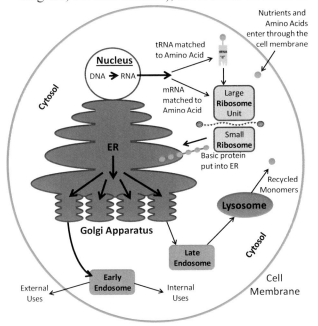

Around this central core, squeezed into odd places, are various other organelles such as a Lysosome, numerous Mitochondria, Endosomes, and a Centrosome, (source of the cytoskeleton).

The diagram shows that the main process flow begins in the nucleus, where DNA is copied to form RNA that passes out of the nucleus into the cytosol. Here Ribosomes assemble the crude protein components (orange), which are then pushed into the ER for checking & finishing. *How* the proteins are checked is only partly understood, but this process does include testing the **shape** that's achieved by each polymer and correcting it where possible.

If the proteins do not fold in the correct way, (and therefore do not adopt the correct shape), they become useless. Yet the ER also tries to adjust errant molecules by applying 'chaperone' chemicals which latch onto them to then assist, check, and correct the folding process.

I use the word checking because at some point, proteins can be rejected, (seemingly being beyond repair), and will then be sent to the **Lysosome** for disassembly and recycling. But what is it that makes the assessment?

At face value it seems that a judgement is being made, because although we might say it is easy to see whether a protein is 'incorrect', (eg. if certain bits don't line up as they should), a failure of that test doesn't say whether a strand is fixable. Yet some are fixed while others are rejected even though chemicals shouldn't be able to exercise any judgement – they should just react. So what prompts an attempted repair to be abandoned?

One suggestion, which matches *some* of the observed activity, is that, no decision is being taken at all - the process is simply a 'race against the clock'. What is meant by this is that there are mechanisms which 'roam around' the ER and grab anything that isn't correct - carting them off for recycling. This would imply that many fixable proteins would also be destroyed in this way. If correct then the process may not be very efficient.

The ER will also 'finish' the proteins by removing bits left over from the formation process, and generally 'topping and tailing' them - which may help to refine the **destination codes** that are built into the protein strands.

Another key function of the ER is described in biochemistry text books as 'sequestering' chemicals such as Ca^{2+}. You may feel rather unmoved by this revelation, but if I translate this into saying that it **stores** such chemicals for re-use later, its meaning will probably have much greater significance to you.

Why should any unthinking chemical process choose to store things?
It isn't just that they float about waiting to be used, they are actually stored in the ER's flattened discs and then returned to the cytosol when required.

A fourth set of activities relates to the production of fats, carbohydrates, & other polymers. Their purposes are broadly for energy storage, signalling, and the construction of cell structures such as membranes and tubes.

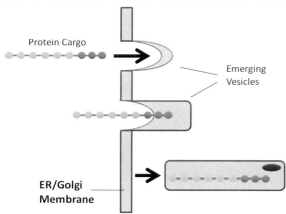

Protein Cargo

Emerging Vesicles

ER/Golgi Membrane

A fifth function, **and one of the most significant**, is that the lipids/fats making up the smooth ER walls, can form 'bubbles' which act as containers to transport proteins, and these may occasionally help some of the proteins to fold correctly as well[12].

When the bubbles break off the ER wall, as a container, they become known as a '**vesicle**'. There are so many vesicles being used to transport cargo that the **entire** membrane is replenished[12] every 30mins - and that's a lot of fatty material which has to be produced by the ER.

These containers can carry more than one protein – generally of the same type: but they are not just for convenience. Conceptually at least, they protect the cargo from heavy buffeting by the myriad of smaller molecules in the cytosol, and also prevent unwanted chemical reactions from occurring in transit. Vesicles are also remarkable in having a **destination code** (red oval), which seems to relate to the contents they are carrying... somehow.

Despite this simple logic, vesicles seem a remarkable development even in terms of evolution, as their formation and use form a complex process whose benefits would only be sensed at the end of a long chain of activity.

Once the vesicle containers exist, the different types of cargo, (typically protein or fat), need to be taken to relevant places where they can be used or recycled. The Golgi Apparatus is the next stage in that routing process.

For our purposes the Golgi Apparatus gets the vesicles to a starting position on the road network that is best suited to their end destination. In some way it filters the different types of vesicle, (possibly using slight differences in their construction or shape – or even by reading their destination code).

Transportation

The astonishing transport system of a cell has a complex mesh of roads, plus some extraordinary **walking** molecules that effectively act as trucks to pull vesicles to their destination. In terms of aiding route planning to a destination there are two basic categories of road network in a cell:

- Secretory pathways mark the main assembly & distribution flows, while

- Endocrytic pathways – (for our purposes), can be thought of as routes for recycling and waste disposal.

However in terms of construction these routes follow two types of 'road':

- Microtubules – tubes which run out from a specialist central compartment, (the Centrosome), like spokes on a 3D wheel.

- Filaments – twisted stands that run outwards but 'mainly' across the microtubules to form a loose **grid**.

Somehow, built into each type of road, there are direction markers which help to guide the different types of walking molecule, (each of which only operates on certain types of road, in specific directions).

Collectively, the filaments criss-crossing the microtubules form the basis of the road grid, which is also structural: forming part of the 'Cytoskeleton' of the cell that helps to give it its shape. However, for the same reason, that network is constantly changing.

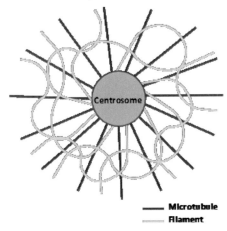

— Microtubule
⋯ Filament

Let me explain. Each cell is in a constant process of replicating itself. It does so by first generating copies of all the main compartments and components that a cell needs, so that there are two sets of each. While it does this the cell has to expand, and therefore the cytoskeleton has to expand too until the moment that the cell splits in half creating two full cells, each with its own Centrosome and road network. Overall, the production of a new cell is known is 'The Cell Cycle'.

The Centrosome is thought to somehow control the ***building*** of the transport network, but there is nothing to indicate that it controls movement along it. Both microtubules and filaments can be extended or reduced in response to both the changing circumstances of a cell, and the position of its organelles. Yet in terms of ***route planning*** across this network the situation is constantly changing.

Walking Molecules

When I first heard rumours about protein molecules that could walk and carry things I thought that it had to be ridiculous nonsense, but the biochemistry text books tell us that they are indeed real and astounding!

As a category, these chemicals are generally referred-to as '**motor proteins**' because they have moving parts which can exert a force on other things, causing one or both of them to move. There are 3 main 'families' of these proteins, each having a number of different versions/types:-

- Myosins – which ***either*** walk along the '**filaments**' carrying vesicles, **or** which pull on muscle fibres to make them contract rapidly or loosen rapidly when they are working together in large numbers[43].

- Kinesins – which can walk along '**microtubules**', (thin rigid tubes made of 13 strands laying side by side like a sheet which is then bent round to form a cylinder). Other types of Kinesin help a cell to divide.

- Dyneins - which can also walk along '**microtubules**', carrying cargo such as mRNA[12,40], but in other forms they can also cause minute flaps on the outside of a cell to beat – allowing some cells to move.

Although the main thrust of our deliberations relates to the movement of cargo inside a cell, it's worth restating that some forms of the three motor proteins types, (typically among myosins), are the things which cause your muscles to contract or relax by pulling muscle fibres one way or the other. Your strength **doesn't** come from the 'chemical shrinking' of your muscle tissues; it comes from millions of your motor proteins which pull fast and hard like millions of tug-of-war teams side by side!

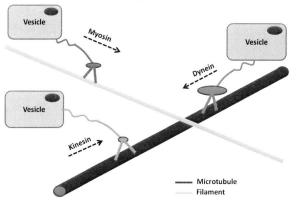

In terms of moving cargo inside a cell, these long motor protein molecules attach themselves to a vesicle, at one end, while at their other end there are two legs, resembling a 'V' shape. The central connection point of this 'V' is where the motor is situated, which either twists/flips the 'V', (as done by Kinesin/Myosin), or which flexes the angle of the 'V' in an alternating 'in-out' manner, (deployed by Dynein). These alternating actions generate the walking movement, but that is not the full story. If the legs just 'waggled' back and forth, the protein wouldn't go anywhere.

One leg must grab and push, while the other moves – which requires intricacy and co-ordination in these mechanisms. They also need an energy source for their actions, and it seems that ATP 'power packs' serve this purpose, while also explaining part of the movement. When an ATP molecule attaches it causes one leg to grip while the other is flipped forward.

Kinesins, (with the exception of K14), only follow microtubules towards their 'positive' end, (moving from the centre towards the outer wall of the cell), while Dyneins take the opposite direction towards the 'negative' end (inwards to the centre)[43]. Myosins, (as above) only follow filaments.

How the motor proteins came to be so direction specific, in a way that matches their cargo, is not entirely clear – other than suggesting that it's another 'miracle of evolution', etc.

As a basic concept, a vesicle being transported may need a kinesin plus a dynein, plus a myosin to move around the road network in different directions, and there are indications that all three forms accompany each vesicle in order to complete a journey, with the inactive motor proteins effectively hitching a ride until they are needed. It is certainly true that at points of intersection the motor proteins have to choose which direction to go in, and if necessary hand over the cargo to another motor protein[42]!

To complete our narrative of the transport system within a cell, 'early' and 'late' *Endosomes* represent other types of routing compartment, like the Golgi Apparatus, (at least in broad concept). 'Early Endosomes' guide the motor proteins to usage areas, while 'Late Endosomes' set the paths which lead to recycling – primarily at the organelle known as the Lysosome. This essentially salvages amino acids & nucleotides from used or malformed components, and then either returns them for use within the cell, or disposes of waste materials out of the cell.

5.2.2   Life's Methods of Controlling its Needs

While DNA is considered to be the instruction manual for each form of life, and possibly the equivalent of a computer program, its main purpose is aimed at large scale initiatives such as 'reproduction of the entire cell'.

We see various mechanisms that perform the actual work of copying and repair, but many of the things that *trigger* these discreet activities remain elusive. DNA doesn't have any obvious ticking clock or pre-programmed start times especially for day-to-day maintenance activities.

Cells come into existence as fully functioning live units, so it's tempting to think that cell reproduction is a continuous process where the DNA code is read from start to finish and then the program loops back to the start again.

In this way, there wouldn't be a *need* for a specific trigger to initiate any single action; although we do see that some cells suspend their 'cell cycle' until they judge that conditions are right to complete the task; and some scientists feel that the cell signalling system also gives the strong impression of having a fixed timer built-in to control operations in the early embryo.

Yet **day to day** operations to create spare parts etc., (rather than the ones for reproduction), **do** require specific triggers and, if the principle of Materialism is to be maintained, they would have to operate in unthinking ways to **start** the process of making particular proteins or RNA, 'to order'.

The underlying point here is that Materialism/Determinism needs each process to have a prior physical cause based in Matter/Energy– rather than a spontaneous start point, or one based in 'awareness'.

As part of a larger body it is quite common for cell activity to be triggered by signals that originate outside them, (whether those signals are electrical or chemical). Yet it is possible for cells to be kept alive in a test tube, which will deny them any external signals from a body, so all of their triggers would have to originate within the cell itself, but how?

Even if DNA does have a crude timer it won't apply where production is initiated in response to a sudden operational need.

In trying to establish what determines that need, as far as we can tell, the active elements of cells, (RNA and Proteins), do **not** refer back to DNA in order to seek instruction from 'the manual'. At best, the mechanisms detect chemical changes or electrical signals from other processes, and may occasionally be triggered by a 'matching' process, but little else.

Yet complex activities do occur well away from the nucleus, in quite separate compartments of the cell. These might do such things as: recognising a shortage of functioning proteins; or identifying the need to undertake a repair; or determining where cargo should be transported to and by which route; plus various other quality control measures.

The generic mechanism which scientists use to explain how dynamic control is exercised and actions are triggered in an unthinking & inevitable way, can be referred-to as a '**Feedback Loop**'. These processes can take two forms:-

- in **Positive** feedback, the outputs *stimulate* their own production.
- in **Negative** feedback the outputs *inhibit* their own production.

Where feedback mechanisms exist, (in either form), they generally operate in one of two main ways: either through

- a process generating a signal which then starts a chain of events; or
- an abundance of chemicals, (or other outputs), becomes so concentrated that they start to flow backwards towards the start of the process, affecting earlier parts of that chain of events.

Whichever combination of these 4 factors is used in a particular situation, the loop will give the appearance of purposeful control when it will actually be applying a direct mechanism that's purely chemical/electrical.

It is relatively easy to imagine how a loop would operate to (say) slow a production process when supplies of raw material are running short; or to maintain the chemical balance inside a cell; or to adjust the speed of a process where there is either a need for something or a surplus.

It is less clear how this would work in deciding which transport route to follow; or in deciding whether a component needs repair or should be scrapped; or even in maintaining a strict sequence within a complex process, that might otherwise divert into many other forms.

While feedback loops are fascinating and have been <u>proven</u> to exist in *some* processes, they have **not** been found for many others - at least not yet.

Materialists will try to argue that each protein acts in a blinkered and unthinking way: each reacting to one chemical circumstance when it arises, to perform one reaction at the right time. If this fulfils one element of a process or fixes one element of a problem, then a number of these things will need to perform their task in order to resolve a complex issue. Any co-ordination will be done by simple chemical or electrical signalling. There will be no awareness or understanding

Yet it is hard to ignore the appearance of purpose or direction when many separate control elements seem to be applied with a clear objective. We see these things happening and we can also rationalise the strategic function that each protein is there to fulfil; not as a happy accident, but being available when necessary, in order to achieve the same type of outcome.

Whether that arises from structural arrangements or dynamic factors there is a strong suggestion that something has generated the strategic objective.

If there is no apparent signalling or feedback loop then the effects must either be very subtle, (to escape our notice), or be the result of something else. Scientists have therefore speculated about other hidden forms of communication/feedback, (such as fields of influence or coded electrical signals across the fluid of the cytosol) – even though there is no direct evidence to support any mechanism.

As a carry-over from Book 1, which looked at the nature of such 'fields of influence' (eg. magnetism or gravity), it is unclear precisely **what** they are, as they are invisible and typically detected by their effects on other things. Yet we do know that their influence can spread out in all directions, although their strength will fade as they get further away from the source.

If this type of short range influence does exist within cells, (and again, this has not been demonstrated to any degree), there could be a much broader signalling ability within cells that might provide numerous, highly tailored feedback loops to trigger changes in activity. Having said that, if this is correct, those coded signals could re-open debates about the use of information in even the tiniest aspects of life.

The only other possibilities seem to lie in 'other types of stuff' whose alternate types of influence could be many and varied – but I have to say again that **there is no real evidence for any of this**.

5.3 <u>Probing the Mysteries – A Summary of Unexplained Factors</u>

When looking at the rich variety of life on this planet it becomes readily apparent that many organisms are designated as being alive but quite a number of them, (from plants, to types of creature), do not have a brain.

It also seems that some multi-celled creatures may even have evolved to **lose** the brain which they originally had, (such as the sponge[118]). If evolution determined that operating without a brain was 'better' it would, (seriously), imply that the brain was a disadvantage – either because it consumed unnecessary power for little benefit, or perhaps because it served as a distraction to good decision making, (boredom?).

One way to interpret these facts may be to assume that, if life doesn't need a brain, the 'essence of all life' boils down to mechanics/chemistry, and by implication that could be assumed for the higher abilities of the brain, too.

Such thinking seems to presume that by not having a brain such organisms may detect something and react in fixed pre-programmed ways, but they won't 'feel' or have any level of crude understanding. But is that correct?

Could it be that brains and Minds have elements which work in ways that we don't normally imagine - allowing a broader set of thinking capabilities even at the most basic levels of life within cells?

We have seen the example of a single celled creature, (Didinium), which swims about seeking prey, which it then attacks with darts, and proceeds to eat – all without a brain. This suggests a crude level of awareness, not just mechanics and chemistry, and if that is true we need to consider how that arises. There is no denying the observations, but what do they mean?

At a more basic level, some of the core functions within **every** cell also display activities which indicate that some crude level of awareness may be in operation. In this respect I am **not** talking about high level Thought functions, but the possibility of basic understanding – an interpretation of signals received; not just a direct reaction to them.

As mentioned before, hardened materialists may not like my use of the terms 'awareness' and 'understanding' - feeling that they are unnecessarily 'emotive' because the words challenge their belief that there can only be basic chemical reactions, (despite what we all experience). Yet these words are not presuming an outcome. They merely describe observed behaviour, and convey valid possibilities that are in keeping with our experiences.

Put another way, it is not unreasonable on matters of the Mind & behaviour, to use terms that describe real factors which we employ all the time, especially where Materialist explanations are (currently) unavailable.

We need a way to determine whether any of the observations which give 'pause for thought' do actually represent something that could genuinely represent awareness – because chemistry has so far **not** provided a credible solution, and the prospect of one is 'challenging'.

> Similar considerations will also apply to our analysis of how the brain and Mind work, in Chapter 12. Do the 'neural networks' in our brain actually think, as we experience it, or do they resemble unthinking mechanical computer chips?

The tables below summarise the examples provided in the explanations within this chapter, and the fuller descriptions provided in the Appendices.

Each of these will have different strengths and weaknesses, and I present a reasonably full list for you to judge the need for any 'awareness'.

However when I put these lists together I was struck by: the **number** of these puzzling factors; plus the fact that they seem to span most areas of activity in a cell/body; and also the complexity of the tasks that they are able to perform.

While we can anticipate that entirely physical factors will continue to be explained in physical/chemical ways, what we are trying to assess is whether matters of control, planning, and implied understanding, go beyond what we might reasonably expect from Matter/Energy – to break its principles.

As a reminder from Chapter 4, these factors can be categorised in two ways due to the nature of their circumstances:-

- **Structural arrangements**, set up *before* the functions of the cell began to operate, which force chemicals to react in pre-determined ways that produce highly *specific* outputs in a manner that is *inevitable*.

  These are the ones whose origin must be explained through Evolution, or God, or some equivalent factor.

- **Dynamic arrangements**, which arise 'in the moment' and must reflect intrinsic characteristics of the cell components themselves.

  These are the ones which should rigidly conform to the known laws of physics, but if not they may point us to additional influences that are in live operation today, such as 'other types of stuff'.

The table below summarises the factors that emerged from section 5.1 but also capture some factors from Chapter 4 and Appendix A :-

Structural Arrangements	Dynamic Arrangements
DNA and the information it contains, including template designs for components	Finding the location of a particular gene within the tightly curled DNA.
Intricate & highly tailored machines such as Enzymes and Ribosomes.	The deployment of Riboswitches at a stage well before they are used.
Codes that put meaning into a line of chemicals.	Self-Assembly of complex structures possibly using scaffolding.
An apparent level of 'pre-programming' that enables the codes to be read by different mechanisms.	The way in which the production of a specific protein might be initiated – ie. the starting of the process.
The production of Haploid chromosomes in an egg or sperm that contain a 'random' mix of genes from grandparents.	How a different mixture of genes is selected for use in each individual, sometimes from the mother's chromosome and sometimes from the father's.
Translation mechanisms.	The pre-selection of tRNA by Ribosomes to match the mRNA.
Quality Control incl. ways to check for specific types of production error.	How a ribosome rejects a protein that has been assembled incorrectly.
Specialist mechanisms to identify and fix damage – especially **Homologous Recombination**.	Identifying that something is wrong in later checking processes, without a template to compare against.
RNA Editing	The matching and alignment of chromosomes after fertilisation.
Chaperone and scaffolding mechanisms, that help to fix problems in construction & folding	Selecting one form of DNA repair out of several possibilities.

It can appear, at first glance, that pre-existing structures which guide activities in a cell, and ensure that they can only occur in set ways, provide an adequate explanation for the way that life controls chemical reactions, but we should remember that those structures and processes still had to be put in place by sterile chemicals. That is particularly challenging when some of the key functions above would have been needed by the very first cell, *before* issues of survival could guide any later evolutionary path.

From Section 5.2 and Appendix B we have:-

Structural Arrangements	**Dynamic Arrangements**
How did a cell membrane learn how to develop and label vesicles within the evolutionary process?	How do the cells of the brain generate creative thought and emotion not just 'causal' responses?
Walking molecules with specialised motors, to transport cargo and to provide the power in your muscles	How do motor proteins plan a route when the complex 'road network' inside a cell changes regularly?
Centrosomes plan and control the development of the ever-changing network of filaments and microtubules?	How do motor proteins know when to change direction en-route, incl. swapping their cargo to a different type of motor protein?
Motor proteins swap their cargo to another walking molecule when a change of direction is needed?	How do enzymes align with substrates so quickly when spinning at up to a million times per second?
Enzymes and other molecules in cells can hold ATP and other chemicals in readiness for use at a later stage rather than use them immediately.	How do enzymes and other molecules know when to use the components they are carrying, or begin walking?
The ability to store and retrieve things.	How do processes within the ER 'know' when to store and when to retrieve chemicals?
What established 'feedback loops' when chemicals shouldn't care what the outcome is? Even if each process is 'mechanical' the effects have to be detected and responded-to.	How are enzymes located in exactly the right place that matches their logical position in the metabolic sequence of a pathway?
How did the remarkable mechanism of photosynthesis emerge in some cells before any life could show an interest or dependence on it?	Why do the proteins that guide Ribosomes to Translocons only work on Ribosomes that have paused their production process?
What coded the 'program' behind the switch mechanism which allows cells to interpret signals from their neighbours & internal mechanisms?	How does M-Cdk manage to control all of the complex sequence of activities in the 'M-Phase' of the cell cycle?
How did Eukaryote cells develop a suicide mechanism in preference to a wrong outcome, plus the means to judge when it should be used?	How do cells judge the suitability of their environment in the G_1 phase of the cell cycle?

A recurring feature in many of the 'structural arrangements' is that they are often **not** single components controlling things alone, but a potentially long chain of them all working in close harmony to achieve an apparent purpose. Of course, that purpose may be an illusion arising from the way that we try to rationalise things, but it is also true that if any links in that chain were missing, none of it would be likely to serve any useful function.

Put another way, we can see how evolution might make changes to individual components to 'see' whether they work better or not, but if the chain of components didn't exist in the first place, random developments would seemingly have to be stored waiting for others to emerge, which then, by chance, happened to work seamlessly together to form a wonderfully intricate set of outcomes which unthinking chemicals shouldn't care about.

This is a real issue, and one which Materialists feel will be resolved in future by an, as yet, unknown but unthinking process.

Fine. However it is also valid for people to ask if the factors being observed could arise out of something more purposeful – whether that is the 'underlying stuff of Thought', God, or something else?

We will look at more of these issues in Ch.7, yet some of the most poignant issues arise from the 'dynamic arrangements' which appear to function beyond structural capabilities because they are 'of the moment'; responding to very fluid circumstances in ways that are unlikely to be pre-programmed.

Not least of these is the ability of the brain/Mind to generate thoughts, feelings, emotions, strategies, concepts and all of the other abilities we take for granted. This however is partly a consideration of how groups of cells (neurons) co-ordinate their activities, and will be tackled in Chapter 12

In order to demonstrate the potential for awareness in cells, I would like to elaborate on some aspects of the more prominent examples from the tables:

a) <u>How do DNA Repair mechanisms select Homologous Recombination from the various options available, and then implement it?</u>

We saw the outline steps involved in this process in section 5.1.3, and as thinking beings we can understand and rationalise what is happening, yet these steps are very hard to explain in the context of unthinking chemicals. As mentioned before, there is a significant difference between these processes and normal sensory detection.

The normal sensory mechanisms in a cell wait until something bumps into the detector, which then supposedly triggers a pre-programmed response. However, these processes **seem to go looking** for things.

In philosophical terms, these repair mechanisms appear to go beyond the **reactive** nature of causality, where an effect is generated by a cause, because they show many signs of engaging in a **proactive** search for information.

Do the mechanisms try to assess the damage before making a choice between a simple re-connection of the broken DNA strands **&** a rebuild? If so, judgements & choices would seem to be made. An alternative explanation may be that it was just a race to see which type of repair protein got to the damage first - which wouldn't require any assessment.

Either way, once a type of repair had been started, ways would need to be found to stop other potential repair mechanisms kicking-in, as they might interfere with the active solution creating a bad repair.

However it does seem that Homologous Recombination needs to detect the scale of damage and the location of any code that might enable the damage to be repaired. It needs to determine if unbroken chromosomes nearby can assist the process, and if so, where there might be a match to the unbroken nucleotide code on either side of a break.

Not only is there uncertainty about how big the break might be, but the position of the relevant gene on the undamaged chromosome is not necessarily going to be directly opposite the break.

Although we can easily understand these concepts they would still be a challenging task for **us** to perform let alone unthinking chemicals.

Simply to determine areas of matching sequences, the process would need to track quite a number of nucleotides on the damaged strand **as well as** the 'host' in order to determine that there was a match.

Quite apart from the need to store information like this, it is the logic of 'where to look' that implies a degree of crude awareness.

b) <u>How motor proteins navigate a changing network of roads to reach a specific destination?</u>

Apart from the remarkable fact that unthinking chemicals have learned how to walk & carry things, motor proteins seem to display surprising abilities in understanding where to go and how to get there.

While recent discoveries have indicated that end destination codes may be built-into each coding gene, and then placed on vesicles which transport the proteins; motor proteins would still need a way to convert that *code* into a physical location with a instructions on how to navigate there. This is especially true as some organelles and membranes move their position in/around the cell, causing the road network to constantly change too, due to the cell cycle. Put another way, there's no known map.

Even if the destination code were to somehow describe a journey, rather than a location, (on the basis of (say) go three strands up and then two along to your right), it is not clear how motor proteins would read the code, let alone how they would cope on a changeover part way through the journey, (eg. if a transfer from a filament to a microtubule, was necessary - prompting a change from a myosin to a kinesin).

Suggestions that **DNA** as the source of the destination code would know exactly how the cytoskeleton would be laid out at any future moment, seem unlikely. Even if we said that DNA holds the blueprint of every component in the cell, it seems to specify how to build the component, **not** to prescribe its movements thereafter.

So from what we know so far, it is hard to see how any route can be planned without a lot of interpretation/awareness and a map.

c) How do Centrosomes determine how to build and adapt the cytoskeleton during the cell cycle?

Centrosomes are believed to control the building and adaptation of the 'road network' of filaments and microtubules that form the Cytoskeleton of the cell.

Once a new Centrosome has been formed as part of the process of bringing a new cell into being, (the cell cycle), one of the early tasks is to create a microtubule spindle and then use it to ensure that all 23 of the duplicated pairs of chromosomes are drawn to the side of the elongating cell which will become the 'new entity'. It must make sure that it has them all, but none of the originals.

It must then do similar things for any other duplicated components and organelles like Mitochondria. How it does this is unclear because there are no apparent checklists, but we do know that as these movements happen the road network also has to adapt to maintain any links!

A further set of dramatic changes in the road network, (microtubules and filaments), has to occur when the cell splits in two.

All of this seems to suggest that the Centrosome has a **proactive** 'understanding' of what has to happen, but there is no knowledge of how it manages to orchestrate this, or indeed how it monitors progress.

It is still possible that Materialist solutions might emerge to present us with an inevitable and unthinking physical process for each of these functions, but it is currently a mystery how such control might be exercised. So although it is not a 'scientifically preferred' option, awareness cannot be ruled out at this stage.

Materialism will still form the backbone of any research as scientists don't have any other testable or observable means of pursuing enquiries, however we may be seeing the limits of purely chemical explanations.

As the questions are pushed ever deeper into the world of physics rather than chemistry, we can expect an ever increasing crossover between the two disciplines. Later chapters will probe these issues to a greater extent.

6 Evolution and its Limitations

In terms of its original remit and claims, the Theory of Evolution has been remarkably successful. It provides a way to explain how all the different *species* of Life could have emerged from simple beginnings.

Enhanced by its genetic explanations it has felt instinctively 'right' to many people, as well as having near universal application for living things. Yet in many others it has also provoked a backlash; often for religious reasons, but also because some feel discomfort in the idea that their distant ancestry may be shared with animals, as the theory advocates.

Being the principal atheistic explanation of Life, it has come into direct conflict with religious beliefs that claimed we were all directly created by God; yet it remains the only theory which has substantial evidence to support its method of operation.

Over the course of one and a half centuries, many diverse branches of science from geology to genetics have found themselves adding to the original evidence, and **all** of that material seems to point in the same direction. In terms of its original claims it is very compelling as we'll see.

However, perhaps through an atheistic need to provide an explanation for the **origin** of Life, the tendency has been to unofficially extend the theory into a process of 'start' as well as one of 'change', and this is where it has hit a number of scientific difficulties as well as ones of faith.

As we began to see in earlier chapters, it **can** claim to be an explanation for the 'structural arrangements' that emerged *after* the first cell came into existence. Yet it lacks a mechanism to explain the development of the first cell itself, and possibly the 'dynamic factors' that were listed in section 5.3

The term Evolution must be therefore be treated with a degree of caution.

To clarify some early points about its original remit, evolution deals with change, but it's a term that is generally applied to species, not individuals, so it **doesn't** concern the way that each creature changes over its lifetime.

The definition of a species can accommodate limited differences between individuals. These are characteristics that already exist within the population such as: **size** (in the dimensions of certain features such as horns, or the body as a whole); **eye colour**; or the **pigmentation** of fur or skin. However it becomes a matter of judgement whether particular differences are sufficient to warrant a new species definition.

For instance, we don't use eye colour as a way to define new types of human, but if you found that deer in a particular country had blue eyes instead of brown/black, you might think about doing so.

Categorization partly relates to whether such variations are intermingled in the population or placed in discreet groupings. Subtle differences which are being shared/inherited across the whole species are the genetic equivalent of shuffling a standard deck of cards and then dealing a hand to each individual. The pack shouldn't change.

Yet this doesn't explain how the characteristics first arose, especially if we believe that the full diversity in the 'Tree of Life' could be traced back to a simple 'first cell'. At different stages, our notional 'pack of cards' would either need to have cards changed, added, or removed.

> As a twist on this narrative we might imagine several beginnings with many 'first cells' arising in different environments, leading to the different branches of life, however there's a lot of evidence to suggest that Life only began once. We will explore this in Chapter 7

Zoologists have carefully studied the differences between species for thousands of years, (with increasing sophistication, as our knowledge progressed), and they have noted one other remarkable thing: that while some individuals within an animal community may have problems, we **do not** see entire species becoming less capable over time. There is a clear trend of general improvement in all species, and that has to be explained.

> (Sizeable populations can see their numbers both rise & fall over time, while some species can even become extinct. But this always seems to be due to competition from other species, or changes in the environment - not from a trend of genetic decline).

There are therefore two main parts to Evolution theory:

1. Explaining fundamental change.
2. Explaining **how** each species always seems to be on a path of steady genetic improvement – an evolutionary 'direction of travel'.

These are the bits that I will focus on, and I will separate the factors which may be involved, from the normal processes of reproduction.

Theory therefore suggests that the process of change should generally work forwards from simple beginnings to become more complex. From this we can speculate that new characteristics might emerge either as dramatic shifts, or by small changes early in the evolutionary cycle which could then lead to ever greater differences later. This brings us to the suggestion that biological change originates from mutation, whether large or small

The term mutation carries with it all sorts of unpleasant connotations because we generally think of it producing unpleasant effects such as illness or deformity. But the term is also applied by scientists to denote beneficial changes when a living organism is improved, as part of the evolutionary process.

The mechanisms that we looked at in section 5.1.3 touched on some of the ways in which those changes might arise through alterations in the DNA code: from errors in the mechanisms that copy or repair it; to the effects of light, radiation, or other chemical agents that might cause damage/change to individual genes. Remember this is **not** the mixing of genes from parents.

Once a mutated gene has emerged it will be used in **normal** reproductive processes to create a new form of being. If the change is beneficial to that individual, theory says that he/she will live longer, providing a much greater chance of spreading that gene to his/her offspring. In this way it would become established within the broader species community, and if the change was radical enough it may even create an entirely new species.

On the other hand, if a genetic change is not successful, theory says the individual will not survive so well, and will have less chance of passing on that gene to his/her offspring – eventually leading to its disappearance.

As described, it could be a brutal process for those involved in an unsuccessful change, but as a means of establishing a steady process of improvement for each species, it is quite powerful.

Evolution **needs** a sense of direction if it is to take us from the simplest of first cells through to modern humans, in the time available – 4 billion years per the chart in section 3.1. When you also consider the main phases of change on that chart and the associated diagram, you can see that the timescales could be even more challenging for the first cell - which emerged after just 200 million years of opportunity/experimentation.

4 billion years may seem like an incredibly long time to us, but in evolutionary terms it can seem quite short when we think of what has to be achieved. We do not see mutations in every person being born. The vast majority of babies appear 'normal', but a small proportion will have noticeable changes. The general belief is that most of these will **not** be beneficial to the individual, but thankfully most will not be significant. Almost all of the ones that **are** radical seem unsuccessful and severe.

This perception is based on hospital studies and also the rate of change that we observe in species populations, but it could be argued that if we only ever register the problems/abnormalities which are drawn to the attention of doctors or scientists, the stats could be distorted significantly. It may be that a myriad of small but positive changes are always occurring, but because they are not seen as a problem they are not registered. There is no information to sensibly make such a judgement as yet.

However there is another interesting observation from cellular biology. Each cell's DNA can be damaged thousands of times each day but there is still only a tiny rate of mutation in organisms. Why? It seems to boil down to three main factors:

- To affect an entire individual the change needs to happen in the DNA of a sperm or egg, which sets the pattern for the whole body. Once a body exists, an individual cell will only have limited impact.

- Although the change to a single nucleotide **could** result in a dramatic effect on a protein, most appear to have little or no effect.

- If a genetic change is severe it is likely to prevent the normal development of the foetus which will generally cause it to miscarry.

6.1.1 A Range of Perspectives on Evolution

The traditional religious way to explain the complexity of life was to say that it had to be put in place by design, and of course, that would imply a conscious and powerful presence/being to be able to do this, 4 billion years ago before any life existed on the planet.

The prime candidate has been God, but in modern times those with a sci-fi inclination have also suggested that it could be aliens from a distant solar system, whose evolutionary development began a few million years prior to ours – making them more advanced than us.

Whether or not that suggestion was initially made tongue in cheek, it has gained a degree of credibility because of the very tight timetable that has been identified by fossil and geological records - for chemicals alone to generate the first cell. One way to buy more time has been to argue that nature experimented across the broader universe before bringing life here. Yet if we acknowledge that possibility we should be fair to all perspectives by saying that development elsewhere could include God too... if He exists.

> The convention I use when talking about Deities is to refer to **a single God who is male**. I do not deny the possibility that there may be many Gods; or that divinity could be female or even without gender, etc. However, it becomes very draining for readers if I constantly refer to gods as He/She/Them.
>
> As a single male deity is the most common belief across world religions, I will adopt that format and ask you to interpret this merely as a convention, and that the underlying principles in each part of the book could be applied to the other views as well.

Beliefs about divine intervention have taken three main forms. Some will argue that God continues to design **every** organism that ever exists.

Other beliefs, such as Deism, will argue that God put the initial mechanisms in place at a creation moment, and then left everything to play-out in their own way. Deists therefore have an easy means of incorporating the Theory of Evolution into their own beliefs, because they will argue that the evolutionary mechanism was put in place by God.

The third way suggests that God uses the things He creates as tools – from the physical Universe to the Life within it. He will let His creations perform as they were designed, but may occasionally intervene to produce a desired outcome.

Aside from the degree of intervention that God may apply in the universe, a key difference between some of these options is that two of these beliefs can accept Evolution as a genuine mechanism. By accepting evolution as an unthinking process it also *avoids* making God directly responsible for experimenting on us, in ways that are often unpleasant.

However, as I am setting out the full range of possibilities, we also need to remember the broader philosophical options that I outlined in Chapter 2.

Following Idealist principles, everything we experience could just be a manipulation of our Minds. In this case physical evolution would merely be a 'narrative' to maintain the illusion of physical substance, although it may also have a more subtle meaning related to our development as non-physical beings. These are logical possibilities even if you don't find them compelling, and as I pointed-out in Book 1 some theories on the nature of existence **have** been advanced by scientists which follow Idealist principles to explain certain findings from Quantum Mechanics.

Yet if you accept the strong likelihood that physical matter does exist, the final interpretation of evolution comes from Dualism/Pluralism. Here we find a suggestion that other types of stuff which underpin our reality, are subtly influencing the workings of Matter/Energy to give it both a sense of direction through various means, and provide moments of true spontaneity or randomness that may give Evolution 'a nudge' towards positive change.

One of the things we will explore later in section 6.2.2 is the hidden need for Thought which exists in various aspects of Evolution theory.

Another interesting consideration is that the mechanism of Evolution, (change), seems to go against most of the other functions in a cell which seem intended to preserve the integrity of good codes and not to alter them. Yet the development of Life, through better capability and increasing sophistication, **requires** change to occur.

Could it be that the process of Reproduction is 'deliberately' flawed to allow such changes to arise? A parallel point is pursued in section 6.4 when we consider why Evolution doesn't seem to have improved our lifespan much since our species emerged.

As a final point, while science has identified a number of factors which might lead to change in a particular gene, (and its associated protein), there are broader questions to address in the emergence of more sophisticated functions such as Homologous Recombination. For such capabilities to arise, something not only needs to individually develop the perfect components for the process, but also associate all of those separate elements into a seamless procedure. I don't specifically know how many there are but if we say 15 or 20, that would represent a lot of things that had to come together by chance to create a previously unknown benefit.

Across this range of thinking, to guide our choice, we each have to consider the evidence available, alongside our preferences. So what is that evidence? Well, it comes in two forms:

- Facts that emerge from scientific scrutiny
- Logical conclusions that come from the interpretation of facts.

Logic can be used to establish a theory; or to show that there are holes in a theory; or more interestingly to show the consequences of a theory.

6.2 A Closer Look at Darwinian Evolution

Although Evolution is not yet a scientific Law, its position as a Theory should not be underestimated in scientific terms. That status is only conferred on ideas which **are** detailed, robust, credible, and with lots of evidence. For that reason I don't feel I'm exaggerating when I say that it is accepted as a virtual fact by most scientists, and is probably accepted by a large majority of the public too in developed countries.

In terms of its original claims there are still gaps in its evidence base but these are getting ever smaller, and perhaps more significantly there is nothing that has yet contradicted its main theme. But it is not absolutely proven, and there are still objectors.

Even with all the evidence from scientific research that is discussed below, from fossils to genetic engineering, there are those who will oppose on religious grounds, and although we might be able to demonstrate that certain types of genetic/evolutionary change are possible today, under laboratory conditions, we cannot go back in time to **prove** how different species actually arose in the past, outside the lab, ('in vivo').

In the spirit of being fair to all perspectives, I will therefore present many of the key objections to the original theory and how scientists have sought to rebut those concerns. You will then hopefully see what remains contentious and what is proven to your satisfaction – allowing you to make a judgement on how far to accept Evolution as a theory.

We also have to be careful about what the theory says. Does it actually claim to explain the origin of life? No. As we have seen it is a basis for explaining diversity, and that is its strength because it **can** demonstrate a mechanism for such **change** in the testing that scientists have undertaken. This makes it truly viable, and also gives it a strong advantage over other proposed solutions which cannot be tested as they rely on unproven factors.

To restate earlier points: suggestions that it can explain the origins of life as well, are **not** demonstrated by science as things stand, (which has only produced one mechanism for evolution, and this **cannot** account for origin). However findings from research into Abiogenesis do seem to be edging that way, because they are beginning to support the possibility of an entirely different, if unknown mechanism, (see Chapter 7).

Some will view the start of Life as a moment that has equivalent significance to the Big Bang as a point of creation – because it seems to be so unique. In this respect a number of statistics suggest that the chances of the first cell emerging by chance are beyond any expectation anywhere in the Universe. That is a big subject which I will also cover in discussions about the origin of Life in Chapter 7.

Yet strategically the claim that Life had a **true** spontaneous start point is philosophically challenging to Materialism/Determinism which effectively demands a cause for every effect – a continuous process. I am therefore focussing the rest of this chapter on 'increasing species diversity', the core issue raised by Darwin & Wallace[20] in 1858/59.

We should also be clear that while the theory helps us to recognise a *pattern* of change, it doesn't necessarily mean that we can explain **how** some of the key processes of life can operate – especially where there are suspicions that 'other unknown influences' may be necessary, (as listed in section 5.4). That is not the purpose of the theory.

I will also present the logic of how Darwinian Evolution and some of its later variants seem to depend on Thought to make it work.

6.2.1   The Evidence to Support Evolution

The evidence which won popular support for Darwin & Wallace's theory was largely based on what we might call 'circumstantial evidence' today. However the theme that the two men were advocating has prompted a lot of further research which has consistently added support for their idea.

That research is powerful testimony. If we equate our analysis to a murder mystery, it has added means, motive, and opportunity... at least in principle.

One of the greatest modern exponents of Evolution theory is Richard Dawkins[19], a biologist by training and a passionate advocate of the principle that natural forces & processes can explain all of the complexities of existence without the need for God.

He begins from the position that evidence for the process of Evolution is abundant, overwhelming, and readily available for anyone who cares to look. That evidence broadly lies within :-

a)   The extensive fossil record which shows a detailed pattern of change for many species over millions of years, plus

b)   Our understanding of DNA and reproduction (per Ch.5), which has shown that mutations do correspond with differences in the genetic code; and as further demonstrated when distinct characteristics from one species were transferred to another, when the relevant section of genetic code was transplanted into the DNA of a different species[24].

c)   the distinctions between similar but isolated species, (eg. found on different islands in the Pacific), as pointed out by Darwin, Wallace & other field biologists since their time, which seem to demonstrate that the creatures adapted to their environments in distinct ways.

d)   people with differences such as a third nipple, or additional/ missing toes/fingers, etc who have undoubtedly changed in comparison to their parents, ancestors, and indeed their species.

As most people are familiar with the general nature of this evidence, I will focus on some of the main counter arguments that have been presented to challenge it, plus the scientific rebuttals which these have prompted.

However before proceeding it's worth noting three other things: firstly that an analysis of the sequence of changes within DNA has always confirmed the backwards pattern in the tree of life which emerged from fossils. Secondly, DNA analysis has shown the presence of significant amounts of apparently redundant genes within the DNA of all species, some of which point to old versions of the genetic code. Interestingly this has received little or no challenge from religious lobbyists. I will elaborate on this towards the end of the section.

Finally, there is evidence which falls under the banner of 'Irreducible Complexity' – the suggested need for a minimum level of sophistication before any mechanisms of life could work... the need for a design. This will also be raised at the end of the section, but first we should begin with the challenges to the main evidence in 'a' to 'd' above.

a) <u>Counter-arguments to the fossil record:</u>

Fossil records do reveal species that have similar but distinct bone structures yet it is also in the nature of species to be created and then eventually become extinct. To put different extinct species side by side and then claim that they form a pattern of evolution is wishful thinking – especially when the chain is far from complete in many of these 'family lines'.

There is no DNA or other evidence to say that one fossil is a progression from another, except by chance appearance. This is especially true if the specimens were found in different countries and even different continents.

The whole of Evolution theory depends on 'link species' which do not exist for most of the supposed tree of life - hence the search for the 'missing links'. The assumption that these links exist is only driven by theory. The alternate assumption is that they don't exist, which is why we haven't found them.

The fossil records show that large dinosaurs suddenly appeared without an evolutionary path. Some became even larger or scalier over time but essentially they remained within type ie. the same species.

Rebuttal

The fossil record that has been discovered is vast, and continues to grow. While there can be significant gaps in the historic trail of some species, most of the key species will have a trail that is largely complete – establishing a clear principle.

While it is true that DNA can't be extracted from fossils, it is important to realise that fossils can be dated in various ways and that this invariably shows a progression of species: we **never** find modern creatures predating their ancestors. Such dating techniques range from:-

- their position within geological layers, that reflect a fixed timeline, to
- various techniques which use the fixed rate of decay in radioactive elements to determine an age.

The typical changes that are evident within the fossil record are small and gradual, rather than a dramatic change by divine intervention. This agrees with the Theory of Evolution.

The dinosaurs also show patterns of progression like this, and it would be wrong to think of them as one species which suddenly emerged. There are a vast number of species within each of the many dinosaur ages, and they were each developing and growing at different rates in different periods.

Different large creatures have existed throughout this enormous period of time. They came and went through a series of different progressions. Even in the very earliest periods when the land began to be populated from the sea, we see a progression over millions of years as the creatures become ever larger, (eg, Proterosuchidae, an early crocodile which survived the P-T extinction event to spawn many branches of early dinosaur; or Therapsids which included early forms of mammal). These were not sudden starts.

'Link species' are not mysterious special concoctions, created as if by magic. They are merely gaps in the fossil record and sometimes it can take a while to find them. But many have been found.

Suggestions that we need to find a strange 'half creature' being partly one thing and partly another, like half dinosaur and half bird, misses the point. There will be many evolutionary paths. There were flying dinosaurs which evolved early-on; those which developed flight later; and entirely different species such as mammals which developed gliding/flight by separate paths.

b) Counter-arguments to the mechanism of DNA and the principle of spreading new traits through inherited genes.

Nobody has ever seen a new species evolve. We only see minor changes within a species which could be the result of many factors not related to genetics. In recent centuries for instance, humans have been shown to get progressively bigger but that is a reflection of better healthcare and diet.

We have even seen scientists tinkering with the genetic code to produce dramatic new features in their laboratory creatures, but they are still recognisable as mice, rats, rabbits etc. even if significantly deformed. They are not a new species, and have only emerged from a planned intervention.

In addition, if evolution is a natural and inevitable process it should be happening all the time in every aspect of life. It should be an unstoppable force, and yet there are species which even science admits have not changed over many millions of years such as the manatee and platypus. They are unique and have no variants.

They are also, typically, discreet to one part of the world and do seem to represent the sudden appearance of a new species, (as well as remaining unchanged throughout the ages).

The recognition of a new species is a matter of judgement and is typically done in retrospect when new traits are established in a population rather than an individual. That takes time – possibly even centuries.

However in the realm of plants scientists **have** seen changes in the genetic code cross-pollinating them to create a new hybrid[95]. Admittedly they didn't observe the genetic code while it was making the change, but this 'before and after' approach is still convincing to many.

In terms of creatures, one way to define a new species is that a particular 'breed' will become unable to mate with others of that species, and in this respect scientists **have** also observed the emergence of new species.

In one example, a large group of fruit flies were progressively sorted by their preference for certain types of environment/food as they bred over 35 generations. At the end of the process some breeds of fly would not mate with those from very different environments[25].

We have also proved that genetic changes do lead to physical changes, in two ways: firstly, scientists have shown that many physical differences do correspond with differences in the genetic code; and secondly, certain genes are known to be the source of distinct properties within a species, and under laboratory conditions, a transfer of that genetic code to a different species has also transferred the physical traits as well.

By way of example, the gene responsible for a green fluorescence found in some jellyfish, (when they are exposed to blue or ultraviolet light), has been introduced into the DNA of another species, (eg. mice), which are then seen to glow in blue or ultraviolet light in the same way[24].

Such tests are highly controversial and many countries have therefore introduced restrictions, both to safeguard animal welfare, and to ensure that such effects are not spread to a wider population before they are shown to be safe in the long term – particularly in relation to new breeds of plant and their ability to pollinate large areas.

Whether you approve of them or not, the experiments did prove that the genetic code in DNA is the source of some dramatic physical characteristics. The green fluorescence is remarkable in marine life as well as land based creatures, and these abilities were not developed by men. They seem to have emerged naturally.

Rare examples where creatures have not evolved does not mean that the process is a myth, as it applies everywhere else. There will be reasons why they haven't evolved but it may take scientists some time to pin-down what those factors are. Relative isolation may be a significant factor.

While demanding proof from science for evolution, (a great deal of which has emerged), the objectors offer no corresponding proof for any alternate source of such changes.

c) Counter-arguments to the slight differences between similar species in isolated communities.

Breeding may change the mix of characteristics in a species but it doesn't create new species. There are many breeds of dog but they will never evolve into a cat. Slight differences do not explain new species.

Cross breeding **between animal species,** (generally among those held in captivity), invariably results in sterile creatures such as mules, ligers, and tigons – but they could never exist as a new species in the wild. Nature stops them from reproducing.

All new species therefore have to be **created**, even if that is mimicked in the test tube.

Rebuttal

The analogy of a 'tree of life' is a good one that fits the evidence. When further changes happen, they vary the particular branch or twig of the tree that they occur within. They do not go back and re-work the past, as the opportunity to manipulate the earlier points of 'common ground' have been lost – the code no longer exists so it cannot be manipulated. That is why dogs will never become cats.

There are thought to be three main ways to generate species, which all reflect ways to forge new specialisms on the genetic code.

- **Allopatric Speciation** uses physical separation and isolation to prevent the mixing of genetic code, and focuses each breed on certain genetic traits, either by losing some abilities, or developing others. A variant of this is known as **Peripatric Speciation** where a small group becomes isolated from the main species group.

- **Parapatric Speciation** involves increasing genetic isolation where only certain types of individual choose to mate with each other. This is often associated with partial geographic isolation, where two communities only mix occasionally. This is believed to lead to increasing specialisation within those two communities making them increasingly focussed on each other.

- **Sympatric Speciation** occurs within a population that is in the same geographic region. This may work in one of two ways. Either
  - individuals may only choose to mate with those that have certain traits, and these factors become progressively more entrenched, leading to an inability to mate outside those limited possibilities.
  - a chance mixing of certain chromosomes will only allow some individuals to successfully mate with others having certain traits.

There are documented cases of each type, and analysis of the genetic code seems to confirm this specialisation.

In relation to mules, ligers, and tigons - not all interspecies breeding results in an infertile animal. Some mules, ligers, etc. **have** been known to breed but not with their own kind. According to Haldane's Rule some females may be fertile, but rarely the males, (if ever). This is primarily due to mismatches in the chromosomes of the different species. If both a male and female were ever found to be fertile then a new species would result.

d) Counter-arguments to observed mutations and unique creatures

The fact that someone has a new characteristic does not mean that we stop thinking of them as being human. They are not a new species, and similar changes in animals do not represent new species.

A number of living species, such as the platypus are local to one area of the world and are unique on the planet, showing no evolutionary path whatsoever.

Just because a species is old doesn't mean that it emerged from a process of evolution which then mysteriously stopped. Indeed, an ancient species which hasn't evolved is proof that evolution is not necessary or inevitable.

Rebuttal

It is not correct to say that there is no evidence of an evolutionary path for the platypus. It is one of a small number of warm blooded but egg-laying mammals called 'monotremes' that all exist in either Australia or New Guinea, (there are also 4 species of Echidnas). Early mesozoic ancestor species are Teinolophos & Steropodon which were closely related[26] and there is some fossil evidence for a much larger version of platypus in the distant past. It is likely that more fossil evidence will be found in future.

Analysis of the platypus genome[27] has confirmed that it is, itself, an ancient link species which combines features from mammals and reptiles. (Suggestions of a link to birds is tenuous). It originated very early in the branching of life and is surprising because it has survived to this day as a living species – however it is not unique in this respect. Manatees, crocodiles, and other creatures are also believed to be very ancient.

The mechanism of Evolution does not **demand** change but it would be most common for it to occur. Changes which are less successful will not be preserved, for instance, if the animal has already reached the peak of its abilities for its circumstances. The platypus does seem to have changed over time to become smaller, but not to diversify into other species.

Other Evidence from DNA

There are three other generic ways in which DNA points to a process of Evolution. Science now has access to the full genome sequences of 50 types of bacteria, 13 types of Archaea, and 3 unicellular eukaryotes alongside the human genome and some other animals; and these have been compared – particularly in relation to their protein coding sequences[12].

As a result of this, three major interesting features have emerged.

Gene Families

Analysis has shown that there are great similarities between many genes, which indicates that they emerged from a common source. As a result, scientists have grouped them into 'Families' as they also have functions within similar areas of a cell, such as copying or repairing the genetic code; metabolic functions (discussed in the next chapter); and signalling.

These families can exist within a single strand of DNA, so we have to ask how the DNA replication processes have produced more than one copy of the same original code? The source of this duplication is probably the result of errors in cell division which scientists **have** observed[12]. On rare occasions the copied DNA is not placed cleanly in the emerging second part of the cell. Some genes can be left alongside the original and these can become incorporated into that DNA while the other incomplete cell will die. In other circumstances a section of DNA code can simply be copied twice.

The additional copy of the gene then has the opportunity to mutate in different ways to the original, and the slight differences which have been seen in such genes do indicate that this is the most likely origin of change. If this type of activity occurs many times over millions of years then we can envisage how the considerable duplication seen within the genetic code has arisen.

Analysis of some prokaryote DNA has shown that 47% of genes can have one or more obvious relatives[12] within the one to six thousand genes that they contain, (between one and ten million nucleotide pairs).

Genes Common to all 3 Braches of Life

Across the different types of cell mentioned above, only 63 gene *families* are present in every cell, (ie. are common to all life); but 264 families do appear in *most* cells – just missing out on one or two species.

This is still considered a relatively crude analysis because it depends on our ability to recognise common features rather than those which have been changed by mutation, but it's a strong indication that there was indeed a common ancestor.

Redundant Code

Among the many duplicated genes we find that cells may only activate a proportion of them. This could mean that some genes are lying dormant waiting for the right circumstances to arise, but there is a strong suspicion that a proportion of it will represent unsuccessful mutations or old genes that have been superseded and will never be used again[96].

Logic that goes against Evolution Theory

In addition to challenging the evidence which has been presented in support of Evolution, those who oppose the concept have also produced logical counter-evidence of their own.

Irreducible Complexity is a generic set of arguments which try to demonstrate that there can be no evolutionary path for particular organisms. It is probably most successful in arguing that there is no evolutionary origin for either the first cell or certain necessary components within the first cell.

As these are more related to questions of origin rather than diversity, I will deal with these in Chapter 7.

Irreducible Complexity can be thought of as a more scientific way to argue the old philosophical notion that certain complex developments in life had to emerge by design and not by a 'random' process.

The 'Design' argument often quoted examples of such things as 'the eye' as being impossible to explain by the action of unthinking chemicals due to their intrinsic complexity and the fact that unthinking chemicals should have no need for an eye.

However the process of evolution does partially explain this because it can point to many different species which show a progression of complexity in the performance of eyes, from the Nautilus which has a very crude eye, to ourselves with quite advanced eyes, or the eyes of other creatures which generate astonishing magnification and detail either due to their different structures, or sensitivity to a wider range of light frequencies than our own. The Nautilus will still gain advantage from a crude eye compared to no eye at all, as it could detect movement of prey or predator, but it wouldn't be sufficient for us, or a bird of prey.

The other significant point we can take from eyes is that evolution doesn't necessarily result in perfection. Despite their sophistication even healthy human eyes are not perfect due to the presence of blind spots and the limited types of light that they are sensitive to, etc. We also know that not all eyes are equal and that some people grow up with eye defects requiring glasses or other lens corrections etc. The challenge back to creationists is that if eyes were put in place by a divine being, why wouldn't He make them perfect? An unthinking mechanism of evolution means that God doesn't have to take responsibility for a seemingly flawed product.

In short, there is clear potential for an evolutionary path, yet the reasons for a 'direction of travel' fall back onto issues of survival, not basic chemistry, and that in turn points to the influence of Thought.

6.2.2   A Possible Need for Thought

Darwin's theory is entitled "On the Origin of Species by means of Natural Selection". In other words, there are a number of elements to his idea.

He didn't say **how** the changes in species arose, but he did describe how they spread if they were successful, or disappeared if they were not, because the process of evolution is dependent, in part, on things which are social rather than chemical/mechanical. This is the factor which gives evolution its drive and direction – '**natural selection**'. However Darwin's term encompasses several factors.

The first part of his argument is that when changes provide an advantage they will enable the individual to survive longer, by having better abilities to cope with their circumstances. Yet that is **not** just a case of having (say) a stronger arm or an ability to move faster. Such things do nothing on their own. Survival is improved because of how the creature is able to **use** those extra capabilities, which suggests that Darwin's theory may depend on some sort of awareness/Thought to provide its drive and sense of direction.

That potential 'need' goes further because part of the theory is that by surviving longer these improved individuals are likely to produce more offspring, thereby spreading their new genes through the population for the benefit of future generations. Yet 'surviving better' doesn't guarantee reproduction, because that is also partly a social thing for any creatures that interact. So the need for Thought/awareness impacts in 2 other ways:

- we select our mates because we find them attractive, so any mutations which they have must either be appealing or at least not off-putting. These changes do not have to be visual but may be ones of health, personality, or ability. Either way the impact will be partially mental.

- any mating creatures will have to be **aware** of each other before they can 'do the deed'. That may be obvious for the higher forms of life but more challenging for the tiniest single celled creatures.

These factors have impacted on the Theory of Evolution, which has itself evolved accordingly! In searching for ways to accelerate the process so that it might reasonably fit within the timescales available, scientists such as Richard Dawkins have proposed the notion of '**positive selection**'.

This is where males and females will select mating partners who show desirable characteristics; suggesting in turn that if the changes are perceived as desirable the genes will spread in the population more quickly.

While this seems a very reasonable elaboration of the principles when applied to higher forms of life, it is harder to see how this would be applicable to lower forms of life, (single cells), where the earliest and most challenging developments must have occurred 4 billion years ago.

While it is probably unrealistic to expect advanced levels of Thought at that time, lower level forms of awareness may be a possibility because of the behaviour we observe in single celled creatures like Didinium. This may indicate that an underlying mechanism may be being being scaled-up to provide ever more advanced forms of Thought, in different levels of life.

Although such behaviour is not observed in bacteria or archaea, we can say that crude awareness or even understanding become important to the process of evolution as soon as they are available to a living entity. They not only seem to speed-up the process, but may also help to explain the development of certain capabilities which appear to depend on them, (as we saw in section 5.3), whose origins have proved challenging. Examples would be: 'Chromosomal Crossover'; Homologous Recombination; or even the apparent exercising of a choice.

Prior to this, we still have to explain the sense of direction needed to drive any evolutionary mechanism **before** the first cell ever existed.

So from the bottom-up perspective, if there was a deeper underlying mechanism which started the development of Life, then it wouldn't be surprising for it to continue through all of its levels – potentially manifesting itself as Thought in the most advanced forms... if it exists.

(In saying this, the scalable mechanism might conceivably be physical or based in 'another type of stuff', and we will look at this in Chapter 12).

Until we find the underlying cause of awareness and Thought we can only speculate, but these factors seem ever present in the mechanisms of life, as well as those of Evolution.

6.3   <u>Mitochondrial Eve and Y-C Man</u>

Various DNA analysis techniques have emerged that provide us with a guessed timeline for genetic change. The underlying mechanisms can be referred-to as 'molecular clocks', which primarily indicate the **sequence** in which genetic changes occurred, but by looking at the average speed of change in humans, can estimate **how long ago** they may have arisen.

In broad terms these seem to strongly support the Theory of Evolution, even though the clocks don't say how those changes came about.

As the DNA of mitochondria is only passed down from the mother, and the Y-Chromosome is only passed down from the father, an analysis of these types of DNA can show us the way in which humans have changed over the course of time, plus the rate of progress made by Evolution.

The initial study of Mitochondrial DNA in this way, was conducted in the 1970s and strongly suggested that we all relate back to a single mother, (single common female ancestor), who lived around 180,000 years ago, in Africa. She was given the nick-name 'Eve', but this **did not** mean that she was the only female at that time, (as might be implied from Biblical texts).

This mitochondrial Eve can be thought of as the first with the distinguishing characteristics of our species, but in more technical terms she is the point where an unbroken sequence of DNA transfers from mother to daughter began – spreading to all women alive today.

That description is important because where maternal genetic lineages are broken, (eg. a mother who only produced sons), her mitochondrial DNA will be lost to further generations. So it is possible that other females existed within the human genetic line, (alongside mitochondrial Eve, and possibly even pre-dating her), whose DNA has been lost, although some of the genetic changes to Eve's line may have come from that other source.

Challenges to the initial findings led to a number of subsequent studies using more human subjects across a wider range of countries, and while the findings have been refined, they have not been fundamentally changed.

Using different techniques it is now believed that 'Eve' lived within one of two periods:

- between 140 and 200 thousand years ago ('kya')[28], with some indicators pointing to 160kya, or
- between 99 and 148kya[29].

It is therefore interesting to see a small overlap in those possibilities.

There is also some debate over her location as the genetics point to a 'fork in the road' between African and non-African lineages around 95-100kya.

Equivalent studies into the Y-Chromosome, (which always come from the male), seem to be more volatile in their dating estimates but have also shown that modern humans can be traced back to a single male who has been nick-named 'Adam' who probably lived in Africa. (One of the key indicators (Haplogroup A) is only found in low frequencies in parts of Africa but are common in hunter-gatherers[33] so his location is not firm).

This **does not** mean that he necessarily lived at the same time as Eve but the dating range seems to be honing-in on 120 - 156kya[29,30]. So there is another narrow period where the two **could** potentially have lived together and even been a mating pair. Yet this is seen by many scientists as an unlikely possibility.

Findings from 2015 now suggest that Adam could have lived as long ago as 200 – 300kya[31] – the approximate time when modern humans are first thought to have emerged. This is a return to some of the earliest estimates from 1990s[32].

Both the male and female common ancestors are likely to represent people who were also a positive result of genetic mutation, (by whatever means).

6.4 Ageing – Design & Possible Causes

We all age, and it is an obvious disappointment that our fate is to decline and eventually die. It has therefore been a puzzle to scientists as to why that happens... let alone an opportunity to make vast fortunes if they can identify the causes & remedy them. Yet the answers seem strangely elusive.

The subject of ageing has prompted a lot of philosophical consideration, particularly in relation to religion and peoples' hopes for a continuation of life after death. If a 2nd life was possible at all, then death could represent a whole series of opportunities to 'wipe the slate clean' and start again – possibly in better circumstances and with a different (better) body.

A new beginning might even refresh our zest for life if it was all becoming a bit stale and repetitive. This thinking is taken to its highest level by those who believe in a paradise environment which we might reach through a higher state of being, or even by entering the paradise kingdom of our God.

Yet to do any of this we would need to preserve the essence of ourselves as we transitioned to the next life – the essential purpose of a soul.

Although concepts of an after-life have generally been dismissed by many materialists, (but not necessarily atheists), it has been a surprise over recent decades to find that some scientifically gathered evidence has been emerging to support the existence of souls, even if it isn't conclusive. We will look at this in Chapters 9 and 10.

However none of this tackles the issue of ageing and how it happens, although it may set a context for any theories about *why* it happens.

Even if Idealists are right and everything is in the mind, we are still likely to experience a deterioration in our bodies if we survive to old age.

Some have therefore likened ageing to a build-up of errors in the body's mechanisms which will gradually lead to breakdown. Mechanically, that's probably not unreasonable as a basic concept, but we still haven't managed to pin down precisely what may be involved.

However there are a number of other factors which suggest that ageing may be an important part of our design, whether by evolution or other means. In effect, it could be built-into our DNA.

General thoughts about Ageing

When we look back over many generations of people, let alone all other creatures, we rapidly see that any organisms which are able to reproduce have a fundamental problem. An ever growing population will rapidly outgrow the environment which sustains it, unless there is a means by which the level of population can be controlled.

Illness and disease will reduce numbers to some degree. Predators will account for others, and may even serve to keep the population as a whole healthier by picking out those which are ill and therefore easier to catch.

Fights and battles will serve to reduce the population even further, yet we still see that some populations can exhaust their food supply, and possibly even harm the environment's ability to produce, through over-grazing.

So strategically, once the available terrain is occupied, the only remaining strategies that will enable a population to be balanced with resources are:

- to limit the number of offspring that each species produces, (which seems to go against the basic instincts of life),   and/or
- to limit the time that each creature/organism can exist.

We can see that nature has deployed both strategies when we observe different species producing different numbers of offspring, and we also see a universal backstop via ageing and death. If all characteristics of life come via evolution, then logic presents us with a strange possibility: that evolution might have developed and maintained these traits, and therefore it may treat ageing and death as 'desirable'.

That may seem truly bizarre at first hearing, and you may feel it is much more likely that evolution simply hasn't progressed far enough to remove these bad aspects of life – but consider this...

> we see a continuing trend of improvement through the process of evolution but this doesn't seem to have improved our life spans very much, as most of our increasing longevity seems to have come from better diet and healthcare – not genetic improvements. In short, evolution seems to be avoiding the issue of ageing – leaving this genetic trait in place.

The most pampered people on the planet still only live long enough to basically see their children and possibly their grandchildren become established as adults and to provide them with guidance on how to be parents themselves. It seems that humans are programmed to die after 2 new generations have emerged and matured: giving a nice double overlap – like tiles on a roof!

We might also point out that the oldest recorded ages across humanity as a whole, do not seem to have moved significantly in history; and that people who migrate from lower average age communities to higher ones, seem to fall into line with the pattern of their adopted home – a strong indication that genetics do not vary much and that society and lifestyle will account for almost all of the differences.

Although the average number of offspring and the average lifespan of each species may vary, they also seem pretty stable. Each creature finds a balance with nature and then seems to stick with it in evolutionary terms.

From all of this, the idea has grown that ageing may be an inbuilt and necessary part of our DNA. One of the first people to propose it was August Weismann in 1889, who argued that Evolution required the old generation to make way for the new. He even saw ageing as a necessary part of the Evolutionary process, despite it reducing the success of an individual life rather than strengthening it, (ie. an effect that seemed to flow in the opposite direction to the normal evolutionary path).

On that basis, people have asked how evolutionary processes could 'perceive' that 'programmed death' had a useful purpose? Those who die cannot reproduce – so what could provide the 'strategic overview'? While some might turn to God, could more basic mechanisms be at work?

Whether we look at the wearing out of our component parts, or a gradual deterioration in our ability to reproduce cells flawlessly, the complexity of our bodies may mean that a considerable number of changes might be needed to our DNA before any noticeable improvement to human average

age might be noticed. On that basis we seem largely stuck with our present 'genetic age' prospects, and nature would probably find it easier to flex other single/discreet factors in our reproductive abilities.

As it is hard to imagine that nature could easily change the average number of offspring that could be produced on each reproductive cycle, it seems a lot simpler for it to change the period that females are fertile – possibly as a response to overpopulation and the struggle to raise young.

Indeed, the differences in average age recorded for the menopause in different regions, (eg. South East Asia (44)[34] as opposed to Australia (52)[35]) is again thought to relate to social factors impacting on age & fertility, (from smoking, to diet, etc) [36], however genetic capabilities would still have to be attuned to these factors, otherwise they wouldn't have an impact at all.

In this respect, genetics seem to be having a passive influence on our ability to survive as a species, by giving us another way to cope with times of difficulty rather than a simple case of which individuals last longest.

Interestingly the menopause is not a universal feature of life and only seems to occur in a small number of animal and aquatic species – such as some monkeys, whales, some dolphins, elephants, the budgerigar and some laboratory rodents. *Why* it occurs in these species is not known, but it is equally interesting that with the exception of 'short finned pilot whales' (which stop reproducing around the age of 40)[39] the menopause doesn't seem to be observed in the wild for these species – only in captive creatures. Of course that doesn't mean that it is a direct result of captivity or domestic environments.... but who knows?

If some species produce offspring throughout their lives it can either seem that survival factors and ageing are the only population control factors which nature has deployed; or that nature has lifted restrictions on the menopause - pushing it beyond the ages when death would normally occur.

In terms of why the menopause might be needed at all as a factor in ageing, people have speculated about the following:-

- older parents may have a greater chance of producing damaged DNA, (although if correct we would expect males to become infertile too at a similar age, when in fact they remain fertile but at slowing rates of sperm production[37]).

- it becomes harder for an older mother to sustain her offspring, while the extra food gathering capacity that a grandmother can undertake could greatly help child survival – especially in times of famine.

- in an environment where predators roam, younger females will be far better able to protect their offspring, (yet if this were correct we might expect to see the menopause as a common feature in the animal kingdom[38] when in fact very few species have it).

Possible Causes of Ageing

Leaving aside the possibility that ageing is built-in to our DNA, and that our biological clocks may suddenly cause hormonal and other changes later in life, there is a lot of evidence to suggest that a continual series of other effects might contribute to a gradual physical decline, and may even accelerate it.

A primary example would be damage to DNA and the resulting mutations that appear in new cells. This may lead to malformed proteins which may either stop working, or alter the effects they were intended to produce.

Although the main functioning areas within Eukaryotic cells, (including the nucleus), have very robust repair and control mechanisms which preserve the integrity of their structures and systems, the Mitochonria compartments, (whose DNA and internal structures more closely resemble bacteria), are a lot less sophisticated and show a much greater incidence of nucleotide deletions and mutations. It is estimated that their degradation is 100 times greater than that of nuclear DNA[12].

Poorly performing Mitochondria tend to produce more ROS by-products (Reactive Oxygen Species), which are chemicals that can cause respiratory problems and may also be a possible source of oxidation damage to neurons in the brain, and even cause some cancers.

Associated with these things are malfunctioning defence mechanisms within the body, (such as the auto immune system), or defective ways in which damaged proteins are removed from the system. A build up of damaged proteins is a major cause of diseases like Alzheimer's and Huntington's.

Strategically we have already seen some processes such as Telomere shortening, (Chapter 5), which limit the ability of cells to reproduce, and do not seem to be repairable by any cell mechanism. However other similar effects can be related to stem cell production which also seems to decline with age. These are immature cells which can regenerate any other type of adult cell; so falling numbers of stem cells will also tend to equate with a reduced ability for our bodies to maintain their quality.

From this it is easy to see why a single change in any gene is unlikely to transform longevity in the body as a whole. However it is interesting to consider whether maintaining stem cell production or finding a way to repair telomeres would produce dramatic effects in lifespan.

If they could, we would face a real dilemma over whether we should introduce such developments into the population. If we don't age and die, how would the rapidly growing population be able to feed itself?

7 The Unknown Origin of Living Cells

As mentioned in Chapter 6, the Theory of Evolution gives us a method by which simple forms of Life turn into more complex forms of Life.

However that process only has **one** way to operate: using the reproductive mechanism of living cells. As a result, scientific explanations for the diversity of Life all begin with the development of a notional 'first cell'.

At this point in our journey back through time, theory hits a 'brick wall' because there is no known process that could lead to the development of the first cell, and that is a major problem - one that the new scientific field of 'Abiogenesis' aims to resolve through the workings of Matter/Energy alone – ie. the Materialist principle.

Yet the dilemma and the challenges deepen when we think that the only mechanisms available to produce the **components** of those cells are the components themselves! Until recently that has been true in the laboratory as much as anywhere else, because scientists have also relied on Ribosomes, mRNA, Enzymes etc. to manufacture the specific polymers too.

You may recall that for the purposes of cell reproduction there are two main types of polymer: those that are based on nucleotides, (DNA and RNA); and those that are based on Amino Acids, (proteins and enzymes). Ribosomes are a little strange in being a mix of the two. From chapter 5.1:-

> Ribosomes are complex programmable assembly machines which exist in all cells, and are the only natural things which are able to construct **proteins**. In that process they utilise two other forms of nucleotide chain: 'tRNA' which (with an enzyme) identifies relevant Amino Acid components; and 'mRNA' that indicates the exact sequence in which those Amino Acids must be strung together.

The new laboratory techniques[101] for creating specific proteins still rely on a rigorous control of the environment in which reactions take place, (not the chaos of the real world); plus a firm grip on the sequence in which these things are put together; based on a prior knowledge of the *precise* chemical profile for each **useful** polymer that they want to generate.

Such technology disguises the full enormity of the task of creating life. It doesn't hit you until you realise what it takes to create even one protein from a bunch of sterile chemicals after the Big Bang. It's staggering.

Despite their ability to directly assemble Amino Acid polymer chains, scientists cannot predict what a **new** version/sequence could do, if anything. The vast majority are completely useless, and those which do have purpose, (which we call proteins), can only be assessed by their function and shape in relation to other cell components where there may be a 'fit'.

In terms of predicting usefulness we are barely on 'base one', and the best that scientists can realistically hope to achieve is an interesting 'tweak' to a protein that already exists. Having said that, nature is in no better position. According to Evolution Theory, its approach has always been to produce something and then try it out - for better or for worse.

Indeed, the difficulty in creating a useful protein becomes a lot worse for nature when you think that the early conditions on Earth were very far from a protected environment. They were a chaotic chemical soup, where any polymer that happened to form could easily be taken apart by the next wave of toxic reactants.

Yet we are here, and something must have enabled that to happen.

We will look at the challenges that had to be overcome to make proteins & RNA shortly; and then consider the *codes* and *descriptions* which had to form; before finally thinking about the unresolved factors from section 5.3 which we categorized as either 'Strategic' or 'Dynamic' arrangements.

Those who believe in divine intervention have an obvious answer to the origin of Life, if God does in fact exist, however He has not chosen to overtly demonstrate His existence except through matters of faith, and so there is a real and prolonged need to consider more pragmatic possibilities.

The evidence for Evolution **after** the first cell existed, is strong, including patterns of change within the genetic code. So if these things do not reflect Evolution, or God's work, we would have to ask why they are there.

Put another way, we shouldn't ignore the story that our bodies seem to be telling us. Yet **prior** to the first cell, there is far less evidence to guide us.

Overall, some modern techniques are able to suggest a likely sequence of early changes within the specific gene codes that have been analysed. This gives an order of events which may reflect the Evolutionary changes that occurred, but this **doesn't** give us an actual timeline – just a guess at best.

These techniques have been applied to critical cell components, such as the Ribosome, (which are believed to have been necessary for the first cell). From this we have logically assumed that the earliest sections of their genetic material must represent part of the code used in the first living cell.

Following this, when scientists compared the results from each of the three forms of Ribosome, (one for each branch in the tree of life), some **common** early elements of the code were identified. This led to suggestions that there may have been an earlier common stage of development, **which may even pre-date the first cell**!

Similar research[102] seems to indicate that Ribosomes may also share a common ancestry with tRNA and mRNA. All of this seems to support the notion that an earlier reproductive mechanism must have existed to enable pre-cell evolution to occur... unless God assembled the new combinations.

If such an evolutionary mechanism did exist it would have allowed sterile chemicals to experiment with different forms of polymer, before eventually hitting on the key components of the first cell.

Possibly because Amino Acids were the first biological components that were shown to be capable of forming naturally by themselves, they have drawn the eye as a possible source of life. Yet that could be a false clue, especially as it has led us to a logical impasse for the origin of proteins: ie. Ribosomes are partly made of proteins but they are the only natural things that can manufacture proteins – a real 'chicken and egg' situation.

However there isn't the same dilemma with components made of nucleotides. RNA components can be assembled from relevant sections of the DNA code by specialist molecules called Ribo**zymes**, which are also made from nucleotides, (the same building blocks used by RNA). Indeed, Ribosomes are partly made from particular types of ribo**zyme** which are now also intertwined with some proteins.

So RNA has more than one way to copy itself using different versions of the same nucleotide components, and for this reason, attention is switching away from Amino Acids and proteins, to RNA as a potential start point for Life. However this is far from a viable possibility at this stage of research. We do **not** have forms of RNA that could cover all of the necessary functional ground for a first cell, even in combinations, (although I gather that some scientists are trying to engineer some to show that it is possible).

Having said this, even if RNA does lead us to an early evolutionary mechanism, we cannot ignore the reality that all modern cells, (Prokaryotes and Eukaryotes), do **rely** on proteins interacting with RNA, and therefore some way has to be found to generate those proteins, and get them to work seamlessly with the RNA before the first cell existed. Given the timeframes available, that is not an easy thing to conceive. As you will see shortly, the concepts involved seem to verge on the impossible.

As part of this we have seen that it's not sufficient for evolution to just have a mechanism. It **needs** a sense of direction, otherwise sterile chemicals will take as many steps backwards as forwards, because they don't care about the outcome. That potentially becomes even more important if this pre-life activity is to avoid succumbing to the principle of increasing entropy/disorder implied by the 2nd Law of Thermodynamics.

So what could provide that sense of direction before there was any survival issue – before the first cell? Some have again argued that the driving influence may relate to 'improved chemical stability' – however this leads to the same challenge as in Chapter 6 - there is nothing to really demonstrate that stability leads to improved functionality. The source of any sense of direction in a pre-life environment is therefore still wide-open.

So, having set the scene for our 'debate', I would now like to consider what it would take to generate some of the basic factors of physical life from the starting point of a new solar system 5 billion years ago, after our planet had cooled sufficiently to produce a crust.

The environment in those days was extremely hostile to life as we know it, but this could also mean that as the environment changed, different processes would be in operation at different times. Ancient processes may no longer function in today's world because *our* environment would be extremely toxic to *them*!

As a starting point therefore, we have to recognise that the earliest forms of life **didn't** exist in an atmosphere that contained free oxygen.

Some of those early cells are believed to have produced the free oxygen that we now breathe, as a waste product from their day-today consumption of nutrients, but in so doing, after millions of years, their own pollution largely killed them off. Fortunately a new form of oxygen-using life emerged to take over, 'just in time'.

Yet all of this speculation relates to periods that are far later than the earliest ones we really need to consider, before the first cell emerged.

7.1 **The Chances of Living Cells Emerging by Random Activity**

You will realise by now that all of the essential elements of living cells are polymers, and that these are built up by stringing the associated monomers together, so we need to consider how those monomers first emerged in a form that could be useful.

The three main forms of monomer that I listed in Chapter 5 are Amino Acids, Nucleotides, and Monosaccharides. These are all medium sized clumps of atoms, (ie. molecules), that each have their distinct features, which allows us to classify them. Those chemical features also enable them to be strung together under the right circumstances, but as we have already seen those circumstances are not readily available in the modern environment - except in the enclosed conditions of a cell.

We have speculated that the origin of life may lie with Nucleotides and RNA as they form the working elements of some key components, but it is equally undeniable that all forms of cell today rely on proteins as well for the bulk of their activities.

Indeed, mRNA and tRNA have no other purpose than to guide the use of Amino Acids as they are assembled into proteins; and DNA is little better. So in many ways the origins of life are entwined between proteins and RNA molecules, which is why I will focus on them.

Sugars and fats are more common in the natural environment and are mainly used for structural and 'energy storage' purposes within a cell, rather than direct functional uses, so I will leave these aside as they won't add much to our sense of awe.

7.1.1   Amino Acid and Nucelotide Monomers

In basic terms Amino Acid and Nucleotide monomers are medium-sized molecules that don't achieve anything by themselves. They are only useful when put together in certain combinations, and the vast majority of such combinations would also achieve nothing on their own.

In crude terms, useful viable proteins, RNA, & DNA do not exist in nature outside the living cell, and have no purpose until they are all working together in 'perfect' harmony within a cell. It is therefore puzzling to imagine why pre-cell chemicals should want to experiment with them at all.

Amino Acids are not simple molecules, but out of the 500+ different versions that are known to exist[45] only 22 are used to make proteins; and living cells require 'left hand' versions of these, not 'right hand' versions. Nature is very picky about what it uses.

> For the sake of clarity and completeness in this section let me say that single celled Bacteria and Archaea require 2 additional Amino Acids[50] above the 20 needed for Eukaryotic life forms.

In contrast, as we saw in Chapter 5, there are only 4 or 5 nucleobases which to some degree can be thought of as modifications of each other. They are vital to life because of their ability to form unique pairs as well as being able to form polymer chains. The much smaller number of their varieties can again suggest that these were the more simple origin of life, but if we follow the logic, things are not as straightforward as they seem.

Outside the body there are many alternate forms of nucleobase, (known as 'Nucleic Acid Analogues'), which also have base pairing abilities, (although many of them are not *unique* pairing combinations). It seems that nature had to carefully select the components it chose to use. In 2014 two new forms of nucleotide produced from analogues were apparently introduced into bacterial DNA. These were replicated many times[46] as the cells reproduced, but interestingly, they never produced any mRNA that incorporated them, (or indeed any proteins that used them), which may suggest that the cells had flagged them as redundant code, not to be used.

In terms of origin, it seems logical to suppose that Amino Acids and Nucleobases were some of the first bio-chemicals to form naturally on Earth but for some time it wasn't clear how this could have been done. Nucleotides are not seen in the Earth's environment outside cells as they are very reactive, and are also very difficult to synthesise in the lab. Indeed it is only relatively recently that ways have been found to do this at all, so scientists still try to preserve/recycle them, or get cells to make new ones.

That said, a 2011 report[47] from NASA indicated that a number of nucleobases had been identified in meteorites and indeed there have been reports of a modest number of Amino Acids being found on meteorites as well – indicating that it was possible for them to form in space. But science has struggled to show how they can be turned into nucleotides.

Interest in all of this was first sparked in a classic experiment from 1953, by Stanley Miller[48] who put clean/sterile chemicals into 2 flasks using proportions that he believed would mimic an early 'primordial soup' on Earth from which life could have emerged, (a point of contention that has been modified by later research).

Miller applied heat as well as bolts of electricity to his flasks and observed the mixture turn pink within a day. Scientists were astonished when 5 basic amino acids and some fatty acids formed on their own within 2 weeks. This prompted an eager press to herald that the experiment proved that the original mix of chemicals on Earth could spontaneously form life.

As I mentioned at the start of the book, this claim wildly exaggerated the findings because, if nothing else, the experiment didn't explain the other 17 necessary Amino Acids, or the origin of nucleotides, or the mechanisms of assembly etc.. Yet a much later re-analysis of his early experimental material, (the preserved residues from his experiments), indicated that Miller may in fact have generated several more amino acids than he thought – but still far short of the necessary minimums.

Yet the experiment did establish an important principle – that these things could form naturally and quite quickly in the right conditions. So the remaining question was how far the principle could be extended.

The other amino acids have proved more problematic – even requiring people to imagine very different chemical soups as the starting conditions for the early Earth. However that is a double edged sword because it has led to speculation that part of the reason for the speed of Miller's reactions was because his mixture was far more chemically reactive than the real original chemical environment 4.6 billion years ago.

The same experiment performed on a revised, (less reactive), mix of chemicals has produced only one very primitive amino acid... on occasions. However in terms of origin, nature had a few million years to play with – so even one Amino Acid opens the possibility to more, with enough time.

It is therefore important to recognise that we simply don't know what the original conditions might have been, so any reasonable permutation might have been correct. A number of these alternate mixes/conditions have been attempted which have even included additional chemicals[49] such as Sulphur or the presence of UV light etc, and from this science **has** synthesised all of the 22 necessary amino acids required for life, ***but not all at the same time***. (Interestingly, increasing levels of hydrogen in the experiments seems to make the results more successful).

Put simply, the conditions in which we might generate some Amino Acids would be very hostile to others, so in order to create all of the mandatory 22 amino acids for life, it would be necessary for the world to undergo a series of dramatic chemical changes as time passed, and each of these changes would need to leave the existing, previously created, amino acids unaffected. However this has **not** been demonstrated.

When we layer-on the need to produce nucleotides as well, the situation of 'overlapping but competing requirements' becomes even worse.

In a similar manner to Stanley Miller's 'spontaneous creation' experiment people have attempted to generate Nucleotides using the base chemicals of a presumed primordial mix, *entirely without success*. (In fairness Juan Oro did synthesise some nucleo*bases*, but not nucleotides, in his Hydrogen Cyanide experiments[49]).

Different forms of Hydrogen Cyanide chemistry seem to be the easiest way to produce some of the nucleobases, (through the formation of intermediate chemicals such as ammonium formate, formamide and diaminomaleonitrile ('DAMN'). However these would not seem to be conducive to the formation of other monomers.

Strategically, some will argue that enough of the principle has been proven to say that because we are here, and nature had far more time than we have had in terms of laboratory experiments, it is entirely feasible to expect that a purely chemical answer to this aspect of origin will be found.

I have a fair amount of sympathy for this but it remains true that the argument for the full range of Amino Acids is far from proven and there are many other people who will argue that other influences would have been involved, even at this early stage in the development of our planet.

Again – you will need to form your own opinion, yet ultimately, I do not feel that this is the area of greatest difficulty for science.

7.1.2 Proteins and RNA

As mentioned earlier, proteins are long chains of amino acids which distinguish themselves from other random chains of amino acids by having a useful purpose, and being specifically manufactured by living cells as a necessary part of their operation.

In layman's terms, as I write, the great strides in science, including the decoding of the human genome, allows us to understand the high level function of approx. 5% of the proteins and other components of a cell, but not necessarily *why* or precisely *how* they perform their tasks.

To make a single useful *protein* life requires an average of some 200 specific amino acid molecules arranged in a precise sequence. A very small number of useful proteins have as little as 100-150 amino acid molecules, but below that the usefulness of an amino acid string is more like that of a building block. (I believe that the smallest viable protein requires 51 amino acid molecules, but it would achieve little without the other proteins). At the opposite end of the scale, some proteins require more than a thousand amino acid components.[51]

The reason for pointing this out will become apparent in a moment when we try to show the likelihood of any single protein emerging from unstructured chemical reactions – even if we assume that all of the necessary Ribosomes and Enzymes were available to assemble them.

The odds against success are truly staggering. In terms of calculating these odds we can draw an analogy between the amino acids and lottery balls. For instance, the original UK National Lottery drew any 6 balls from 49 giving odds of approximately 15 million to one. The balls could be drawn in any sequence, but each number could only be used once in any draw.

By contrast, an average 'winning' protein must only select 22 specific types of 'ball' from a range of 500 which are all in the drum, (not 49). The process must somehow avoid using the other Amino Acids, but each of the 22 can be used more than once. The draw pulls out 200 balls not 6, and more importantly they must be assembled in a precise sequence, **not** drawn in any order, so the odds of success become almost unimaginably impossible as a chance event.

I understand that the odds of achieving just one of these average sized proteins from 'random' chemical reactions has been calculated as 10^{260} (which would be written longhand as 1 with 260 zeros after it)[12,50]. To understand the size of this number I've heard various colourful analogies: -

- I am told that this amounts to more permutations than there are atoms in the entire Universe.

- it would be like a tornado ripping through a huge pile of scrap metal, plastic and other bits, to leave behind a fully assembled and functional jetliner... or in this case a single protein!

The simplest protein of 51 amino acids has odds of 10^{66}, which is still a million million million million million million million million million million times less likely than winning the UK national lottery jackpot. Almost all of the other permutations would be useless.

If we extend the principle to complex proteins with over a thousand amino acid molecules instead of 200 then, quite simply, the probability of a single such molecule arising spontaneously is off the scale.

Yet when we look at odds we have to be cautious. Every lottery draw does produce a result which matches the odds. Those odds only have significance if we are seeking a *particular* result: yet

Nature doesn't generally look for specific outcomes, it seems quite happy with any result.

So it is quite possible for a useful protein to emerge relatively early in nature's experiments, but there is no prospect of nature recognising that it is useful without the other specific proteins with which it must react. The key point now is that at this stage in our logic, nature *does* have to look for specific outcomes to arise in the same place; and the odds will start to bite.

They will do so in five ways. Firstly, if we are now looking for **many** specific proteins to emerge by 'random activity', each with the same astronomic odds - those collective odds multiply enormously.

Secondly, if nature has to compare every version of an Amino Acid chain with every other version, in order to determine which polymers work well together, the number of experimental permutations multiplies the odds enormously once again.

Thirdly, if there was any contamination from unwanted chemical reactions in the wider environment, the number of permutations rises dramatically.

Fourthly, nature will need **many** copies of every useful polymer in order to conduct its experiments. This is for two main reasons. At one level, with more **permutations** of Amino Acids than there are atoms in the Universe, nature would rapidly run out of Amino Acids, (and indeed atoms), if it tried to keep every permutation of protein until it found the right ones. In addition, proteins only have a limited lifespan – presumably made worse if we imagine them emerging from a toxic chemical soup.

The significance of this is that even if nature defied all odds to produce all of the necessary proteins in the same place at the same time it would still need to experiment with them many times before a living cell is likely to emerge. With odds of 10^{260}:1 for a single protein, there can be **no** expectation that a **second** example of the same proteins could *ever* arise by chance in the same locality even with all of the 13.7 billion years of the Universe's existence.

Finally, in a pre-cell world, nature would **not** seem able to keep tabs on which experiments produced something useful and which didn't. Each new protein would effectively begin its series of experiments with a 'clean slate' raising the odds significantly once again.

The only way to stop the odds escalating is to imagine a pre-existing **evolutionary process** that can reliably copy proteins, alongside a way to identify, preserve, and encourage success – a sense of direction. Even if we finally identify such a process, the odds of success remain mind boggling.

We have already seen that in a world without proteins, an original evolutionary process is likely to have been exclusively based on nucleotides and RNA until they somehow managed to extend their reproductive abilities to Amino Acid chains.

At this point we not only have to ask *why* unthinking nucleotides would pursue an interaction with Amino Acids, (which would have to be quite a dedicated/prolonged process in the circumstances), but also determine whether RNA was finding a way to *copy existing proteins*, or was instrumental in the 'experimentation' that *developed* the first useful proteins? With no realistic prospect of the necessary proteins evolving by chance, many people will be inclined to consider the latter possibility.

As we formulate our ideas we then have to remember that :

to make the 1st cell, these factors needed to **pre-exist** in an environment that **had no need of them.**

In today's world mRNA 'merely' acts as a coded template to build **established** proteins, and evolutionary change is primarily introduced through damage to DNA plus its faulty repairs – not RNA experimenting.

So to turn the roles around and say that RNA was the means by which nature experimented with new forms of protein, is a significant step.

This whole subject is fraught with practical difficulties as well as philosophical ones – including purpose & direction.

DNA has often been thought of as a **later** development than RNA, which was used to preserve things that were found to be useful. Yet logic would suggest that it would either need to arise **before** or **at the same time** as RNA if it was really to help the speed of the evolutionary process by not having to 're-invent the wheel' on each cycle of experimentation.

The simultaneous development of DNA, RNA, and Proteins increases the task that nature had to achieve without any controlling influence. In addition, science deems that DNA's main function is to be the long-term storage of <u>information</u> by an unthinking chemical, using a **code**. It has no other function, and the chain of other processes/components that are currently associated with it, also have no purpose without DNA.

The complexity of DNA suggests that it took a very long time to develop but we don't see a stable form of nucleotide outside a cell, and haven't identified an environment where nucleotides/RNA could exclusively mix with Amino Acids to perform their dedicated experiments. We will see later how this has influenced Abiogenetic research.

Of course, part of the explanation is likely to rest on dramatic changes in the Earth's climate over billions of years, however it also smacks of good fortune if each climatic change only happened **after** life had progressed to the 'next stage' on each occasion.

7.1.3 Sets of Chemical Codes working with Accurate Descriptions

Sterile chemicals don't think, and yet codes are almost always associated with thought and purpose. They also tend to introduce complexity.

As we saw in Chapter 5, living cells deploy three sets of codes which work seamlessly together in the process of reproduction. DNA is used to form 2 other codes, (tRNA and its negative mRNA), which are initially used to identify Amino Acids and then to put them in sequence by pairing-up again.

That's not all: we know that four sets of **destination codes** are deployed in the identification of end locations within a cell's transport network. The ones used by mRNA (copied from DNA) are transcribed into the Amino Acid sequences within a protein, then into the RAB code used by vesicles.

In short, there's a lot of coding going-on between different types of sterile molecule in a cell, and they do have real purposes.

The obvious question is: how could those codes emerge from 'random' (unplanned) chemical reactions *prior* to the first cell, seemingly without an instruction manual, (if there was no DNA), and no end objective?

The point about a code is that it isn't a direct copy of the item being described; it is an indirect form of information exchange, and requires the code to be 'understood' by both the user and sender if it is to be effective.

So not only do the protein/RNA mechanisms have to exist, but they also have to apply the code in a useful way. What's more - the chains of understanding here are quite long and complex, which means that if there is an end purpose, (as there seems to be), 'maintaining the concept' before every component is in place is a huge challenge to the theory of origin.

All of this goes against suggestions of 'random' activity before the first cell. Scientists are as baffled as the rest of us, in understanding how it happened.

Yet it's one thing to have developed a set of codes, and quite another to have accuracy in the way that the codes are used to describe something.

Conceptually it is easier to get a detailed description of something if it exists. If it doesn't yet exist then the concept will either be quite loose, or it will have been subject to a proper design. As sterile chemicals cannot design, materialism requires the biological objects we are interested in to be brought into existence by other means – trial and error, evolution, etc.

If the descriptions are of a complex assembly like a cell, then there is a 2nd requirement – completeness. In other words, natural processes would need to ensure that the first set of DNA included everything necessary to make the first cell, not just getting half way through and then stopping.

This is important because it's very hard to imagine how all cell polymers could have come into existence at the same time. Indeed, the background conditions might easily include many polymers that had no useful purpose at all, so something would have to determine which were useful.

There is also a third and more challenging aspect to this because we have seen that the majority of DNA comprises **non-coding** genes which effectively control how the **process** of cell replication should operate. A physical **process** description is difficult to copy from anything intangible.

If we equate a process to button-pushing on our computers, then many people will realise that our sequence of trigger actions can be captured by 'macros' which can then play back the steps, however that requires a lot of programming and machinery to allow this to happen. Our fingers also have to press physical keys on the screen or keyboard. Yet in the evolutionary development of molecules we can only imagine that it would have been chemical bonds which were formed or broken in a series of reactions. There doesn't seem to be any 'keypad mechanism' to store the sequence.

While I admit that my analogy is crude in relation to the functions of a cell, the principle is still sound and the three points need to be answered.

What could generate the code in each of the three circumstances?

One potential way to resolve the dilemma is if either the RNA or DNA was the source of nature's experimentation, (as seems to exist today).

This would imply that all of the replication mechanisms existed before proteins and that somehow, changes in the DNA or RNA code **drove** the experimentation which early evolution must have represented. The design would effectively come first – it's just that it may not be a good design.

While this would mean that the DNA/RNA code for every polymer attempt was *preserved* up front, there's an implication that the **process** would also need a means of determining which steps were successful or not, (as DNA isn't thought to be long enough to contain every failed experiment).

With the need for several proteins to work together; and a precise sequence of steps that would ultimately need to be performed; it becomes very hard to see how unthinking chemicals could determine a usefulness for each element of cell activity before the first cell existed with its DNA instructions. In most cases, even if 3 good proteins in the ultimate sequence were put together, they wouldn't achieve much more than all the rubbish – so how could they show enough potential to be preserved and built-on?

Part of the problem concerning our ideas about the origin of the first cell is that we don't really know what the first cell was capable of. There is an assumption that it was crude, and that many of the sophisticated elements which we see today evolved later. However there is still a minimum level of complexity that must apply to any cell, especially when they all use the same underlying mechanisms.

It is this which prompts us to consider how signalling and control mechanisms emerged to enable the first cell to operate. There is so much of this crucial activity in existence today that it seems almost impossible for a first cell to exist without many of them also being present. But how?

While some processes such as energy generation could well have earlier uses, it's unclear why many of the other functions including signalling would be required before the first cell, (and the principle of 'need' underpins the Theory of Evolution through 'natural selection' – see Ch. 6).

Signalling strongly implies a sense of crude awareness, especially when there is no mechanistic purpose. So unless there is even a concept of how sterile chemicals would see benefit in signalling, we again have to consider where that sense of direction and even foresight could come from.

The new science of Epigenetics[52] might help to explain what is happening and possibly why. This field of research looks at the influence of chemical add-ons to proteins and other mechanisms in a cell – which causes them to either act differently or to become more specialised. But it's early days.

On the other hand we see that biochemistry is now turning to quantum physics for some answers, (eg. the navigational abilities of some birds is now attributed to delicate balances in quantum fields in the bird's brains[53]).

While this is 'producing some fruit' as discussed more fully in Chapter 12, Book 1 pointed out, that physics & cosmology have their own major issues which they are struggling to resolve, and scientists in these fields are also trying to overcome those issues by resorting to suggestions of 'other types of underlying stuff' that we can't yet detect.

To quickly state some examples: 'Dark Energy' is now an almost accepted part of science, but we can't detect it. There is also the evidence of 'hidden field' activity in the dual slit experiments, etc... and of course, there's the old philosophical possibility that other types of stuff may be necessary to explain Thought, emotion, and control. Within the topic of Life, such considerations not only touch on issues of spontaneous or random abilities, (see Chapter 2), but also suggestions about the possibility of 'a life force' and ways to explain the nature of the Mind, (as we will see in Chapter 12).

Whether such things could provide the basis of a hidden 'sense of direction' for early evolution, or an explanation for 'emotions', remains to be seen, but if so, they could be a turning point for all the mysteries of life.

In the wider body, control mechanisms generally have 3 elements :

- A sensor or receptor - which detects levels of activity or chemicals in the body
- A control centre - which gets signals from the sensors and interprets them before sending a signal to an 'effector' to make a change to operations.
- An 'effector' - which might be an organ; muscle; other body part; or cell mechanism that has to make a change to its activities.

Yet in cells the sensor molecules give the impression of combining two, or even **all 3** of these elements in one small combination of atoms, indicating that the molecules are far more capable than the chemistry would suggest.

In these cases, researchers have tried to show that our perception of 'control' within cell functions may be no more than the 'flicking of a few chemical switches'. However when we see motor proteins seemingly working-out a route to an end destination on an ever changing network of roads, 'switch flicking' doesn't quite seem to cut it. The process would not only seem to need an awareness of where things were located, (a constantly updating map or plan), but also a great number of switches to cover the options, and neither seem to be there. Yet research continues.

Even if these elements *were* there, what process could have created them to perform the tasks in such a co-ordinated & purposeful way? There were no switches before the first cell, and there's no brain in any cell today.

As a further example from earlier chapters, if a strand of DNA contains several genes that do the same thing, (either one from each parent, or left over copies of prior mutations), only one will be activated... but how does a cell identify the best version if it is not the latest; or choose from two equally viable options, and then stick to it for the life of the individual?

These are real challenges for science.

7.1.4 Origin of 'Structural Arrangements' & Evolutionary Awareness

As we saw in section 5.3, the process flows of a cell not only encourage particular types of chemical reaction, but also prevent other unwanted reactions from occurring, due to pre-existing structural arrangements which control activities. Many of these mechanisms are types of Enzyme with varying degrees of complexity, but each one is tailored to a specific task.

To simply say that the overall process works because of these components is not an explanation; it merely pushes the question of control backwards in time, to the factor(s) which put those highly tailored mechanisms in place.

We might guess that something could possibly emerge through evolution to resolve a problem that was being encountered, but before the first cell existed many problems would not have arisen. If the mechanisms arose beforehand - anticipating the issue, this would strengthen suggestions of design; which is why most Materialist explanations imagine evolution later.

However, the level of co-ordination & sophistication being demonstrated by some processes, (such as Homologous Recombination), which also use some structural tools, all seem to suggest a more proactive influence.

So how might these structural mechanisms have been achieved? Could it just be the action of unthinking chemical reactions, or would other things such as crude 'awareness' be involved?

The word 'awareness' is often interpreted as an emotive term, but I struggle to find alternatives when the mechanisms appear to go beyond a simple sensing of something, (eg. an event), to form a basic understanding of what those senses imply - as we also saw in Homologous Recombination (5.1.3).

While scientists have found that DNA can act as a crude instruction manual, it is unclear how those instructions can be carried by the enzymes themselves, and as discussed already, we have no idea how 'intangible steps in a process' could be captured, let alone stored using a code. **Proactive** actions in a dynamic situation push expectations even further.

We have also seen that there are more overtly physical issues too. Let's return to the question of why replicating forms of RNA (nucleotides) might suddenly focus on copying something other than themselves – ie. chains of Amino Acids. Is there anything which makes proteins more chemically appealing than copying themselves? Not that we know of.

Put another way, the only known link between nucleotides & Amino Acids is the enzyme which links them to tRNA, so even if we suppose that there was a 'happy accident' which produced it, there's no reason why replication mechanisms should then focus on producing the different forms of tRNA, (having different nucleotide combinations), to accommodate & experiment with the specific types of Amino Acid needed for Life - the basis of the 'code' being used. These 'chains of understanding' are quite long.

There are puzzles even within the mechanics of the replication molecules. If you read Appendix A, you will find a more detailed description of how Ribosomes work: co-ordinating activities based on several sets of in-built sensors, which track different stages of its operations, and cause it to physically adapt both its shape and its actions as a result. This is all for quality control purposes – which implies an awareness that quality is good.

It doesn't mean that one for one cause & effect solutions aren't possible, like a series of switches, but the more complex the scenario, the more numerous these pre-programmed options would need to be. Amid all of the unanswered points of control that we listed, (and others perhaps that have yet to be revealed), we have to ask ourselves, what level of control needs to be displayed before 'awareness' is seen as justified possibility in cells?

The way in which the human eye could have evolved *after* the first cell has shown that incredibly complex things might emerge by physical means. Yet we still need to exercise caution when trying to explain the origin of these functions/mechanisms such as motor proteins which all include the additional 'awareness factor'. It's all too easy for both sides of the debate to make false assumptions about what is physically possible, but developments prior to the first living cell **do** still hold enormous challenges for science.

Motor proteins are used to pull/push duplicated cell components to opposite sides of a cell before the process of cell division occurs, so there's a strong possibility that sophisticated control did feature in the first cells.

What could possibly drive the development of walking molecules if there was no desire to create life amongst sterile chemicals that shouldn't care? How did chemicals 'appreciate' the need to containerise cargo and move these things to specific destinations; or engage in group activities like 'tug of war' (which is how muscles move)? Perhaps the driver came from elsewhere – but I personally see no pre-life 'need' for raw chemicals to do this. 'Need' only seems to arise with the concept/reality of the 1st cell.

While we have to be careful about which developments came before or after 1st cell, it's still remarkable to think why/how developments such as motor proteins came about, not only with the level of power & efficiency we observe, (many times more effective than car engines[43] in terms of relative size), but also their collaboration.

These miniscule 'strongmen', when working together in their millions, are the things that actually give you the power in your legs and arms: (the muscle fibres don't twitch on their own)!

Similar principles seem to apply to all of the structural factors that we observe in cells, and they inevitably colour our perception of what Evolution is being asked to explain.

For me, it's particularly interesting to think how a cell membrane might enclose the initial cell components, at the exact moment in history when they all came together for the first time? (Given the odds, it's hard to see how it could happen many times). That would be a remarkable coincidence.

If not, then we might consider that gelatinous blobs were regularly capturing those protein and RNA components and that some of the experimentation happened within them, (as this would give the mechanisms a protected environment). It's pure speculation, but it may give us a clue to the sort of conditions in which life might develop, insulated from the worst excesses of unstable chemical mixtures.

Alternately, we might consider that undersea volcanic vents might offer some potential, by offering a degree of chemical stability below the waves, and possibly a source of fatty acid bubbles that could provide a membrane.

7.2 Potential Ways that Life on Earth may have Emerged

We have seen that the odds against developing even a single useful protein by ad-hoc chemical reactions are enormous, even if you had the means with which to assemble them. When you then add the requirement for **many** specific proteins & types of RNA, **plus** the codes which they utilise, **and** all of the other structures and mechanisms they need, it is not surprising that some people believe that the emergence of the first cell from base chemicals was a unique event in the history of the *Universe.*

The profusion of life on Earth may mean that this unique event just happened to occur on our planet approx. 9.7 billion years after the Big Bang, (4 billion years ago). Yet to some, even that timescale would seem challenging for a series of 'random' reactions that had no sense of direction.

As we know, the general way in which timeframes are imagined to be reduced is by believing that unthinking physical matter managed to establish **processes** which helped to steer the development of Life. If such processes can be demonstrated, the origin of the living cell might still be a unique event, but it could now occur either here on Earth within a 200m yr. window of opportunity; or many billions of years earlier, elsewhere in the Universe, allowing time for cells to cross the vastness of space, (say by comet, or even alien spaceship (!)), to seed our planet.

As strange as some of these ideas may sound at first, they all have their logic and all try, in their different ways, to reconcile the evidence available with the extreme odds concerning proteins etc. that cannot be ignored.

Yet I do have some difficulties with the 'comet'/'meteorite' options as they do not offer much protection to the cells on their journey across the incredibly vast and cold distances of space – especially if we talk about distances between solar systems or even galaxies, where we could be talking about millions of years travel time. Cells have a limited lifespan.

Then there's the 're-entry' problem, where all the surface/accessible layers of these rocks would burn off in the atmosphere, and the interiors are also likely to get very hot, so normal cells would not be expected to survive other than by remote chance. We are **not** talking about raw chemicals here.

You can probably see where the notion of 'seeding' by spaceship after life has developed elsewhere, begins to gain a degree of credibility, even if you may not be fully persuaded! It avoids a number of serious problems.

So is there any evidence to back up the 'comet seeding' idea? Some ancient bits of space matter which have hit the Earth (meteorites) have been analysed and found to date from the birth of **our** solar system, not beyond. When such rocks were analysed, a number of them were found to contain some of the amino acid chemicals which are necessary for life, (reflecting Stanley Miller's experiment), but not cells or even proteins/RNA.

While amino acids are occasionally found in relative profusion within these rocks, we already know that these monomers can form naturally here on Earth; so the seeding of amino acids does nothing to explain the origin of cellular life. In short, while a succession of strikes by comets and other space material may have added to the planet's stock of water and minerals, there is no evidence to say that they brought the mechanisms or coding for the first cell. The materialist search for an explanation of the first cell therefore focuses on the natural emergence of Life here on Earth from raw chemicals within 200 million years, without 'external influence'.

Any solution must explain our origin without resorting to undue levels of 'luck' and also answer some core questions, such as sources of control, and a viable means of 'evolutionary direction' by unthinking chemicals.

Of course, it is still a logical possibility that each of the 3 main branches in the tree of life was based on a separate 'first cell' and so there would be three start points for Life not one. Yet some facts incline against this idea.

Firstly, the odds magnify significantly. Secondly, while each type of cell does have its own unique version of the Ribosome, the atomic mapping of the different forms of Ribosome has indicated that a set of common evolutionary changes may have pre-dated all three types of cell. In other words, there may have been an earlier common ancestor, but possibly **not** as part of a cell as we know it.

Thirdly, there are the common reproductive mechanisms of DNA, tRNA and mRNA, which also seem to have atomic level similarities with the Ribosome. Finally, if three similar forms of Life had emerged independently, why do we not see many more?

What we can say is that any physical mechanism would have to be based on chemical processes. So are there any ideas about the circumstances which might have enabled such developments?

Well, until recently, there have only been some outline concepts. There was talk of warm muddy pools; undersea vents; and even crystalline starts to life: but at this strategic level of detail none of these ideas could really scratch the surface of what would be required for a 'credible explanation'. We need to generate basic methods of reproduction & metabolism.

Superficially in nature the formation of crystals may seem to act as a crude form of reproduction, because the chemical structures of those molecules forces them to sit alongside each other in a regular geometric pattern. Crystals also grow within environments that can support them with a source of minerals, avoiding the need for a metabolism. Yet nobody thinks that crystals are alive, so could they be a place for experimentation where this crude form of reproduction might enable a basic form of evolution?

In short, the crystals themselves are unlikely to do this because they do not let the minerals evolve; they just assemble them in an inevitable pattern.

RNA remains the best hope of a purely chemical answer to evolution, and as mentioned earlier, crude forms of RNA **have** been shown to replicate themselves. Yet, to do this they need a regular supply of monomers, and a protective environment where their delicate chemistry won't be affected.

Caves might offer some form of protective environment, and on the early Earth caves may also have been a lot warmer than today, helping to facilitate reactions. Darkness would protect any RNA from harmful UV light, (as would the dark atmosphere of the early Earth), however we assume that the air would also be an ever-changing mix of chemicals which would make any surface-based development of life quite vulnerable.

One of the earliest forms of Life, (known as stromatolite), still exists today off the northwest coast of Australia, (Shark Bay). We might think of it as a very slow growing form of coral or 'bacterial rock'[14]. From this we might speculate that the sea could offer a degree of protection and stability from the chemical soup above. At deeper levels, we also know that undersea volcanic vents support life, and do seem to provide relatively stable conditions. However they are not particularly known as a source of nucleotides and RNA – those would seem to come from elsewhere.

Recognising that cells have a fatty outer membrane, the idea has grown that a form of replicating RNA might have 'experimented' with polymers **within** a protective cocoon – perhaps bubbles of oily fats on the banks of a warm muddy surface pool on the early Earth. This would imply that cell membranes were one of the first developments towards life, and that RNA and Ribosomes developed within it. (Suggestions that those bubbles may instead have been made of mud or lava have only added to the chemical challenges and have **not** been seen as likely).

However, whatever the mechanism, given the scale of the things that had to emerge from evolution and the relatively short amount of time available, we would expect such experimentation to have been undertaken on a vast scale not in rare and isolated circumstances.

One difficulty for this notion is that fatty bubbles generally only form in liquids that would not support the formation of nucleotides and RNA, (which in themselves are very difficult to make). Even if we suggest that it was possible to make RNA in the early Earth atmosphere, and these came into contact with the surface of a pool producing the fatty bubbles, those globules would generally have already formed by the time they reached the surface, making it difficult for RNA to enter any bubble. Nucleobases/tides are very reactive and seem unlikely to reach/enter the bubble in pure form.

Not only that, if RNA was to replicate and then generate an evolutionary process, it would need a regular supply of more nucleotides to build the new molecules, and those monomer raw materials would also have to enter through the wall of that fatty bubble over a prolonged period in an early Earth environment. None of this has really been demonstrated.

On the positive side, work by Leslie Orgel has shown that simple forms of RNA **can** replicate themselves in lab conditions but he wasn't able to generate RNA that was longer than 14 nucleotides, (incredibly short).

Research by Jack Szostak[119] demonstrated that this form of RNA could be contained in a fatty globule, and its reproductive abilities made far more efficient with traces of a certain type of mud, called Montmorillonite, (and possibly other similar forms of clay). The clay within the membrane seems to act like an ultra-crude form of enzyme in cells, helping reactions to occur.

His team has also shown that the bubbles can poach each other's fatty materials, allowing them grow as their contents get bigger due to the RNA replication inside them; and that such bubbles can also form with multiple layers – a form known as a 'protocell', which can subdivide into many smaller cells each containing some of the RNA contents, when shaken as in a strong water current.

However it must be said that an RNA strand 14 nucleotides long will not achieve anything unless it is given a very long time to evolve with a regular supply of necessary building material – especially nucleotides. That constant supply of monomers remains problematic – especially on a large scale to allow for massive experimentation.

Indeed, it has also been very difficult even to demonstrate the formation of such RNA, (which needs sugars to bind the nucleobases), as sugars are difficult to imagine in the early Earth environment. Cruder forms of RNA, (such as PNA), might have been available, but they have not been shown to replicate. So there's a mystery over what could have generated the first replicating molecules in conditions where a fatty bubble could enclose them and then re-supply them with more nutrients/building blocks.

The reactions within the protocells were made possible with the addition of magnesium but this tended to destroy the fatty cell walls unless citrate was added. Magnesium is not a common material, and the use of citrates to stabilise it is very hard to imagine as oranges and lemons didn't exist then.

So has the research into abiogenesis produced a mechanism which is viable, let alone widespread? Does any of this demonstrate how life could get started? Not really.

While these experiments do demonstrate **some** of the necessary capabilities for an early form of evolution in the lab, it is far from a complete picture, and the different elements have not been brought together into a single viable process within a common environment similar to the early Earth. However the experiments **have** put a lot more flesh on the bones of a possible materialist solution.

The question we face is: has enough of the principle been shown to say that something viable might be expected to emerge with more research?

We need to remember that even the crudest of living cells requires many different codes/components/features which might be worked-towards with a sense of direction, but at this stage of development basic RNA chemicals seem to have no such mechanism. A series of changes is likely to have left them with as many backwards steps as forwards ones.

It has also been very hard to show that the basic replicating form of RNA which has been discovered, can grow beyond 14 nucleotides on its own. New sections of nucleotides can, in some experiments, be added to these very short RNA strands – but they have to be developed elsewhere first.

How? We either have to imagine that other undiscovered forms of RNA were far more capable; or a significant number of different forms of RNA somehow managed to combine at the exact moment when two or more protocells burst/subdivided - leaving the new longer form of RNA enclosed in a new cell. It has the feel of a rare occurrence even if such RNA did exist.

As the environment inside a fatty bubble is quite limited and the conditions necessary to generate them seem unlikely to be commonplace, an alternate suggestion has been made - that more sophisticated forms of RNA emerged before they were enclosed by fatty bubbles.

If the simplest form of chemistry resulting in the production of nucleotides, (often portrayed as a cyanide-based mix of chemicals), was dominant in say the early atmosphere, there would be a much broader environment in which experimentation could occur. To my mind this seems to take us back to the notion that everything just happening to come together at the right moment - requiring a lot of luck and a leap of faith.... But who knows? Are these outline principles sufficient to persuade you?

8 Collective Consciousness and Meaning

In this chapter we take a step back from the mechanics of our bodies to look at some broader concepts about Life and the factors that could give it a deeper purpose and possibly even 'meaning'.

Most readers will find these to be fun, but some aspects do point to real issues, and those who adopt them as full beliefs will treat them very seriously indeed.

We will be primarily looking at two 'strategic' ideas which have emerged from the concept of 'Collective Consciousness'.

Before you put the book down thinking that we are about to get into very weird and fanciful territory let me say that collective consciousness is born out of observations from nature: including the incredible organisation displayed by ants and termites; through to aspects of human behaviour and awareness across cultures. Some aspects of these concepts are being tested to see if there is anything to them.

So I hope you find the chapter interesting as well as a bit of light relief.

All life on Earth exists within an environment that sustains it. Because life consumes some of the resources of the Earth, living organisms are often portrayed as parasites that give nothing back. But **Gaia** theory says that this is a two way relationship, and that we do give something back to the planet by being part of a self-regulating system within and around it.

The other concept we will be considering is the extent to which minds might influence reality. At an obvious human level, our individual minds control our bodies, but through the communication of ideas we can also spread our thoughts and co-ordinate the activities of large numbers of people to produce much larger effects on the planet.

So collective consciousness allows everyone in a community to share a common vision of what things are and how they seem to operate. That may not sound like a remarkable thing, until you remember that our minds undeniably form an impression, from electrical signals alone, of both 'shapes' and what is happening. So whether you are a materialist or an idealist, our impression of reality is a mental construct from within our minds. How is it that they all seem to form a common image?

From this, the idea has grown that collective consciousness may not only make us all think the same way, but may also allow us to shape our environment by changing our collective thoughts about it: to form a new vision and a new reality – a *subconscious* way to influence events. The **Global Conciousness Project** is testing that hypothesis.

In terms of the philosophical range, I tend to position Gaia philosophy as 'Emergent Idealism', while the 'Global Consciousness Project', takes us closer to full 'Idealism'. Yet at their core is the idea of Collective Consciousness which could potentially be explained on a Materialist basis.

We should therefore begin by considering why collective consciousness is both a credible concept and one that may not be entirely down to chemistry.

Most basic definitions of Life try to distinguish it from 'non-life' and tend to focus on physical mechanics, however as we progress from there, definitions increasingly shift onto the varying levels of consciousness that are apparent in different organisms/creatures.

Ants and termites are perceived to only have the tiniest brains, and yet their communities are highly organised and co-ordinated for the gathering of food, the nurturing of young, and in generating remarkable structures.

A termite mound has many chambers which are suited to different purposes, (from nurseries at the right temperature and humidity; to farming areas creating the right environment for specific types of crops that they harvest), and across all of these is a sophisticated 'air conditioning' system.

Can chemical signals between these tiny creatures really account for the design and organisation that is observed in (say) the construction of cooling fins? Wouldn't some sort of thought be necessary too, and if so, would this equate with the size of brain that science observes in termites?

It can be argued that humans generate a form of collective consciousness through physical means (eg. talking via the muscles in our mouths and transmission of air waves), and mental means, (elaborate languages and concepts), via one of the largest brains in the animal kingdom.

But termites... ? The mechanics alone suggest that there's something beyond chemical signals to enable the sharing and development of ideas.

Life is probably the only force in nature which can understand the effect it is having on the rest of existence, while displaying self-control, reasoning (as part of survival), and sometimes acts of spontaneity and randomness.

For this reason many people have argued that Life is distinct from the mediums in which it hitches a ride, and that physical life may therefore have an additional component beyond the bunch of chemicals that make up their bodies, although we cannot say what that might be.

We have seen some pointers to this within living cells in Chapters 5-8, and from Book 1 there are also factors from the world of physics, such as the 'faster than light experiments', which break the established mould and strongly imply that sub-atomic particles communicate with each other – another potential basis by which thoughts could be coordinated.

Put another way, Book 1 showed a number of respects in which Idealism could be supported by the findings of physics and quantum mechanics, so it should not be dismissed out of hand just because you might be sceptical.

8.1   The World as a Living Entity & Gaia Philosophy

Modern Gaia theories straddle the full spectrum of religious and atheistic beliefs because, in a similar manner to all good religions, there are aspects that have some foundation in reality, and they can also work in harmony with other beliefs.

Scientifically, if we consider the circumstances of Earth in comparison to an equivalent lifeless rock of a planet in another galaxy, which is the same distance away from the same type of sun, we tend to imagine that conditions here are much more moderate.

While that moderation may start in the basic provision of life-giving conditions like an atmosphere and water, there's no doubt that it is enhanced by the beneficial effects which living things have on the planet... and yes there are some benefits – life doesn't just consume and destroy per the agendas of certain pressure groups.

The hypothesis presented by James Lovelock[54] and Lynn Margulis in 1974 suggests that the living and non-living parts of the Earth form a self-regulating, complex, and interacting system (the Biosphere), that can be thought of as a single organism.

> By way of example, if the level of carbon dioxide in the atmosphere rises, (causing greater global warming), plants grow more readily, and in the process remove some of that CO_2 thereby reducing overall levels, and moderating the planet's temperature... over time.

> Of course, while the effects are logically true, the scale of the impact generated by biological factors is unclear.

Through such processes, the actions of plant life alone are thought to have changed the atmosphere and the chemical balance of the oceans[54] not only to enable life to thrive, but also to regulate heat making it a more even and gentle climate overall which in turn helps to moderate volcanic activity and the movement of tectonic plates[55].

The idea was originally strongly criticised, but it found increasing favour as science has shown that the associated processes do genuinely produce such effects to some degree, however the key point of contention is whether they are driven **by intent**.

This is where we see the scientific, philosophical, and religious theories of Gaia diverge.

The key process in Gaia theory is 'homeostasis' which some believe needs conscious control, but the scientific interpretation is effectively that these are simply inevitable, natural interactions that just happen to be beneficial.

The step change for the philosophy, over the science, is to think of the Earth and all of its living inhabitants as being a single organism, (a theory which in part is tested through the Global Consciousness Project, (below)). If that is true, then the organisms may not just produce a self-balancing mechanism but also one that drives change on a planetary scale.

If you are also religious, the further question is whether God, or some other influence, set up this interaction between planet and Life?

Inevitably as a way to reconcile competing beliefs, a variety of religious thinking has blended Gaian ideas with either: the Taoist force/way; Buddhism and the interwoven influences of life; Pantheism[56]; Neo-Paganism; and even Judeo-Christian religions.

Of course the ultimate link to God would be that the biosphere extends to and possible emanates from Him... which is actually not dissimilar to the ideas of ancient Greece!

The name 'Gaia' was apparently proposed by the author William Golding after the ancient Greek goddess Gaia – one of the primordial deities, and the personification of the Earth. The ancient Greeks proposed that their Gods literally formed the fabric of the environment – so it's easy to see the parallels, even if Gaian philosophy today is much more 'new age', and associated with the notion that all life is linked through a common 'network'

In popular culture Gaian ideas have been heavily used in such films as Avatar and other media storylines including Final Fantasy, ("The Spirits Within"), plus computer games etc.

Gaia hypotheses, and associated ideas of eco-systems, can happily sit alongside the theories of evolution as they show that the Earth and its inhabitants continue to adapt to their circumstances.

It is only recently through increasing scientific knowledge of eco-systems that we've become aware of how complex the inter-dependencies can be, as part of a single natural system. It is also remarkable that such self-balancing mechanisms should form **without** the conscious help of the creatures involved.

> We see plants which are entirely dependent on insects for pollination/reproduction; or predators which unwittingly regulate the population sizes of other creatures to bring them into balance with the resources available.

> It's all very intricate, but equally, such eco-systems have had a long time to emerge, generating survival niches/opportunities for different creatures to adapt-to and exploit.

So in basic terms we might say the Materialist perspective is: that once Life existed it moved forwards to exploit the opportunities that it found, while the more Idealist elements suggest that the need for Life, and a presumed evolutionary process, were driven by a sense of purpose/direction.

Personally, I can't see that seas, atmosphere, and rocks will have any level of consciousness and yet it is correct that an evolutionary development of the first cell **would** require a sense of direction. However that direction doesn't necessarily have to be based in consciousness.

For me, there is some merit in considering that another type of stuff which underpins reality may provide this - but of course, there is the possibility of God too.

Finally I should say that Gaia theory **doesn't** seem to offer any view on life after death, or the continuity of the soul. *That* remains firmly in the territory of established religious beliefs.

8.1.1   Global Consciousness Project

Hopefully it is not an exaggeration to say that the majority of people will associate consciousness with the mind, and therefore the brain.

Yet we see remarkable levels of control and co-ordination even within cells that definitely do not have a brain.

Amongst ants and termites we observe spacial awareness in the way that they explore territory, but this seems to be taken to an additional level of purpose when their mounds include design features such as cooling fins, and where we see cultivation of specific crops, or eggs and young being transported to other chambers when a threat is perceived.

They seem to display a common vision and shared purpose.

We also seem to share a common image and perception of the world and its activities. These seem to form from the electrical signals which are processed by our brains, and might be reinforced by the concepts we share through language etc. So the general impression seems to be that although we could each form very different perceptions about what is happening in life, we co-ordinate in order to largely share the same vision.

Within this of course, there is some room to manoeuvre because, for instance, what I actually see and experience as 'red' and label as red, you may actually experience as blue, but still label as red, due to the different images that our minds may form. This could explain why we all like different colours.

In truth, nobody knows if our minds do construct the same images & experiences, or not. Yet if we do imagine the same things in the same way this would seem to be evidence that either

- our brains are built the same way, which is why they produce the same effect, or
- our minds are genuinely connected together in some way, so that we all share a true, common perception.

So for the moment let's stay with the *less* rigorous proposal: that we always appear to recognise shared circumstances in a consistent way - not only by our own standards, but also in the expectations of others. One way to explain this common view might simply be that all of our perceptions are constructed from the same independent reality that we all sense. In other words, if it is there, there is only one way to see it.

However the alternative, as we have seen, is that we could all imagine things in different ways but that our perceptions are linked dynamically, to enable us to share a common vision - a form of 'group psychosis'.

This could apply to all sorts of every-day activities from the way in which we collectively react to the smell of bacon, the taste of chocolate, the sounds of music, or the words on this page. However even here we see variations in peoples' likes and dislikes.

But might we see less variation with regards to big strategic events which capture the public imagination? Could it even be the case that a global shared vision may actually shape events before they happen – and not just in human terms but in the natural world as well?

In this respect I am reminded of anecdotal evidence of a folk-lore phenomenon: that significant human decisions can spark dramatic downpours and even storms, *in reality*, not just on stage!

There are quite a number of historic moments which are reported to have been followed by a sudden storm or deluge. The latest one I can think of can actually be seen in the original TV video footage[57] of the archaeological excavations in Leicester which uncovered the grave of King Richard III. Just after the first digger had broken the tarmac over where his bones lay, a dark cloud rapidly moved over the site and there was a sudden sharp downpour – prompting comments on camera at the time.

I also remember a documentary about the decision by Hitler and his advisors to go to outright war in World War 2, (in relation to the Polish invasion, I recall). In it, there was an interview with a German lady who had been on Hitler's staff at Berchtesgaden and was on duty at the time. She related how, in the half hour leading up to the decision, the sky began to rapidly fill with black clouds from all directions - **not** like a weather front. They were mixed with very unusual colours: reds, oranges and dark purples amid the darkening sky. Then, almost immediately after the decision, an enormous and very powerful storm broke out with high winds and many bolts of lightning – which she interpreted as an omen of doom.

These occurrences might easily be dismissed as coincidence or an elaboration of events that can't be checked – but they could also be pointers to rare effects. I'm not sure that anyone has assembled a historical list of examples, but I suspect that until such things are verifiable in the modern age they will be treated with scepticism. Richard III may be the first of these.

However it is in relation to the general principle of thought affecting matter that The Global Consciousness Project may offer a way forward. It was born out of early experiments some 50 years ago which suggested that certain types of equipment, (random number generators), could be sensitive to human thought.

As you can imagine, it's an interesting notion but it is highly controversial as it challenges all sorts of perceptions.

The Global Consciousness Project (GCP) a very long-term international initiative which is privately funded and largely run by academic establishments, (the initiative having emerged from initial research by Princeton University in the USA). Over the past 30 years, since it adopted its latest format, it has sought to demonstrate whether or not human consciousness can influence various random number generators that are scattered around the world. There are now 70 devices.

The random number generators run 24/7, year after year, and when major world events happen, the patterns of numbers are scrutinised immediately before, during, and after those events to see if **non**-random patterns have arisen above the level of 'background noise' that normally exists.

Surprisingly the researchers claim that they **do** show significant spikes of such activity around those times. Yet others disagree, saying that the way in which the data is processed by researchers effectively skews the results – and that different methods do **not** show spikes. Other critics have taken a different view saying that spikes of activity can occur in any statistical sample, and the levels of spiking being claimed are still relatively small, so the results are not that significant.

Yet I find it interesting that the challenges have not deterred the backers who seem to think that the findings are sufficiently encouraging to maintain the significant funding that's necessary for this research, for many decades to come... and many of those backers are highly skilled in statistical analysis too.

For interested observers, I suspect that it's the timing of those spikes, which correlate with many dramatic events over an extended period, which generates continued interest in the exercise.

It's refreshing that there **is** a willingness to consider such 'lateral thinking' in the face of severe scepticism & tight purse strings. I ask you to remember this when we consider equally contentious research, in Chapter 10.

One of the most eye-catching claims was that significant levels of non-random sequences were recorded shortly **before** 9:11 and prior to specific moments during those terrible events, (eg. when each plane struck the towers and when the towers collapsed). Other events that were analysed included the results of the OJ Simpson trial, and the funeral of Princess Diana – all apparently showing some spiking. But is it at a significant level? Let's just say that while the funding seems to be continuing, there have been no dramatic conclusions or claims.

To be clear, there is no apparent way in which anyone could interpret future spikes to make predictions, as the timeframes are short and there is nothing in the data to indicate *what* might be about to happen or *where*.

However all of this seems to be based on the notion that our collective consciousness is extending to the wider environment, and yet as things stand, none of the findings indicate **how** these effects might happen even if they were real. Of particular interest are the spikes in activity just **before** a historic 'moment' occurs, and the causes for it. People can only speculate about this, and I suppose that general notions may take two forms :-

- an act of great significance produces some sort of 'shock wave' effect that runs ahead of the event, affecting the environment & equipment,
- our collective human thoughts subconsciously make these events happen, effectively shaping the world around us in a pro-active way.

If our collective consciousness does make things happen because our collective view has been altered, (not the other way round), this may be partial evidence that everything about our existence is purely in the mind – the Idealist view of existence.

Yet as things stand **the case is far from demonstrated**, let alone proven.

So where do the benefits lie?

Well my interest in this continuing exercise is to demonstrate whether or not a subtle effect is real; and to potentially establish a point of principle about whether Thought could have an effect beyond our bodies.

To do that, spikes in activity would need to be much more significant than they are, and must appear on numerous occasions, so it is likely to be some time before any claims could be made.

If the results can ultimately do this, they may point us towards the underlying cause of this effect; which may in turn help to demonstrate whether Thought is always tied to Matter/Energy, or can be independent of it – a basis for ultimately considering ideas about the soul and an afterlife.

Some will therefore see it as a threat while others will see it as an opportunity. What do you think?

8.2 **Various Ideas about the Meaning of Life**

> "The answer to the ultimate question of life, the universe, and everything is........... 42 !"   Douglas Adams
> *The Hitchhiker's Guide to the Galaxy*

How many times have we heard the question:

> 'What is the meaning of Life?'

Philosophers will typically jump on this to say that it is probably a meaningless question, which is why Douglas Adams' answer is probably as good as any other; perhaps even better than most given its great humour.

To understand what they mean you have to drill a little deeper: for instance, how do you interpret the word 'meaning'?

Are we asking about *why* Life arose, or its *purpose/objective*, or perhaps whether it has any *intrinsic value*? Similarly, what does 'Life' mean in this question? Are we confined to human life, or all life? Are we talking about experiences, or the fact that it exists at all? Two more sample quotes might illustrate the challenges :

> "Life is problems. Living is solving problems."
> Raymond E. Feist, *Silverthorn*

> "The purpose of life is to stay alive. Watch any animal in nature - all it tries to do is stay alive. It doesn't care about beliefs or philosophy. Whenever any animal's behaviour puts it out of touch with the realities of its existence, it becomes extinct."
> Michael Crichton, *Congo*

If Life is just a simple fact without original purpose, then the only meanings are either found in what you experience, or what you do with life. In other words,

the choice would be ours, to live lives *with* meaning or without it.

If we look at current astro-physical theories on the ultimate fate of the universe we see that all physical life will probably cease one way or another at some remote point in the future – so you might wonder what the point of it all might be, if nothing that we achieve will ever have any lasting significance? Once again, we may be drawn to the conclusion that the meaning is what we choose to get from it, while we live.

If you believe that our souls are immortal then they will live beyond the existence of this physical universe into the existence of future universes –

which would preserve 'significance' in the memory of our achievements and again, the meaning/value we attribute to them.

On the other hand if the answer lies in saying that we are here to fulfil God's plan for us, would we be saying that we have no intrinsic value other than to God?

Well for a start, I think most people would see value in ourselves. It may not be significant compared to God but equally from this perspective, the significance wouldn't *just* be down to God either. As an extension of this we might argue that there **is** meaning in the simple fact that we exist.

From these various lines of thinking it's easy to see that we can find meaning in what we want; which returns us to the age-old desire to avoid death by achieving immortality, or re-birth into a new life... in which case Michael Crichton wasn't far off the mark in his quote above.

Yet Crichton doesn't say **why** we want Life. We know that people can commit suicide, so <u>survival is partly a choice</u>. Once again I tend to presume that we want it because we enjoy experiencing it, or we want to achieve something, and so we again get meaning based on what we choose to obtain from Life.

Of course, many religious people are striving for a *pleasant* continuation of life instead of a *less pleasant* one, however in terms of meaning this doesn't seem to add much because at a simple level, this logic only seems to combine the desire for more 'experience' with an objective that it should also be enjoyable.

Yet within religious principles we also find a quest for self-improvement. Does that have meaning – other than to us? Life would exist in a 'higher' form rather than a 'lower' form, but does that give Life itself a meaning or a reason for being?

In abstract terms philosophers have considered various factors that might bestow meaning on Life and have come up with 4 main candidates :

- Supernaturalism
- Objective Naturalism
- Subjective Naturalism, and
- Pessimistic Naturalism or 'Nihilism'

Supernaturalism

Roughly, supernaturalism maintains that both God's presence plus a relevant relationship with Him, is both necessary and sufficient for securing a meaningful life. This usually goes further to imply that there are both appropriate and inappropriate relationships/practises we may adopt.

Objective Naturalism

This suggests that there's an intrinsic meaning or value within things that is nothing to do with what we personally attribute to them, or how we perceive them. Meaning would be gained by associating our actions with objectives that do have intrinsic value.

It also suggests that meaning could exist without any reference to God, or a supernatural realm.

So as an example, if we chose to spend our lives counting leaves in a forest or hopping in a circle, objective naturalism would probably say there was little or no meaning to our activities because they had no intrinsic value.

Subjective Naturalism

As you might guess, Subjective Naturalism says that we can each attribute our own meaning to each event or activity based on our desires, values, or personal objectives. In short, 'meaning' is getting what you want from life.

Pessimistic Naturalism: Nihilism

Roughly, nihilism is the view that denies that a meaningful life is possible because, literally, nothing has any value. This can be argued in different ways from :-

- the denial of God and a spiritual existence, (which would be the only things that could confer value if only they did exist) , to
- the absence of satisfaction, or the presence of boredom.

However critics will say that virtually no life is completely without satisfaction and that it's wrong to emphasise an end state and ignore the present and its potential.

I realise that these thoughts may not answer the question to your satisfaction however I hope that the range of thoughts and their tendency to come full circle will at least provide a basis for your own exploration.

9 Scientific Evidence for Life beyond the Body

Death is hereditary and inevitable, but *your* results may vary.

Anonymous

The underlying basis of most religions is to provide people with the hope and belief of a continuing life, after physical death on Earth. To many non-believers this amounts to wishful thinking and nothing more, because they assume that there's no evidence for an after-life... but that doesn't reflect the full position. There **is** a reasonable amount of evidence, but as with all of these things it can be interpreted in different ways.

Having spent such a lot of time in this book looking at 'hard science' it was hard for me to write these two chapters, as they provoke such strong reactions on both sides of the 'debating line', and also because we enter a subject which is inevitably driven by 'soft evidence' based on testimony.

Yet the scientifically gathered evidence is there, and if I am to honour my claim of fairly considering all major options about life, I feel it is necessary to present it and allow you to make a judgement, rather than become a blind denier of its existence and its possibilities.

As much as anything, I have given more space to the topic than I intended for two reasons:

- Much of the generalised reporting of these findings, even on some of the popular encyclopaedia websites, has largely avoided presenting the evidence, choosing to focus on criticisms of some weaker aspects of the research, without giving people the opportunity to judge the positives.

- While some of the criticisms are fair, they are not fatal to the findings, but the majority of adverse comments seem to me, as an outside observer, to be little more than generalised mud-slinging.

These chapters are not about religion or faith. They consider the potential **evidence** for the existence of Souls through

- Out of Body experiences, (OBE), and
- the possibility of Reincarnation.

I must stress again that this is scientifically gathered evidence by independent academic teams of professionals with international reputations to defend. These are honest investigations, not 'quackery', but that doesn't have to pre-determine what we make of it. Like researchers we should be careful not to jump to conclusions, either way.

(Reports of phenomena which are **not** backed by scientifically gathered evidence are covered in Chapter 11).

While being wary of fakes, we first have to establish a base position by considering whether the experiences were real for those that experienced them. For those cases that are credible we can then try to determine causes, and seek to explain what those experiences might represent.

If the testimonies are genuine, they are facts which have to be explained, one way or another. **Every** philosophy would have to accommodate them, somehow – whether by Materialist means or as evidence for a Soul.

The sensitivity is clear – that the stronger cases have not been answered satisfactorily by Materialism as yet, and while they may appear to offer evidence for the Soul, they do not sit comfortably with some religious views either: even some permutations of religions that accept reincarnation.

> For the purposes of this book I will regard the Soul as the means to preserve the essence of an individual so that it may transfer to another life/existence after physical death. To do so, it would presumably capture their character, preferences, memories, etc, (even if they are not relevant to the next life), otherwise the new being could not be regarded as the same individual. A permutation of this is that souls may fragment after death and may combine with other souls to form a new hybrid individual, (as in some Buddhist beliefs). There may be other characteristics.

So while the findings have produced no firm conclusions the patterns and the trends that they suggest are likely to challenge almost *everyone* as they seem to have elements which run counter to most expectations, (whether as a believer or sceptic).

That doesn't mean we have to accept any viewpoint but equally it would seem wrong to 'bury our head in the sand' and refuse to consider them on the basis of dogma alone.

From a headline perspective, out of body experiences suggest that the Mind or Soul of the individual can leave the physical body and observe events around it from a modest distance. Initially, all reports seemed to describe the 'spirit' of the person floating **above** the body, looking down at it, but I gather that some induced effects, (generated for the purposes of research), have caused people to envisage themselves **across** a room[114].

Two critical differences with the induced effects are: that the false impression of reality is generated while the subjects are awake, and secondly, by giving them a false or pre-fabricated image through a set of virtual reality goggles, while also touching the subject's skin so that they associate genuine feelings with the false image[114].

In these cases therefore the image is **not** generated by the Mind of the subject, whereas in real cases, the people affected generally had their experience while unconscious and often with their eyes closed - yet reports suggest that they were still able to accurately describe colours, clothing, equipment, and the activities around them, from above.

The 'headlines' in relation to possible reincarnation are that if the experiences being reported are genuine, and do reflect a specific person being able to live again after death, by being reborn, then the only way in which that could truly happen is if the identifying features of an individual are transferred to the new body – which would require a Soul.

That is why these two subject areas are of relevance to us.

If you are sceptical about reincarnation and believe that any adult with some practise could put on a convincing story, then let me tell you that the scientific investigation of reincarnation focuses on the testimony of thousands of young children[62] whose claims begin around the ages of 18 months to 6 years. Their lives are then followed over many years, and their testimonies across all of this period are investigated, analysed, and in the strongest cases, thoroughly cross-checked.

Anyone who has had children will know that to get them to learn something real is hard enough. To get them to lie convincingly and with this level of scrutiny would be a very rare achievement. So to find 3,000 cases in a 30-40 year period, (which is what happened according to various web encyclopaedias), would seem very hard if not impossible to justify as an all-embracing conspiracy theory.

In order to follow the principles of this book, I will present some of the generalised criticisms up-front so that you know what to look for; while more specific challenges will appear against the case notes themselves, particularly in the next chapter dealing with Reincarnation.

Section 10.1.3 will provide a detailed consideration of the counter-explanations, which were also tackled as part of the research.

This might sound quite heavy, but all of this relates to material that is easy to understand and which you should find interesting.

As before, I feel that if there is genuine evidence of something it shouldn't be dismissed, but should be properly explained one way or another.

If there are criticisms – fine, but they should be fair and specific to the evidence presented. Materialism may not have an answer to the stronger findings as yet, but that should mean that more research is needed, not that the peer-reviewed findings should be dismissed altogether.

9.1.1 Context for Ideas about Life after Death

When people consider the possibility of life after death there are many subtle terms, (including their underlying ideas), which play to similar themes but which have important differences between them.

Resuscitation means reviving someone who has technically died, (per. some definitions) - effectively bringing them back from the brink.

For the purposes of this book I consider **Resurrection** to mean: bringing somebody back to life after they are definitely physically dead: either by them re-occupying the same physical body; or allowing the same 'spiritual entity' to live again elsewhere with the same identity.

The Shorter Oxford English Dictionary, (which is still two large volumes), has a surprisingly short definition for Reincarnation:-

"To incarnate anew. So Reincarnation."

Belief in **Reincarnation** is perhaps better described as the rebirth of an individual within a new physical life on Earth, which will carry a separate persona. The child will have to grow again and build a new identity with new experiences. For those who believe in the cycle of life, (birth, life, death and rebirth – 'Samsara'), it can be argued that rebirth may generally explain the traits and personalities that we display from an early age, but only a few people may recall specific aspects of their previous lives.

Resuscitation is definitely real. Resurrection and reincarnation are beliefs, but they both represent a continuity of life after physical death. However while reincarnation is generally portrayed as an ongoing process, resurrection is normally portrayed as a single event for each individual. It is therefore conceivable that resurrection could mark the end of a prior sequence of reincarnation, (and indeed, getting off the cycle of life is a common aim of many religions which believe in reincarnation).

'Liberation from Samsara' can be referred-to as 'Moksha' (in Hinduism and Jainism), or Nirvana (in Buddhism).

There seems to be a more relaxed view of Out of Body experiences, possibly because the people involved don't die and as a result they challenge fewer religious perceptions. There is also the fact that increasingly, science indicates that there are real physical effects to substantiate the experiences that people have[114].

However in situations where a person definitely dies, and then comes back from the dead, the cultural stakes are a lot higher.

Probably the best known person who is famed for coming back from the dead is Jesus Christ – who forms the basis of Christianity. However even his example cannot be taken as ***proof*** because although Jesus was a real historical figure the only evidence that we have for his resurrection are a small number of ancient texts which you either believe in or you don't. Quite a lot do.

Furthermore, because he was a human being who returned to Earth from the dead without rebirth, (or a modern medical team), his can be seen as a *one-off* event, even in comparison to other religions, so we **can't** draw any conclusions from a *pattern* of similar activity.

Despite the official stance of the Christian churches in support of Resurrection, various studies[61] have shown that approx 25% of European and American Christians do have some level of belief in reincarnation - yet they remain Christian. So a blending of ideas would appear to be happening and possibly in Canada too. In Baltic countries belief levels are much higher, (Lithuania 44%; Russia 32% - E.Haraldsson[111]).

People in western cultures should therefore remember that **large parts** of the world have sizeable populations which believe that reincarnation is **a fact of life** – not some weird marginal belief. It is an inherent part of Hinduism and Buddhism, as well as many other beliefs from the Druze in the Middle East, to the Tlingit Indians in Alaska. Encyclopaedias even suggest that some parts of the Jewish faith have elements supportive of reincarnation, (eg. Kabbalah and the Hasidic following).

There are some potential theological advantages to ideas about God, in the suggestion that various rounds of reincarnation could be followed by ultimate salvation (say) through resurrection. For Christians there is just the small matter of doctrine to be overcome; while other religions will argue that breaking out of the cycle of Samsara is indeed an ultimate goal, but it is achieved by other means than resurrection – primarily Karma.

The research which has been conducted does not even attempt to investigate such matters. It just looks at the authenticity of reported events.

It is the presence of reincarnation cases over thousands of years which has led Eastern religions, particularly in the Indian sub-continent, to accept that the phenomenon is rare, but should be incorporated into their doctrine.

It seems that in many cultures people will still regarded it as a very distressing and undesirable situation[62]. You will soon see why the people afflicted by this phenomenon resort to help and support groups, even if they are within their faith community.

However this very dark view is not universal. Other communities may still regard reincarnation as undesirable but not disastrous; it just has to be managed while respecting the relationships of current lives[62]. In some parts of China the affected person may even be deemed to have special powers of healing, while the Tlingit in Alaska foster a positive attitude by actively looking for the return of ancestors, to welcome them back into the family.

However these are all matters of belief and attitude. There doesn't seem to be any profit expectation in such claims. Newspapers/researchers don't normally pay for any of these stories, especially Out of Body experiences which I believe are regarded as 'commonplace' and not newsworthy.

In terms of possible reincarnation, families who are approached about a dead relative are generally very wary, and would almost never pay money out even if they happened to be wealthier and believed the story to be true. There are even social taboos against such requests in some communities.

Of course, there is always room to speculate about other motives for fraud, (eg. religious principle, etc), but such ventures would still rely entirely on the credibility of a very young child who would have to flawlessly learn and deliver a fake storyline... as well as callous parents who would groom them for this motive over many years. I have **never** heard of such claims in reality, and they certainly do not feature in any of the stronger cases.

So what does the evidence tell us?

At this stage in our considerations I just want to talk in general terms about the *types* of evidence and the *patterns* of activity, plus the different ways in which the evidence can be viewed.

When professionals report the testimony that they are given, we can generally be confident that **what they report as being said** is probably true, especially when there are other professionals in the team to verify the testimony. So the emphasis then turns to the people giving the testimony.

If we consider the many reports of 'out of body experiences' given to emergency and hospital personnel, it is hard to imagine that a person who has just been resuscitated at a roadside, or who has come straight out of an operation, will have their mind so bent on deception that they immediately fabricate a tale at that moment.

On that basis, the testimony of what the person actually **experienced** is also likely to be real, even if the individual may be jumping to conclusions about what it might **represent**. Yet, at this point we **are** recognising that an event **is** real, so it has to be explained – not dismissed.

Yet the testimony will still be regarded as scientifically flawed as it has not been gathered in a controlled and 'untainted' manner.

Does that make it any less real? I would say no, but it means that the analysis of what has happened will be limited as a result of 'indiscipline'.

However it doesn't mean that it is worthless. The specifics of each case may be hard to test for accuracy after the event, but when people always describe the same sort of symptoms/effect, (ie. that they float above their body and look down on the efforts of people trying to save them), that consistency is hard to ignore, (people don't co-ordinate their dreams etc).

The same principles apply when looking at the far trickier, and more emotive subject of Reincarnation. The testimonies in these cases are not, generally, obtained at moments of high drama and immediacy. They are quiet comments emerging from otherwise normal situations, so while the professional people reporting the claims might still be regarded as not faking the evidence, closer scrutiny has to be applied to the people making the claims, and on whether those claims can be verified in any way.

> The professionals in these scientific studies are leading figures within Universities and other institutions of high standing.

In terms of professional reputation both out of body experiences, and particularly reincarnation are difficult areas for many people to venture into as this is not 'mainstream' and will inevitably lead to strong challenges on credibility. Funding will also be an issue, which is why a number of very credible people are known for their work in other fields as well[111].

I found it particularly gratifying that some of the large scale research projects into OBE ,which we will consider shortly, were undertaken with the full co-operation of major hospitals in the UK, USA, and Austria.

There are no natural scientific advantages or commercial benefits associated with the study of reincarnation, and funding for the more prominent exercises did **not** come from religious institutions, but from private sources channelled through Universities and other credible academic institutions which could provide independence and rigour in the studies.

The few people who undertake serious research in these areas have worked within different teams[58,111], and the opinions/findings they publish do not reflect the view of just one person. When publishing their work in a credible journal, or under the banner of a credible University, their findings will be peer-reviewed and will not be published if serious challenges emerge that are not addressed satisfactorily.

Such challenges **have** occurred but were generally covered/explained prior to publication. I have **not seen any** suggestion that researchers have deliberately fabricated evidence.

That said, because funding is always limited, researchers will always have to decide where to invest their efforts. One or two meetings will generally indicate whether the fundamentals of a case make it strong or weak. There may be elements which are very credible, but if there are very few worthwhile facts to verify from a child's testimony; or the circumstance in which a case emerged, undermine its credibility from the start; there is little point in pursuing them in detail, as they will never be persuasive.

While in theory it would be nice to have a lot more researchers in the field of reincarnation to provide a broader spectrum of opinion on the detail of specific cases, this is probably not the main area of difficulty. That will continue to lie with two main factors:

- The very limited number of strong cases which people have to work with: (ie. more researchers would probably mean that they would still be tackling the same strong cases and would be unlikely to generate many more findings about them).

- Researchers are rarely, if ever, present at the first meetings between a child showing the symptoms, and the family of the suspected deceased – a moment when some of the most poignant testing of a child's knowledge will occur in comparison to what they have previously declared.

As already mentioned, there seems to be a ready supply of OBE cases, although they may not often reveal high quality information under controlled conditions. Equally, while 3,000 cases of reincarnation may not be a huge sample, and only a few of these are strong, the information as a whole can still be useful in identifying common *principles* which seem to apply, or other consistent *patterns of activity* in the way that events play-out. These could be pointers to underlying mechanisms, and have led to suggestions that the patterns are identifying characteristics for such events. People glean what they can, but from the perspective of scientific analysis these are still early days.

Yet such exercises are not possible with resurrection which is portrayed as a one-off event for each individual. Believers typically expect that it takes the dead into a spiritual existence rather than returning them to one here on Earth. In practical terms, that matches the normal experience which people have when loved ones die – their bodies are not reactivated; the essence of the person is no longer there; and it doesn't return.

Most materialists will, of course, believe that this marks a final end for the individual, but it doesn't have to. If the Soul is real and in some way physical then who knows what might be possible?

However, if you wish to argue that circumstances are profoundly different to the perceived norm, then the onus is on you to prove the case.

Equally, if we are interested in finding out about the truth of our existence, then we should look at the examples presented. Each person will then be able to consider if those cases are persuasive. As part of this, it may be that the evidence and findings from OBE will turn out to be a stepping stone towards a better analysis of reincarnation cases.

In the meantime, I find it interesting that when sceptical journalists and TV cameras have accompanied researchers in their early interviews, many attitudes seem to change. The very human stories and real emotions reveal much more than disengaged reports and abstract statistics.

The book by Tom Shroder[59], and the TV series which followed the separate case of Cameron Macaulay, (still on U-Tube), are both compelling examples - which also reveal the high standards being applied by researchers. We will look at both in Chapter 10.

As you come to make your own judgement on these cases I suspect that you will be asking yourself where the balance of probability lies. Does the outside possibility of one solution, outweigh the strengths of another? None are conclusive.

9.2 Near-Death and Out of Body Experiences

As mentioned at the start of the book, we seem to assemble a mental image of what is happening around us from large numbers of sensors around our bodies that send electrical/chemical signals to our brains. While our eyes see an image directly, our Minds do not.

The typical Materialist explanation of how our Minds work within the principle of true 'cause & effect', is that our mental image of the 'current moment' emerges a fraction of a second after it happens, but in parallel, we have the ability to interpret what is happening, and try to anticipate in abstract terms, (rather than visual terms), what may be about to happen.

In addition, if we think about pin pricks, or pulling our fingers away from a hot surface, there is evidence to show that some of our bodies' reflex actions enable them to take instant safeguarding measures rather than wait for a later instruction from our brains.

All of this is important when we try to rationalise what is happening in 'Near-Death' and 'Out of Body' experiences. The anecdotes are well known in popular culture:-

- A common 'Near Death' experience is a 'Tunnel Effect' where the person feels that they rise up towards a point of intense light, generally accompanied by a feeling of unconditional love and/or communication with 'beings of the light', (who might be perceived as deceased relatives or even angels).

- A typical 'Out of Body Experience' is where the person feels they have floated out of, and invariably **above** their body, so that they're looking down on it and are able to watch what is happening around them while they are unconscious.

One Materialist explanation that I heard suggests that the 'tunnel of light' is actually a failure of the mechanism which enables us to visualise; causing our mental image to collapse; concentrating the 'light' in one shrinking place in our imagination. There may be other explanations but in essence they argue for a physical breakdown.

The generalised Materialist explanation I have heard for 'Out of Body Experiences' is that the body continues to receive signals even if it is unconscious, and the physical Mind will try to rationalise them and build a mental picture accordingly.

The difficulty with that type of explanation is that neurologists and anaesthetists say that unconscious brain activity shouldn't permit this. In addition, while the body may continue to hear, smell, and touch, if the eyelids are closed then no matter what they do, they cannot see, and yet people are reported to have accurately described the clothing being worn by emergency personnel[116] and the types of equipment being used etc.

It may be that the patients caught a glimpse of people before their eyes closed and then projected those impressions accordingly, but there are apparently reports of accurate descriptions of people who arrived later.

The trouble is that this is all hearsay/anecdotal evidence which has not been gathered on a scientific basis in controlled conditions.

This is why attention has been drawn to the numerous reports of OBE incidents that arise in hospitals[115] and particularly in the operating theatre, where people have accurately described conversations, clothing and equipment, as above[116]. It has offered the potential to start gathering more controlled information. We will look at the first of such exercises shortly.

Before then I want to quickly raise an alternate form of Near Death experience where there are famous cases of people being in a coma for days, weeks, or even months with very little discernible brain activity who claim to have had very intense and detailed experiences of 'another place'.

> One of the most eye-catching is the case of Dr. Eben Alexander, a neurosurgeon, and a person who did not originally believe in near death experiences in any way. He entered a coma in 2008 after contracting a rare form of meningitis, and was saved by colleagues at his own hospital. It's in this context that he gained access to his own medical records and saw the outputs of the brain monitoring equipment. He could clearly see that in medical terms his neocortex had shut down - which should have removed all higher consciousness, thought, and emotion, yet he testifies very strongly that it didn't.

> He describes intricate roving experiences that were not 'out of body' as such: more like an intense dream; a level of consciousness that shouldn't have been possible with his level of brain activity.

In Materialist terms there needs to be a way to explain this, if closely monitored brain activity **doesn't** show the active mechanisms. One way to do this is to suggest that despite the perception that we have about the intricacy of modern equipment, it still isn't sophisticated enough to detect some of the underlying mental activity that may be occurring.

However, if we are getting into the realm of unknown effects, then there is the potential for other undetected things to be occurring too.

Once again there is need for better, more targeted information to indicate whether there is anything more than mechanistic/chemical processes at work, and we can only find that if we go looking.

As we have seen in the movies, it is quite possible for a person to be clinically dead for a few seconds, even a minute or so, with no heartbeat and no brain activity, and then be resuscitated. It is in these moments that some 10% of people[70] seem to report a near death experience and the glimpse of an afterlife. That's a lot of people.

Although there are suggestions that out of body experiences have been reported for thousands of years, they have only really been taken seriously over the past 70 years or so.

I heard that some references to this emerged during military research into oxygen starvation in pilots, either through depressurisation or through lack of blood flow to the brain from high 'G' manoeuvres. The military did not research the experiences themselves, they just sought ways to avoid them, however they still report such experiences today[115].

However the first generally acknowledged report to gain attention was from Raymond Moody[69] in 1975 who assembled a number of characteristics that indicate when such experiences might be occurring.

The Horizon Research Foundation[70] reports his findings as a montage of such features in the following way :

> A man is dying and, as he reaches the point of greatest physical distress, he hears himself pronounced dead by his doctor. He begins to hear an uncomfortable noise, a loud ringing or buzzing, and at the same time feels himself moving very rapidly through a long dark tunnel.

> After this, he suddenly finds himself outside his own physical body, but still in the immediate physical environment, and he sees his own body from a distance, as though he is a spectator. He watches the resuscitation attempt from his unusual vantage point and is in a state of emotional upheaval. After a while, he collects himself and becomes more accustomed to his odd condition.

> He notices that he still has a 'body', but one of a very different nature and with very different powers from the physical body he has left behind.

> Soon other things begin to happen. Others come to meet and to help him. He glimpses the spirits of relatives and friends who have already died, and a loving warm spirit of a kind he has never encountered before: a being of light appears before him.

> This being asks him a question, non verbally, to make him evaluate his life and helps him by showing a panoramic, instantaneous playback of major events from his life.

> At some point he finds himself approaching some sort of barrier or border, apparently representing the limit between earthly life and the next life. Yet, he finds that he must go back to the earth, that the time for his death has not yet come.

> At this point he resists, for by now he is taken up with his experiences in the afterlife and does not want to return. He is

164

overwhelmed by intense feelings of joy, love, and peace. Despite his attitude, he somehow reunites with his physical body and lives.

Later he tries to tell others, but he has trouble doing so. In the first place, he can find no human words adequate to describe these unearthly episodes. He also finds that others scoff, so he stops telling other people.

The world has moved on since those early days, and such experiences are now accepted as common, genuine, and subject to scientific analysis – but it has **not** been proven that they truly represent the spirit leaving the body.

Out of Body experiences do not have to occur in life threatening circumstances. They have been known to arise in situations of severe illness or intense pain, car accidents, in cases of severe dehydration, or conditions of sensory deprivation, and have also been described by people who have been in a deeply relaxed state - say on the verge of sleep.

However a large number of cases **do** arise in hospital operating theatres, which therefore offered the opportunity for a controlled experiment.

It is in this context that 15 medical centres across the UK, USA and Austria began a study in 2008 into 'Out-of-Body Experience' (OBE), and Near Death Experiences (NDE) using techniques which attempted to verify patient recollections, and also included placing strange objects such as photographs, toys, a hammer, etc. in places that were on top of equipment or beams – essentially high above the patient and in places that could only be seen if the patient's spirit did float above their body.

The study, called AWARE was led by Dr.Sam Parnia and was intended to demonstrate whether consciousness might continue beyond the point of clinical death, where there is no heartbeat or detected brain activity.

The AWARE experiment concluded in 2012 and findings[71] were reported in 2014. Across 2060 cardiac arrests just one case **could** prove consciousness and auditory awareness some minutes after the heart stopped beating and at a time when "the brain ordinarily stops functioning and cortical activity becomes isoelectric."

The experience was therefore **not** compatible with an illusion, imaginary event, or hallucination – ie. it was real. However the patients did not seem to officially report the hidden objects.

This has led to a further study AWARE II which was due to finish at the end of May 2017, but at the time of concluding this section (Nov. 2017) the report has not been issued.

Based on hearsay alone, I gather that part of the reason for AWARE II was that a number of patients did claim in later conversation that they **had** seen strange objects around the theatre but hadn't mentioned them because they thought that it was too bizarre and might have invalidated the study. If that was true, such reports wouldn't be valid evidence for the study as they emerged after prompting.

Scientists **are** able to induce similar effects through the use of drugs or even through electrical stimulation of some parts of the brain, (especially the temporoparietal junction), or more recently through the use of virtual reality headgear in combination with reinforcing sensations such as touch. Whether this truly represents the original phenomenon is disputed, and such effects may not therefore represent 'the full experience'.

As mentioned earlier, two critical differences with Near Death experiences are that in experiments the subject is conscious not unconscious, and in the latest Swedish experiments, the images are not constructed by the Mind but are generated by pre-programmed equipment[114]. Even so it was interesting to see which areas of the brain seemed to be stimulated at these moments – namely 'Place Cells'[114] in the Hippocampus area of the brain, (which have been likened to a GPS system), and also the posterior cingulate cortex which seems to bind the feeling of where the self is located with the feeling of owning a body.

Research into OBE has identified a number of classical stages through which somebody may go, presented below. As in the case of the evidence from reincarnation, repeated patterns do suggest a real process.

Apparently it is not uncommon for some stages to be missing from the standard sequence, however within the steps you will find descriptions of the common feelings and impressions that people have experienced when going through this phenomenon.

- *Withdrawal stage*: People's interaction with the physical environment is lost with **sensations not being registered, and their attention is elsewhere**.

- *Cataleptic stage*: Normal physical movement is affected and additional sensations may be perceived (**such as noises not present at the time; having sight through closed eyelids, or possibly intense vibrations**)

- *Separation stage*: The mind appears to move away from the body although it often retains the sensations from the body. It is also often reported that the body seems to restrain the movement of the spirit – **trying to pull it back into the body**.

- *Free movement stage*: If the spirit is able to move beyond a certain distance movement becomes unimpeded. There seem to be great variations in reported visual/mental clarity.

- *Re-entry stage*: **The feeling that the mind needs to return to the body** may increase, **leading to a voluntary return or a fast 'snap-back' to the body**. This may be accompanied by a transition to waking or a period of sleep.

There does seem to be strong evidence to suggest that these experiences are common to all human cultures, and probably all periods of history. We just don't know what they mean.

In a similar manner to the scientific findings about **what** our cells seem to be doing in critical functions, (Chapter 5.3), we have descriptions of activities, but not necessarily an explanation of **how** the individual elements achieve what they do. This becomes particularly important where we deal with issues of awareness, consciousness, and Thought which challenge our ideas about mechanical/chemical functions.

We may therefore detect that an area of the brain is active, but we don't know what it is doing or whether it is tapping into another more subtle capability. Questions about the Soul will inevitably linger.

Where the evidence will lead science is as yet unknown, however we can all imagine that any consideration of different planes of spiritual existence would need very compelling reasons for a scientist to risk his reputation.

If AWARE II or other similar studies do produce visual confirmation of objects in an operating theatre it will be a game-changer, as it would be hard to imagine how accurate visual awareness, and consciousness of this nature could occur, floating above a body without something like the Soul.

However we are not at that stage yet.

10   Scientific Evidence Suggesting Reincarnation

What allows science to give credibility to some evidence and not to others? It's <u>not</u> because somebody with a label of 'scientist' has gathered the evidence. Such robustness entirely depends on the ***method*** by which the evidence is gathered, and the thoroughness of the avenues investigated.

Generally, claims that are based on physical evidence will have much greater credibility than those which are not, because there's something tangible which can be inspected and scrutinised by many people at different times. This could, for instance, be historical evidence in newspapers or official records. On a less rigorous basis, photographs of a deceased can bear an uncanny resemblance to their supposed reincarnation - the person born later, (when they reach a similar age in adulthood[63]).

However as a general principle, if there are factors which can taint the evidence, then the method of gathering it must ensure, as much as possible, that it's not contaminated.

Such guidelines also have relevance when people gather human testimony. The researcher must avoid asking leading questions, and should return to key points so as to test them from different perspectives. Such evidence must also be recorded in its entirety, not just the bits that people want to hear, (both as a reference for analysis, and to ensure that later testimony isn't altered).

Following the general introduction that I gave in Chapter 9, to the scientific evidence which explores whether Life could exist beyond the body, this chapter now presents some of the cases related to the study of reincarnation. By its very nature, this is less clinical/precise and relies on testimony given by young children who seem to be referring to past lives.

The strength of such testimony lies in a number of things:-

- It is logically compatible with the notion: that if a life transfers into the body of a new child, recollections about the past life should be apparent from an early age, rather than suddenly emerging in adulthood.

- It removes many layers of suspicion about an ***adult's*** ability to lie convincingly. Children will not have the necessary experience to do this.

- While a child can build elaborate fantasies, they are not necessarily realistic, and are highly unlikely to accurately reflect the intricate details of past events – so if they can be verified, they are powerful testimony.

- Even if we suppose that a child between the ages of 3 and 6 had been carefully groomed to remember a lot of detailed facts, they are unlikely to deliver them in a convincing way: eg. they might talk of 'him' or 'she' instead of 'I'; or via the emotions they display; or phrases they use.

- If young children are asked 'who told them' the facts, or even if they were asked not to tell anyone, any guilty glances or other similar reactions would almost certainly reveal a fraud etc.

In addition to this we can add a number of factors that can aid our belief in the genuine nature of any testimony:-

- Are there facts which nobody should normally know?
- Is there a means by which such facts could become known to the child?

In many of the stronger cases from 30 years ago it was still common for such children to be in an environment where locations 50 miles away would represent an insurmountable barrier even for the family, and **without** a TV or nearby library to provide sources of information, (even if you can imagine that these would have details about a particular family that is not in the headlines in any way).

More recent cases may possibly show that there are no internet facilities in the household which could provide a sub-conscious source of information. However as time goes on, such barriers will be eroded making it harder to *demonstrate* a complete separation between households.

In a number of cases there have also been cultural barriers to the families involved associating with each other, such as the caste system in India.

Quite apart from the testimony of the children there are the statements of many adults who witnessed how events panned-out, not just from the affected families, but also many 3rd parties, which are also cross-checked.

These factors don't eliminate the possibility of a broader conspiracy, but they make it a lot harder to justify.

However we cannot ignore some fundamental concerns about such cases.

Firstly, it is virtually impossible for researchers to get involved from the earliest moments that 'symptoms' start to appear. Cases do not tend to emerge until the children have persuaded their parents that something really unusual is already happening.

More significantly, researchers are rarely involved prior to the first meeting between the two families involved, (the child and the suspected deceased). This critical meeting is where claims and facts are first aired & tested – representing the strongest moment when errors or inconsistencies would appear, (which could potentially be subconsciously 'ironed-out later' as real details emerged).

Yet, there **are** some cases where researchers were present at that early stage, and as awareness and experience grow, more of these may arise.

With these things in mind, I have placed a lot of emphasis on the works of the late Dr. Ian Stevenson[58] and his team from the University of Virginia, who, over many decades, ventured out across the world to find and research cases which could act as verifiable evidence.

Since those initial efforts a small number of other researchers such as Antonia Mills, Erlendur Haraldsson, and Jim Tucker have also pursued enquiries into the subject[111]. There are also sceptical journalists such as Tom Shroder[59] who have witnessed the effort that goes into such studies, and who provide independent verification of the care taken in gathering evidence and establishing its authenticity.

Some of the cases which Stevenson investigated were done in close collaboration with other scientist whom he trusted to maintain standards while monitoring the evolution of cases over many years. These include Professor P.Pal, Professor B.L.Atreya, and Dr.S.Pasricha whose research also seems to show that these cases *contradict* the beliefs of local religions in how reincarnation supposedly operates.

Stevenson's work was apparently largely ignored by the scientific community for many years, but over time, and due to its popularity, more people came to assess it and to take it seriously, even if they strongly disagreed with the concept of reincarnation. One leading psychiatrist (Harold Lief) applauded the methods used but also said of Stevenson that he was either... " making a colossal mistake, or he will be known, (I have said as much to him), as 'the Galileo of the 20th century'."

Critics have often accused Stevenson of being gullible and have pointed to weak examples within his case studies, but they *haven't* been able to explain the strong examples. In one pointed observation he was accused of being misled by bogus translators who wanted to bolster the evidence. Stevenson had in fact already declared this having been misled once in this way, which had threatened his publication, but he had re-interviewed the people involved in the case with a genuine translator and re-confirmed his understanding. As he also wrote in his book, he began to use multiple translators thereafter[62].

Other commentators have also accused him of 'confirmation bias' in that he didn't present cases that didn't support his ideas, as counting against it. However this *isn't* a game of swinging the stats to get over some imaginary threshold. As I said earlier, a single case that is proven would establish the principle.

Yet we are unlikely to see such proof, (ie. that is beyond all doubt), due to the nature of the beast. The best that can probably be hoped-for is a body of strong cases which present reasonable credibility.

Stevenson and others have pointed out some cases that they did disprove, and have also set aside weaker cases after preliminary investigations. With limited resources it is understandable that the efforts of their teams should be focused on those which are strong and likely to provide credible examples. I don't understand how this can be seen as 'confirmation bias'.

To my mind other challenges have been much more targeted and reasonable. Robert Baker Jr., (University of Kentucky), suggested that an effect known as Cryptomnesia might explain some examples. This is one of a small number of specific 'real world' effects which might explain these incidents, and I will explore these in section 10.1.3 below.

For the moment, let me just say that the stronger cases haven't been disproved in these ways, and although you never know what new evidence may come to light, there were often good reasons why Stevenson and his team didn't believe that these were factors in those cases.

Other people have also been cited as being in opposition to reincarnation but their comments were actually made in respect of other matters. As an example, Sarah Thomason, (linguist at the University of Michigan), considered rather different material – of people in adulthood who appeared able to speak a foreign language fluently under hypnosis without any tutoring/training, (an effect known as Xenoglossy). She concluded that in the 2 cases she considered, the level of language didn't reach fluency and that the effect was too weak to really support such claims.

Again – that's fine, but it doesn't address our subject, reincarnation.

Prominent web encyclopaedias state that most scientists either ignored or dismissed the findings without looking at them. Even without stats to prove that, it would not be surprising, but it's also true that Stevenson does have his academic supporters[112] who **have** scrutinised the evidence.

There have been peer reviews at the University of Virginia where he was based, (and where his department continues); plus the checking required by prestigious journals prior to publication[113]; plus the corroboration of other researchers involved in the cases. Even critics do not seem to suggest that researchers have faked the testimonies. So to my mind, the question is whether the children have been lying, or their stories enhanced, and what the cases represent.

Yet there's an understandably high degree of scepticism about reincarnation in western countries. Leaving aside questions of religious or other social conditioning, the norm for almost every person is that we do not remember a past life, or even sense it. In addition, few people in the West will have encountered someone in their area who has been subject to this.

Equally, if this was true of mankind, it should be a global phenomenon and yet there is an acknowledged disparity in the number of cases being reported in Europe, (not North America surprisingly). Stevenson's team investigated this, and we will look at their findings later in the chapter.

While there **is** logical *speculation* to explain why it may affect some communities more than others, based on what we can glean from patterns of activity; the truth is that nobody really knows. Some will argue that the phenomenon simply isn't reincarnation but symptomatic of something else, yet even if that were true, why shouldn't the same number of false cases arise in Europe too? We will see later.

10.1.1 <u>Weak Criticisms and Statistical Findings</u>

Objective criticism is a fair part of the process of testing a theory, but I feel that attempts to discredit something rather than disprove it are unhelpful.

It is clear that studies into the possibility of reincarnation will not be popular in certain quarters, yet in the past, a prominent criticism had been that there was no evidence worthy of testing. Now that there is such evidence it seems weak to criticise people for having looked.

For similar reasons, critics now have to justify their claimed 'overwhelming evidence' against reincarnation when they hadn't attempted to seriously test the argument before the robust cases which are being debated.[112]

We have to decide if we want to know the reality of our situation, or whether our intention is merely to uphold doctrine of one sort or another?

That said, the evidence coming forward should be robust enough to pass scrutiny and reasonable challenges. While we will each find our personal threshold for believability there is a difference between things that are 'not proven' and those which are actually disproven. We have to look at every case on its merits, as a single example might prove the principle.

As an analogy, for centuries the dominant belief was that the Earth was the centre of the Universe and all the stars rotated around it. The theory that the Earth went around the sun was discredited for many years, but it wasn't disproven, and eventually new facts emerged to prove that it was correct.

Whether we are in the same position with reincarnation remains to be seen, but we are certainly **not** able to say it is genuine. There may be real claims, but we **don't** know what they represent. For most people in the West it is not proven, but in other parts of the world it is an accepted fact of life.

There seem to be three main types of generalised and unspecific criticism about the evidence itself. All three are truisms – meaning that they are almost certainly correct to some degree, but they are being used to suggest things which are not demonstrated:-

a) A majority of cases come from those communities which believe it to be true - which suggests that in some way the evidence is unreliable.

b) There could be faked testimonies within the 3,000 cases - which can suggest that fakes exist in every case.

c) Researchers haven't followed every case to its conclusion - implying that investigators have been less than rigorous, and may even have avoided crucial evidence where it didn't suit them.

Let's look at each in turn.

<u>Evidence Mainly Comes from Communities which Believe in It</u>

There are many examples which come from communities that do not generally believe in reincarnation, but it is also inevitable that **any** family which is genuinely afflicted in this way and wishes to report it, must to some degree believe it is possible, even if it is a cry for help. It is also inevitable that communities which are prepared to accept the possibility will be more willing to consider it, rather than bury the story, and may also be better prepared to offer support.

From the outside observers' point of view, the only thing that matters is whether the evidence stacks-up within the realms of reasonable doubt. If the facts can be verified then they should stand on their merits.

If a case is submitted for scrutiny to independent researchers, then surely that must, in itself, show an openness to see what it may represent.

Those who make such veiled accusations should be specific about the taint which they envisage and the evidence to justify such claims. It would also be valid to consider their motives for such statements – including their own faith bias.

There could be faked testimonies within the 3,000 cases

Well of course there might, but it doesn't mean that every case is affected in this way. Moreover this is largely justified by the *possibility* of faked testimony in some of the *weaker* cases which have received less scrutiny.

If people have accusations to make about the stronger cases which have been well researched, then they should be specific about them.

Researchers haven't followed every case to its conclusion

Again, we already know that every research team has to balance the limited resources available and will only target the stronger cases because, almost by definition, the weak cases will never be persuasive. The weak cases will never be taken beyond a preliminary assessment.

There is no valid objection here.

I understand that researchers on the strong cases will pursue every lead that is possible, and from the published records I have seen, will carefully record those avenues which have been checked.

We are entitled to make our personal assessments about any gaps we may perceive, and regard them as a flaw if necessary, but the generalised implication that researchers have been sloppy or even deliberately evasive needs to be justified. Occasional mistakes are one thing, to imply a systemic failure is quite another. Without specific justification we have to again consider the motives of the 'accuser'.

I must again point out that this is not a 'numbers' game. A single case could establish the principle, and so every case must be considered on its merits. But having said this, we do have to be very wary about the credibility of any testimony that is given.

In this respect, some people may try to set standards that I feel are unrealistic. A prime way to establish the authenticity of testimony about a past life, is to demonstrate that little known historical details are true. However to me, it seems churlish and pedantic to demand that this can only be regarded as acceptable if a remarkable truth is revealed like the location of the Arc of the Covenant, or the Lost Treasure of Montezuma, or the arrangements for JFK's assassination etc. which nobody in the world knows.

We need to be sensible about these things, but not foolish (in either sense). The level of proof needs to be pitched at a level that is appropriate to the circumstances. It is not necessary to go over the top in this way, but equally the evidence needs to be credible.

That said, there are cases discussed in 10.1.3 below, where the stories and facts being described are truly remarkable. Some children claim to have been the victims of murder and even name their attackers – which in one case has led to a confession and conviction. Smaller scale than JFK, but very significant non-the-less.

As we turn to consider the positives from the evidence, the number of cases does allow for some statistical analysis.

One of the most significant features is the pattern which each case tends to follow over the years. Stevenson[62] concludes that the symptoms **don't** suddenly appear in adulthood. They follow the logical path which you might expect if a life were to continue from one body to the next.

The traits and partial memories of a prior existence seem to carry-over at birth, and build up rapidly in the early years as the children learn to talk and find ways to express their feelings – reaching considerable strength around the age of 5 or 6. While some memories will stay strong throughout a person's life, the majority seem able to focus on their 'new lives' by the time they reach their teens. It is not clear whether the memories have been suppressed; have faded; or have disappeared.

What we can say is that these are not transient stories for a moment of glory. These are real people who have to live with the condition for many years.

Another commonly reported characteristic **is** that many 'prior lives' have apparently ended in either traumatic circumstances, (often accompanied by birthmarks – although that association must be judged separately)[62], or in situations where the person experienced powerful emotions, such as when they didn't wish to leave the one they loved, (eg. a husband or new child).

The suggestion is that the physical or emotional trauma was the factor that either disrupted the normal process of 'blanking-out' the past life, or which left memories so powerful that they couldn't be erased.

The studies also reveal findings about four other beliefs concerning reincarnation and spiritual existence:

- Approximately 20% of cases[62] claim that a person has changed gender, and there are several reported examples where people believe they have moved to a higher or lower 'caste', (in those communities which have such social distinctions)

- There was almost **nothing** to suggest that people being reincarnated had any memory of life in the form of another species. In other words, there was no evidence of a spiritual progression from a bird, animal, or other creature into a human being. The one example offered to Stevenson, (at least the only one that he reports), was of Wijeratne, a schizophrenic boy who actually denied having made such claims.

- There was **no** credible evidence to suggest that the period between lives offered any opportunity for a dynamic interactive existence. Only one person seems to have claimed that he was spoken to during this intermediate period by a 'spiritual authority' telling him to go back into his former life as he had not fully died.

- Tom Shroder reported that Stevenson had a number of cases of 'near birth' where someone claimed to have entered the body of a newly born child – even recognising the parents, but had then been drawn back to their original body through resuscitation, etc.

  In the one case where timings were recorded it **was** apparently confirmed that the moment of resuscitation, and the death of the newborn, **did** seem to coincide. However the cases could not be presented as those individuals had prior knowledge of each other. Although these cases were not strong evidence, they did seem to support the idea that ensoulment did **not** occur at conception.

It will be interesting to see how the stats change as more cases are studied.

The final point I want to make at this stage takes us back into the reason why I wanted to address this subject – as a pointer to the Soul. I mention it for your general interest.

Why is it that most of us do not remember past lives?

One **highly** speculative possibility tries to reconcile this with the very rapid growth in human population over the past 150 years. Until then the number of people alive in the world had been relatively stable for many centuries – if not longer. One generation of souls would die and a similar number would be born. Yet the sudden improvement in healthcare and food production has led to dramatic changes in this rough equation.

If you follow the broad logic: a great surge in numbers may need to be accompanied by the generation of an equivalent number of new souls – which could mean that a significant number of people may be 'first timers' with no past on which to draw.

As I said – it is a highly speculative idea.

10.1.2 Sample Cases Suggestive of Reincarnation

As mentioned earlier in the chapter, the scientific investigation of reincarnation focuses on the testimony of thousands of young children[62] whose claims begin around the ages of 18 months to 6 years.

In the stronger cases, their lives are then followed over many years, and the testimonies across all of this period are investigated, analysed, and thoroughly cross-checked.

Again - anyone who has had children will know that to get kids of this age to learn something real is hard enough. To get them to lie convincingly and with this level of independent scrutiny would seem to be a rare achievement. So to find 3,000 cases in a 30-40 year period, (depending on which website you refer to), will give most people pause for thought.

A good proportion of these cases were regarded as 'weaker', because of the small amount that the child 'remembers' from a supposed past life; or because these occurrences were only drawn to the attention of researchers when the subjects were much older; or in circumstances which might make them easy targets for criticism; etc.

A much smaller number were therefore worthy of more detailed investigation, and out of these the strongest cases were published.

Yet we should also remember that these are not abstract academic issues. Behind every case is at least one family, and generally two, whose members will be deeply affected by the circumstances, because they have such profound implications.

It is the clear feeling of emotion from the families which seems to persuade sceptics who have accompanied researchers that these people are not trying to deceive and if anything are crying out for help. This is very evident in Tom Shroder's book[63], and the video of Cameron Macaulay's case, (discussed later), which shows actual research interviews in progress. They give you a strong sense of the real people involved in these cases.

I will present some of Stevenson's cases, (such as Sukla and Suzanne), after the following generalised narrative which is intended to give you a flavour of how such cases tend to emerge[62] **as described in his books**.

I do this so that you can appreciate the human context and because it is also useful to illustrate the typical pattern that emerges in these cases.

Imagine that you have a child who, at the age of 3, suddenly and sheepishly tells you that:

> "You're not my real mummy / daddy. Their names are ....
> Why are you looking after me?"

Your own child then starts to talk clearly and precisely of names that are quite different to you and your spouse. The way that they say it may also throw you, as it doesn't seem part of some role play or fantasy. Perhaps you can also sense that the child knows they're on dangerous ground when there's such a close bond and an absolute dependency on mum & dad. They seem upset by it. Then even more surprisingly, they might say

My name isn't ..... it's ..... I want to be with my real family.

At such a young age it seems that they've barely learnt how to say their true name with confidence, and yet they come out with this. You would presumably be a little unsettled but perhaps you'd pass it off as a bit of fantasy... although the child would seem a bit too young to dream up things like this.

But then it's repeated – perhaps after a few days or weeks and the comments become more elaborate, yet at the same time the stories maintain a consistency that surprises you. They might draw pictures of them, but not in a way that suggests it's a game, so you start to think... and as far as you can recall, they've never met people with those names. Did this come from the TV perhaps? Yet in some communities there is no TV.

He or she may then give descriptions of siblings or grandparents which never falter, (perhaps talking about a large nose or red hair), plus their 'real' home (say) with the 'yellow walls' in a place called.... and so it goes on for months and even years.... but with nothing that relates to you.

The children may also refer to themselves in situations where they are an adult and in language beyond their years.

Seeing that you become upset when they talk like this, you can tell that they start to bottle it up, but occasionally you can see it in a wary look that they give you or when it comes out after a bad night when they've dreamt about 'their family' and missed them terribly.

You may choose to hush it up, or you may consult a doctor – but it doesn't go away. So you start to check-out the details to see if any have a basis in fact. A step change happens when some of the details turn out to be correct. Perhaps the village or town is real but far away, and it does have a street with the relevant names... etc.

In the stronger cases the child is taken to that place and on their first visit they guide you to 'their' street and 'their' house, and through this you find a family. The child may also recognise people they have never met before, calling them accurately by their name and perhaps referring to some event in their past. Through this, or the checking of other details that they mention, the names of a relevant deceased can be identified.

If other people do become involved there will initially be some interest and excitement, but then the mood will typically change. People will either say that you've been coaching the child in a perverse lie; or the child and your family will start to be treated like a freak show. The other family, (of the deceased), may also be wary of your intentions, or on the flip side, they may start to have an unwelcome level of interest in your son or daughter. But all you want is for this to go away and for life to become normal.

On top of all this, Stevenson reports that many children can be distracted by their memories and forget to live life in the present, affecting their schooling and development even though they are often regarded as very intelligent. At headline level there is nothing about this which is desirable.

Hopefully you get the idea of what life may be like for these families.

This pattern of events was described by Stevenson in several cases – for instance[62] the case of Sukla (b.1954) from a place called Kampa in India who from the age of 18 months was seen to regularly cradle a piece of wood, calling it 'Minu' which she described as her daughter. This expanded over the next couple of years to include details of her 'husband' and his brothers, and lots of other details about her 'real' family who apparently lived in a district called Rathtala in the small town of Bhatpara nr. Calcutta – which did in fact exist a great distance away, but had been virtually unknown to her family before then. Apparently as a 3 year old she also claimed to be a member of a different, higher caste, (Brahmin), and was reluctant to eat with the others of her family.

Through a series of obscure connections a candidate for the husband was approached through one of his brothers. The family was still living in that very small and largely unknown district (Rathtala). The brother confirmed that one of his siblings, Haridhan, did have a wife called Mana who had died in 1948 leaving behind an infant daughter called Minu.

Professor Pal verified reports that Sukla first met the other family aged 5, instantly recognising several people and correctly naming them, yet it was the strong emotion and tears that she displayed when meeting Haridhan & Minu that was so compelling to everyone who saw it. Professor Pal[62] witnessed these emotions - even tested her in later interviews with false stories about Minu falling ill, that produced concerned & tearful reactions.

Those present describe how Sukla went on to recognise many objects in that household and knew some of the history of the family as would have been known to Mana up to the time of her death, but nothing beyond that.

Through such dialogues both families testified that they became convinced Mana had been reincarnated as Sukla. Haridan even began to visit this child every week – apparently much to the annoyance of his new wife and despite the social barriers created by the caste system. During these visits 5 year old Sukla's attitude towards Haridan seemed entirely that of a wife towards her husband. Towards Minu (an adult) she behaved like a mother. Yet with others she resumed the persona of a child.

Stevenson and others monitored & researched ongoing events, confirming that these contacts were maintained over many years causing increasing friction with Haridhan's new wife and generating increasing social embarrassment, (on reasons of modesty), as Sukla moved into her teens. Due to these mounting tensions the families became increasingly estranged, gradually allowing Sukla to suppress/lose the direct memories & move on.

> The main points of interest in this case are that Sukla clearly gave names and places that allowed a connection to be found – not by members of her family but by interested 3rd parties.

> She accurately named people on first meeting Haridan's family, and knew a lot of background facts. However this was **not** witnessed firsthand by researchers. While this could be collusion between the families, there was no indication of this even with enquiries in the different areas - indeed, it would be very unusual for different castes to socialise, and almost impossible for Sukla's family to obtain personal details about Haridan's family.

> Perhaps more significant were the genuine emotions that Sukla showed and also the powerful reaction of the husband, Haridan over many years despite the objections of his actual wife. Why would he persist if it was a lie? Dedication to a religious cause?

Yet in other cases, an unlucky few seem unable to shake off 'the past', and it affects them for the rest of their lives; often in very detrimental ways:

> In a very similar case to that of Sukla but which was based in Lebanon, a child named Suzanne Ghanem[63,64] was mentioning her 'previous family' in a surprising level of detail and with great clarity. Her real parents and siblings considered it to be make-believe, but before the age of 3 she had mentioned the names and relationships of 13 close members of the other family.

> It turns out that word of the little girl's claims had spread, and it was actually the Mansour family who approached the Ghanems wanting to know more! Farouk Mansour had lost his wife Hanan around the same time that Suzanne had been born.

> The names of the 13 family members apparently checked-out, and because Hanan had died in America undergoing a specialist operation, the time of her death had been precisely recorded.

> Only slight errors in the little girl's testimony seemed to arise – for instance she said her husband had been in the army when he had actually been in the police.

> Stevenson met Suzanne quite early in the investigations but only after the first meeting with the Mansour family. Yet the facts were historically accurate and given the timeframes it wasn't realistic to expect that Suzanne at that age could quickly learn any omitted or mistaken names.

> Stevenson particularly noted that her fierce attachment to her previous memories was unusual[63].

Although the different families had never met before Suzanne was 5 years old, she instantly recognised several member of the Mansour household, **even passing an immediate test** when her 'husband' Farouk was introduced to her as one of his brothers, but she contradicted it. Suzanne had intimate knowledge of 'her former self' as Hanan, and also of her relationship with Farouk – which is what persuaded him. She also asked her daughters Leila and Galareh whether they had inherited her jewellery (which had been her express wish). Quite proactive and confident for a 5 year old.

A year or two later Suzanne was also greatly upset when she learned that Farouk had remarried, having promised he would never love anyone but her... even more so when she saw that it was to a former friend of hers. (*He had tried to keep it from her*).

She kept in touch with Farouk throughout her life and according to later reports, **she never married** – but was this for other reasons?

Suzanne had been born 10 days after Hanan's death and, aged 21, bore a remarkable likeness to a photograph of Hanan when she had married Farouk, (at the same age).

Interestingly, the Druze in Lebanon believe that reincarnation is real and that it always happens as an *immediate* transfer to a new body that's about to be born... in the case of Suzanne, (above), 10 days before birth. They also casually refer to reincarnation as 'takamous' (ie. changing your shirt).

If there had been prior collusion between the households it would be remarkable that the Galareh family would have been so determined to prove a point that they deliberately schooled their child in this way. Stevenson made many visits to Suzanne and the family over many years. There seems no doubt that if this was a lie, both families persisted with it for decades.

Stevenson found a lot of cases in Beiruit, that did reflect this belief and were also relatively recent, enabling more facts to be checked. (I don't know if 'immediate transfer' was true of all cases in that region, but it clearly *wasn't true* of all cases that Stevenson reported).

While this may reflect the Druze' believe in reincarnation, (unlike the other major of branches of Islam), if reincarnation was occurring Schroder considered that it may also be a sad reflection of the violence which that community had suffered in the recent past. It was certainly true that some well documented cases did claim to reflect the turmoil at that period. Examples quoted by Shroder[63] included

Deaths which supposedly arose from a little reported but severe bombardment of Druze positions by the US battleship New Jersey on 8th Feb 1984.

Tom Shroder became convinced that these people were not intentionally trying to deceive anyone, yet he was unable to explain the evidence which came to light. Equally, if someone wanted to make up a story and highlight the effects of US military actions, that example would be a good target.

Returning now to a point I made earlier, it was Stevenson[65] who indicated that while a regular flow of cases can be found on every continent including North America, there is a marked 'shortage' of such cases in Europe. He was unable to give precise ratios, but from the tables of evidence which he presented over a comparable period, the incidence of cases from Europe were only 3% of the numbers elsewhere[65], although the data made no allowance for the differences in scale, (ie. size of Europe compared to the entire rest of the world).

This disparity has been considered by many observers as a reason why reincarnation cannot be true, however such logic carries a number of assumptions which may not be correct.

Firstly, there *are* European cases, it's just that they are fewer in number. It was against this background that Stevenson felt obliged to publish a series of modern cases from Europe[65].

> In truth, few of these cases are as compelling as those from other parts of the world, and a number of the 40 examples were of adults who had recurring and unusual dreams about historical events.

Out of several hundred cases of claimed reincarnation in Europe that were brought to his attention, only 22 apparently related to young children in circumstances that met his standards of verification. (He rejected many cases either because they didn't come to light when the children were infants, or he was unable to get an older person to provide witness testimony to events as many had died by the time of his much later investigations[65]). For this reason he stated that it wasn't possible to say whether the 'incidence level' was on a par with elsewhere, but that the cases simply weren't being reported with the same conviction.

While differences in religious belief, or a strong scientific culture will play their part, why would this distinguish Europe from (say) the USA, or Russia? Those who suggest that this may reflect genetic traits, (ie. that there is something different in the make-up of Europeans), ignore the fact that the USA is full of people with a European heritage.

Another suggestion is that Europeans have proportionately safer lives with far less incidence of traumatic death than in other parts of the world, including the USA with its gun culture. However this ignores the massive carnage of the two World Wars and of course the many conflicts in prior centuries or even in recent decades, (eg. in Bosnia/Croatia etc.) – prime sources of traumatic death.

Surprisingly, in general conversation I have found that many people in the UK were not at all surprised that such cases **wouldn't** come to light, if they were indeed occurring. One main reason stood out :-.

> Fear of the press and its potentially devastating intrusion into people's lives could easily encourage adults to suppress all knowledge of such a condition. The expected effect of such publicity in the West bears no resemblance to the effects in Asia and Africa, but it is perceived (rightly or wrongly) to be worse in Europe than the USA.

The bottom line is that we don't know, but cases do continue to arise. The study of such cases was continued after Stevenson's retirement by Jim B.Tucker who has also written on the subject, including his 2005 book "Life Before Life: A Scientific Investigation of Children's Memories of Previous Lives". In his research he has pursued cases in America, (such as Gus Taylor who claims to be his own grandfather), and Cameron Macaulay, the young Glaswegian boy whose case featured in a 2008 documentary by Channel 5 that I believe is still available on You Tube.

Cameron, as a young child, is seen on camera telling of his former life on the remote Scottish Isle of Barra, yet the Macaulay family had no connection with that place. There were no records of TV programs about Barra, and the family didn't have a computer or internet facilities with which Cameron might have inadvertently picked up information about it.

His story never varied even from the earliest age and he provided many details that were subsequently verified, even though they didn't originally concur with official records on the island. This was because the official records only covered islanders who primarily lived on Barra, but once the property that Cameron had described so vividly had been identified, it became clear that the former owners, (with the correct name - Robertson), had been based on the mainland.

If you get the chance to see the film it is fascinating to see how this young child reacts under questioning, and when he is taken to Barra for the first time. It is also intriguing to see how the Macaulay family were so affected by it. The film gives a real flavour of the interviews and circumstances described by Ian Stevenson concerning other cases.

In this case however some of the key facts in the case couldn't be verified. The boy claimed that his former father, a man called Shane Robertson was killed because he didn't look both ways, (interpreted to mean that he had been run over by a car – seemingly confirmed by Cameron with a nod), however nobody of that name was recalled by a living relative of the Robertson family, and neither did anyone die after being run over. Research was continuing to see if there had been any non-fatal injuries of this nature in the Robertson family and other potential explanations for the different name.

Strangely for me in the reports, I do not recall the child saying what his own former name was, or that of his former mother whom he was clearly missing even when in the arms of his current mother Norma. The only name offered was that of his previous father, Shane.

Jim Tucker is continuing the research in this general field, and the last publication that I saw from him was in 2014, "Return to Life". We will see what the future brings. Having made these points, I feel that we should move on.

I therefore return to the central question: if the evidence which Stevenson and Tucker present is not considered fraudulent, and teams of researchers have undertaken extensive verification – then what does it represent if the phenomenon is not reincarnation?

10.1.3 Non-Spiritual Explanations for a 'Reincarnation' Phenomenon

Grandad, I didn't believe in reincarnation when I was your age.
Anonymous

If you deny that reincarnation is possible on religious grounds (eg. because you believe that life can only continue through the direct intervention of God and the process of resurrection), it may still be possible to explain the symptoms of the phenomenon through some form of possession, however this is generally dismissed on the grounds that possession has different symptoms[62].

> In short, a 'possessing spirit' is often portrayed as retaining full memory plus thinking abilities from the past, whereas in reincarnation the memories are typically patchy and often get stronger when places are revisited, or people from 'the past life' are encountered.

Yet most of the objections to reincarnation lie in the denial of spirituality altogether. There are 5 main suggestions for how the phenomenon could be explained without the existence of a soul, including some options that are perhaps even more bizarre than the notion of reincarnation itself.

These five factors were the possibilities that Stevenson and his team also investigated around each case[62], to determine if they could explain what was happening. If they could be ruled out then it would strengthen the argument for reincarnation: They are:

- Fraud — the construction of a falsehood through the indoctrination of a child and the acting-out of scenarios by accomplices who pretend to be 'witnesses'.

- Cryptomnesia — the child somehow learns about or comes into contact with an individual then forgets the experience of how they gained some knowledge, before regurgitating it

183

as part of a recollection that appears like a memory. If the parents did not have knowledge of the original circumstance they would be genuinely surprised by such comments.

- Genetic   -   somehow memory is encapsulated in a person's
  Memory   genetic code which is passed-on through the reproductive process to offspring within the same family - possibly only surfacing after many generations.

- Chance   -   the random imaginings of a child happen to coincide with the circumstances of an individual who may have lived. Public prominence would be given to those cases where facts were substantiated, whereas those cases which didn't find a fit would be forgotten and dismissed. This also covers the possibility of mental illness.

- Extrasensory -   supposes that information might be gleaned by the
  Perception   child through extrasensory means which we do not understand. If the child could, for instance, read the mind of a relative or friend who knew the deceased.

  Challenges arise where we seem to be dealing with memories rather than regurgitating facts and there's an absence of anyone alive who knew the deceased personally. Here it has been speculated that such mind-reading *may not be bound by time and that direct contact could be made with the deceased in the period when they were still alive*, (in the past)!

  Well perhaps, but I personally find that this is less credible than belief in a soul. It would also suggest that memories from the past are real 'tangible' things that could be accessed.

  Of course, mind reading is only one type of extra-sensory ability, so there may be other non-spiritual ways in which information could be transferred, or so it is claimed.

Stevenson reports that his researchers not only looked for these factors individually, but also in *combinations* and he has stated where these alternate possibilities might exist, even if they can't be proven either. However such **explanations have not always been found**.

As already mentioned, every case includes a *number* of facts & events that build a picture of the overall circumstances. Some of these could potentially be explained by non-spiritual means, however each 'strong' case will have a characteristic that makes it stand-out as a real puzzle, and these are the factors which have to be resolved. Take the following remarkable examples:

> There are reports of a child named Titu Singh[66] who began to tell of a past life at the age of four. Over a period he claimed to be Suresh Verma, who had a wife, two children, and a radio shop in a distant town - Agra. Witnesses (such as a local schoolteacher), heard the boy's claims that he had been murdered and could name his attackers. The radio shop was found and from the new owners, the Singhs were told where they could find the Verma family, who had moved away.

> Both families are adamant that they had never known about each other previously. While some might choose not to believe this, the true critical factor is that the named attacker later confessed to the murder which had previously been unsolved.

> Stevenson reports a similar case - Ravi Shankar in India[62], who claimed to be a boy who had been beheaded to get at his modest inheritance. In this instance two previous suspects were named by the boy as his murderers, however that case was weakened by the fact that the families did have passing contact before the revelations came to light; and the men were not brought to trial.

In the Titu example the key factor for me is that people don't **confess** to **murder** in order to prove some **academic point about reincarnation**. They will only do so if it is true; or if they come under extreme pressure during interrogation. There are no reports of such bullying, and the confession was supposedly *only* brought about through new facts that were revealed by memories from a past life. Yet without a specific endorsement I can't say whether the investigating team adhered to strict standards.

So if you dispute this interpretation, the claims would need to have been faked, probably as a result of collusion, with their 'suspicions' being given extra credibility by claims of reincarnation. If so we would have to marvel at the commitment of the boy's parents in risking the future wellbeing of their son by training him to perfection in a multi-year campaign which had no guarantee of success, in order to expose a murderer for the benefit of another family with no apparent blood ties. Research into the case seems to confirm that the families hadn't known each other before the revelations.

The other case of Ravi Shankar was weakened by the 'murderers' having already been suspected before the claims of reincarnation were made, (indeed one had made an unofficial confession which he later denied/withdrew). Yet aside from the new evidence which the boy revealed, part of the strength in that case came from a birthmark in the shape of a line across the boy's throat which matched the neck wound of the victim.

According to Stevenson, Ravi Shankar's father was suspected of severely beating the boy in order to try to **stop** him making the claims, which the father found both disturbing and potentially threatening to the entire family, (as the murders may have taken steps to silence them before they were arrested).

(Stevenson reports[62] many other cases of supposed reincarnation where birthmarks with particular relevance to a past life, have also been in evidence – yet there have again been challenges to this).

Now people may think of ever more elaborate claims of collusion, or they may speculate about other aspects of these cases which nobody knows about, and which may yet come to light to reveal a different 'truth', but from the stated facts in these cases there is certainly good reason to consider the possibility of reincarnation.

We should also look at the 5 'down to earth' alternate explanations in turn –which I have labelled A-E, below.

In the following paragraphs I will refer to the children's comments as memories in order to preserve the spirit of what they are describing and what those around them consider to be true. Published cases are not thought by the scientists to reflect false statements.

A - Fraud

Fraud <u>has</u> undoubtedly been attempted, particularly where the claims of reincarnation first arise in adulthood, but from my reading of the literature this is very rare in child cases. If there were fraudulent cases in the published material then it would have been very hard to disguise from professional researchers using scientific methods. It would also require a high degree of training.

So what is it that persuades researchers that people are being genuine? There are five main reasons:

1. People do not seem to gain either financially or in other ways from such claims, and more importantly **they do not seek it.** In general the afflicted just asked for guidance or an explanation. Neither the media nor researchers made payouts for information, and on the whole, families didn't gain by any publicity or notoriety except in minor ways. There were no campaigns or spin-offs.

   If a 'prior family' was identified, money and assets did **not** generally transfer between the families; and doesn't seem to have been requested. The families were often wary of each other and in many cultures there is a matter of honour that prevents such requests.

   There seems to be overwhelming evidence for this, so we have to ask how else 'benefit' might be obtained, and the primary suggestion is that the stories are generated to reinforce local beliefs that people wanted to uphold - in short, to provide evidence which supports their religion. Such accusations are generally done by academics far away from events.

From the books I've read there are **no** suggestions from local communities that religious officials ever prompted the families to do this, and I'm not aware of **any** evidence to support it. So is this just mud-slinging that seeks to preserve an alternative faith view?

People are obviously aware of the implications for belief – especially when researchers turn up on the doorstep. Yet if religions are not orchestrating such activity we would have to conclude that such a fraud was a matter of 'personal initiative' by those concerned.

Would a 3 year old be aware of the debate? Would 3000 families and all of the witnesses want to get involved in this over 30 years? And what of the claims that arise in communities which do not believe in reincarnation?

2. In the vast majority of cases *nobody later claims any deception.* (There *are* some rare suggestions of deception, but the motives of the accusers can also be suspect in these instances).

What's more there is a strong level of confirmation from very diverse witnesses. Stevenson stated that the general incidence of conflicting reports or inaccuracy from adults giving testimony about what was said or what happened, was about 10% of statements but those differences tended to occur in matters of minor detail rather than the main points of a case.

From an academic viewpoint it's in everyone's interest to remove fraud. Clearly there are many cases which do pass the test, so if we acknowledge that something genuine is occurring we should seek alternate explanations.

3. Communities believe that **such revelations cause problems,** (even in communities which accept reincarnation), *so there is an active disincentive to do this.* As already mentioned :-

    - the child might become ostracised and ridiculed by other children due to their strange behaviour and claims, or they may simply be introverted and do less well at school, even though they were often seen as very bright for their age.

    - unwelcome media interest which may either make direct accusations or may draw the wrong sort of interest from other individuals wanting to twist the circumstances into a battleground for their debates or ambitions.

    - parents of the child might be worried that the family of the deceased person would try to entice the child to leave their natural home.

- it has caused marital problems in the family of the deceased if the surviving spouse had remarried but they were persuaded that the child was indeed the reincarnation of their former partner – as we saw in the case of Sukla earlier.

There are also scenarios which can be inherently undesirable. Documented cases include :-

- a Ceylonese boy, 'Wijeratne', who claimed to be his father's executed brother - a murderer who had killed his wife, and who was a figure of deep shame in their family history[62].

- in several cases the family of the deceased had far worse economic circumstances than the family of the child[62], or they were of a lower caste.

- a whole raft of cases in Burma where children claimed to be reborn Japanese soldiers who had been killed along the path of battle against the British in 1945. By all accounts, the ordinary Burmese truly hated those Japanese soldiers in the 2nd World War – to such an extent that at least one child was reported to have been burnt alive[63].

   Yet 20 children continued to complain about the spiciness of Burmese food and wanted proper Japanese food, and to wear proper Japanese clothes etc.[63]

4. **The age of the children** who begin to talk about past lives most commonly between the ages of 2 and $4^1/_2$ years, (on average - age $2^1/_2$). It's very hard to argue that so many young children could be taught to remember so many false facts and present them with such credibility and consistency.

5. **The 'personalisation' of the testimony** and the general manner in which the children made their comments is compelling. They do not say that 'this' happened, or 'that person lived there' (which would be expected from rote learning). Instead, the children naturally put themselves in the memory, saying things such as "I was swinging in a tree when...", or "I have children and we live there", or "I died in a car just like that", etc.

Again – we have to remember that all of Stevenson's cases seem to be of young children, and there are thousands of cases.

B - Cryptomnesia

Cryptomnesia is the subconscious accumulation of knowledge which comes out at a later moment as part of a dream or false memory[67]. This is perhaps the strongest theory to explain such testimonies by normal means, yet it still doesn't account for many cases reported by Stevenson[62] from Asia & Alaska where newspapers and radios were largely unknown outside the large cites at the time, greatly limiting the access to relevant information – especially when the cases referred to quite obscure parts of history. Furthermore, in many cases the population of these remote villages were wholly illiterate, and therefore unable to read the scant public records that existed.

In such circumstances information could only be transferred through human contact and yet at such a young age this could not be envisaged without the knowledge of the parents – especially in Asia where parents remain close, and girls never leave unaccompanied by an adult.

In the reincarnation cases there is generally witness testimony to verify that the parents only learned relevant information from others after the claims came to light – sometimes via the researchers themselves.

Yet it remains possible that information did transfer to the family before the claims were made and that they did then forget being told. If so, there are 2 other problems :–

- the child would still have to be schooled in that information, which would mean that the parents would either have to be consciously aware of it, or they would be aware that somebody else was grooming their child.
- if Cryptomnesia was at work, it's unlikely that the communicator of the information would also forget the encounter - especially when the matters were very personal. They would then have to lie about it.

When Cryptomnesia has been clearly identified by researchers in the West[67] (although **not** in reported cases of child reincarnation), the evidence has generally emerged through the technique of hypnotic regression in adults. Sources of information have then been traced to specific passages in books or articles which have been regurgitated and not adapted to fit new circumstances.

The statements lack the 'personalisation' of the narrative, (mentioned earlier), where descriptions should be given from the deceased's perspective. Stevenson only found 2 examples of proven Cryptomnesia where some level of 'personation' had occurred, yet those seemed quite strange – allowing the researchers to identify the books where the characteristics had come from.

In the "Blanche Poynings" case (reported by G.L.Dickinson in 1911), the slightly odd personations came from one book which the subject's mind had associated with a historical character.

The other case was of a medium who adopted the personalities of the composers Weber and Beethoven when under a trance, and it was later discovered that he had read about them extensively, (report by R.W.Pickford – 1943).

189

Stevenson drew several distinctions between these and his subjects, the most obvious being that these cases of reincarnation involved children not adults, and they had not been hypnotised. Perhaps more importantly, he concluded that if Cryptomnesia relied on books, these would be completely insufficient to give the child a true living sense of the real person who had died, at a level that was sufficient to persuade living people who had known the deceased.

C - Genetic Memory

Given the latest speculation about memories being stored deep within the levels of sub-atomic particles/matter, (which we will consider in Ch. 12), it might, theoretically, be possible for genetic material to carry and then transfer memories from one person to the next, even to the extent that the memories of different ancestors could be combined in one individual, as genetic code is exchanged at conception. Still, it seems a long shot.

Even if correct, the speculation about such a mechanism still requires a direct genetic lineage with the deceased, whether they are children, grandchildren or later generations. Genetic memory doesn't seem able to explain memories that supposedly come from a deceased uncle or aunt... but perhaps something else applies in these cases.

As a mechanism it is clearly impossible where there is no family connection, or supposed memories could only have arisen after the death of key people in the genetic line.

Another major challenge is that if such a genetic mechanism were valid we'd expect to see parental memories appearing quite commonly in children across the general population. Other than the published claims of reincarnation I don't know of any such claims.

So what leads to such suggestions of 'Genetic Memory'?

A large part of this comes from beliefs that reincarnation happens within families, and in this respect people will often latch onto distinguishing birthmarks that had relevance to the deceased. Beyond this, continuing physical characteristics such as a distinct shape of nose or a rare eye colour within the family *could* be largely explained by genetic transfer, but new birthmarks, (supposedly reflecting wounds incurred by the deceased), could not.

D - Chance

In a country of many millions of people it may be quite possible to match an imaginary past life to a historical reality using some particular points within a child's general testimony. So we have to ask whether *all* of the facts fit, or whether the people who suggest a possible link to a past life are being selective in their use of details?

One of the characteristics of strong cases is that there are lots of details which are verified.

Equally, on reverse logic, the odds of a chance match within a small community are highly unlikely. So where this happens, the circumstances of each case become very significant.

Alternatively we may find that people wishing to make their desire for reincarnation come true, could sub-consciously 'massage' their recollections in order to fit real details as they became known – either losing some inconvenient statements or perhaps adding-in one or two new facts, but **only** after the subject has been told about them.

In these circumstances we would expect to see testimony changing over time. On the whole, with some minor exceptions, this doesn't seem to happen in published cases by Stevenson and others.

E - Extrasensory Perception

The trouble with this type of possible explanation is that it has far less evidence for the phenomenon than reincarnation itself, so in contrast to the widespread belief in reincarnation, my straw polls suggest that communities across the globe find this far harder to accept.

Why is this offered as an explanation? At the 'high' end, those who are scientifically minded like to consider all possibilities from an even starting position, and as we are in the early stages of investigating such claims, (in historical terms), the possibility of extrasensory abilities is arguably on a par with reincarnation.

Yet the 'low' reason may be more of a driving force.

Those who wish to deny any suggestion of a spiritual existence might see less threat in extrasensory abilities as they are often expected to be firmly based within the proven reality of physics, (if they exist at all), whereas reincarnation can only really represent either an illusion or the Soul.

The implication from the low argument is that spiritual realms cannot exist, yet principles already advanced by scientists, such as **hidden dimensions of existence**, **parallel universes**, or even Dark Energy could potentially equate to the same thing, as they are all undetectable as things stand. Indeed, the evidence for extrasensory abilities is only based on *tentative* evidence that is far from conclusive. We will cover more of this in the next chapter dealing with the Mind.

If we assume for the moment that extrasensory abilities are possible, then Stevenson saw them as offering ways to get information, but he **didn't** see such techniques as being able to provide personality and behaviour which were also demonstrated in the reincarnation cases.

If extrasensory abilities are to work within the known laws of physics they have to operate in real time and they would not be able to go back in time to retrieve facts or traits. Nothing in the Laws of Physics allows anything to go back in time, however it is conceivable that some incredible sense could trawl the minds of people still alive for a memory of the individuals concerned. That's a lot of minds to tune into before you reach the right one, (assuming that they are looking for something specific).

Yet the mechanism could be argued to operate the other way around: that some people either transmit details, or make their minds available to trawling when others are closed. This would imply that children with this capability might just regurgitate the first minds they come across.

However, for me, the biggest challenge to this thinking is that if such extrasensory abilities were true, and previously unrecognised/undetected, why it should only manifest itself in this way for 3000 people?

So having run through the 5 hurdles which each case must overcome if it is to establish credibility in the eyes of sceptics, can we point to any cases where all of these explanations can be discounted? That's for each of you to decide, but I personally find that **no** case is conclusive.

In large part, for me, this is because you cannot be sure that all factors have been reasonably eliminated. Some cases may come close, but there is still room to wonder. The perfect scientifically researched example has yet to emerge and may even be an impossibility.

However it is equally true that the strong cases have **not been disproven** either – far from it. On this basis I would argue that there is enough credible evidence to warrant further investigation, especially when there are so many cases and strong patterns have emerged in the way that this real phenomenon operates... even if it isn't reincarnation.

Aside from the volume and quality of the evidence that I have referred-to in the different books; I remain surprised by:-

- the mundane nature of described events, (not major things which might tempt people who wanted to concoct a story to catch the headlines);
- the consistency with which individuals present their testimony over many studies and many years;
- the degree to which the best cases could be individually and independently verified on key points; and
- the 'modus operandi' or 'fingerprint' of reincarnation – ie. a distinct and consistent pattern of how such events unfold across the globe.

These are no passing fads to gain attention. The occasional researcher who comes knocking on the door marks a very brief moment in time for these people, who have to deal with it on a daily basis – often for many years and sometimes for the rest of their lives.

Taking the evidence at face value in order to consider why only a very small proportion of people seem to be affected in this way, many people have been struck by the frequency with which the prior life, at its end, had suffered a traumatic death.

This has been suggested as a possible cause, as well as a way to explain the lower incidence of such cases in the West and particularly in Europe. Yet this ignores the fact that Europe, the USA and Canada and elsewhere have all been party to major wars in the past 100 years, and there are incidents of car crashes, robberies, and other accidents in every country.

A refinement to this theory comes from the sensitivity shown by (say) a woman who died leaving her young child, or a youth terrorised by shelling. Perhaps it may reflect the different abilities that people have to cope with trauma. But are we really saying that people in Europe are better able to cope in such circumstances, accounting for the reduced incidence?

I have already mentioned the Burmese cases of imperial Japanese Soldiers of 2nd World War supposedly being reincarnated[63]. Are there examples of Western troops being reincarnated on home territory? *Well there are* – although not to the same level. The example quoted by Stevenson was of a German member of a bomber crew who was shot down over England and seemingly reborn into a British family, although the German individual could not be specifically identified[68].

Before we leave this subject let me make a couple of points to balance perceptions. Although the findings **are** as I have described them, it would be wrong to suggest that there are no examples of people who have benefitted from their perceived condition. Some of Stevenson's subjects seem able to speak a foreign language fluently, from their memories rather than through any formal tuition. They have sometimes used these abilities to progress their own careers quite successfully. The technical term for such unlearned language skills is Xenoglossy and Stevenson wrote a book on two outstanding cases in his book 'Unlearned Language' (1984).

Challenges to the origin of these abilities have taken a number of forms. Sarah Thomason (a linguist from the University of Michigan), re-examined Stevenson's cases and found that while they were not faked the language couldn't be regarded as fully fluent. In other cases the criticism has been that the pronunciation was significantly incorrect – the suggestion being that it was picked-up by overhearing people, (such as unidentified tourists, or foreigners who live nearby).

In a separate example, a child from a poor background (Parmod) with little education believed he was the reincarnation of a successful businessman from a different part of India and different social caste, (persuading the family of the deceased as well). He was monitored over many years and with no help from the 'previous' family, used his memories to begin a business of his own which grew into a substantial operation[62]. However, was this just normal entrepreneurial talent?

So where does this leave us? Essentially, as a crude yardstick, various websites that had originally been highly critical and dismissive of the research now seem to grudgingly acknowledge that the phenomenon must be real but in the minds of many of their contributors, it still cannot represent reincarnation. Yet there doesn't seem to be another credible explanation for the stronger cases so I would argue that the jury is still out.

The lack of an explanation leaves us considering the possibilities, but if it is true, then there is no logical reason why Reincarnation shouldn't be God-given in much the same way as Evolution might be God-given.

In addition, the presence of reincarnation doesn't disprove the doctrine of resurrection and can only support ideas about the Soul.

Philosophically while it leans towards Dualism and Idealism, it is still possible that these cases may one day be explained by physical means, but Materialism probably needs a dramatic advance within physics or quantum mechanics to enable it to do so.

11 Non-Scientific Evidence re: Life beyond the Body

Before I return to mainstream research, (this time into the Mind), I wanted to complete our exploration of the mysterious aspects of life – some of which undoubtedly exist, and others which remain hearsay.

In this chapter we will be exploring factors which are widely reported but which have not yet been investigated scientifically in any great depth. They play to the margins of belief because many people will initially feel that they cannot be taken seriously. They seem to be wild claims that go against all of our normal day to day experiences, and also lack any substantive evidence. However that may be rather harsh in some of these fields, (such as hypnotic regression), where the evidence is real but 'tainted' by scientific indiscipline.

In addition, there is no doubt that these areas are dominated by both 'cranks' who have reported events that have been proven to be false, and also untrained/amateur researchers who have made basic mistakes which invalidate the evidence. Yet there are things about them which prevent us dismissing the claims altogether.

At one extreme, the reports of ghosts have persisted for thousands of years and yet even today there is no proof, (which is quite telling), so people are sceptical even if they find the idea fun. Yet hypnotic 'past life' regression is treated far more seriously, and the successful, (but rare), use of psychics by police opens up a whole new level of consideration.

A small number of examples from each genre may pass our basic tests of credibility even if they are not proof, and the sheer number of cases which keep on being reported, (despite the obvious public scepticism and ridicule), should be pause for thought. If even one of them turns out to be true, what would it tell us? In the light of one potential revelation from the AWARE experiment (previous chapter) we may find leads to new avenues of research, and perhaps even a window into Thought and the soul.

I have therefore written this chapter so that we have a rough awareness of both the evidence and opportunities should any findings 'firm-up'.

Probably like you, when looking at the list of headings I thought "Is this for real"? But in reviewing the chapter I am again reminded of the number of surprising sources that kept me going. Please stay with it.

The benefit will be in finding those things we can clearly set aside for the moment, and those which justify us keeping a watching brief!

We can generally sense when reports have a 'ring of truth' about them, and just because the amateurs who were available didn't cover the angles properly, doesn't mean that the things didn't happen.

In the West, reports of reincarnation and out of body experiences were also dismissed out of hand until somebody was prepared to collect the evidence in a scientific way, (as we saw in the last two chapters). That evidence now demonstrates that genuine things are happening even if we can't explain them. However in the areas we are about to explore, reliable evidence has **not** been gathered on a scale that will give it credibility.

You will probably be pleased to hear that I **won't** be boring you with definitions that might try to demonstrate what is 'scientific' vs what isn't scientific. Let's instead begin on a more strategic point:

If an event/object is real then it is evidence of something; but of what?

This simple sentence has two major components. It firstly implies that there's a need to demonstrate that an event/object is real. Secondly, it requires a degree of precision with which to describe the end concept accurately *in the context of a particular objective or purpose*. For instance:-

Person 1 might describe glancing through a door to see a few gleaming metal things lined-up on tables, each of them having a white 'face plate' on the front... but he/she hadn't entered the room in order to touch them, so it was possible that they were just an image/illusion. Yet one object stood out as being the most impressive.

Person 2 said they had seen these things and touched them; even going so far as to measure one of them quite precisely. It was made up of a series of 26 brass cogs set in a frame, with a spring and a white dial on the front. The dial had two arms which rotated when being pushed by the cogs. This person had the precise measurements of the cogs plus the force of the spring and could predict how fast each of the arms would turn. It was a wonderful piece of conceptual art, and all the other devices seemed to be variations on this theme!

Person 3 took a different tack, saying that they were all mechanical clocks which could tell the time of day if only you had a reference point with which to calibrate the findings. Observing how they moved by comparing them side by side it had become apparent that each of these clocks moved at *slightly* different speeds yet gave *wildly* different readings so you couldn't tell which was the most accurate or even which one approximated most closely to the right time of day. They could all be way out!

However the original question had been – which was the most valuable object in the room?

Given the obvious uncertainties about how value could be attributed, (age, beauty, accuracy, etc), which of the above people would you say provided the most relevant scientific evidence to answer the question?

Well, knowing the question becomes an important starting point.

Person 1 may have provided the most relevant information by describing which would be of greatest value to him/her in the absence of a market. While Person 1 couldn't say whether these objects were real... the question was one of comparative value so a judgement based on the appeal of the image alone could be just as valid. In contrast the other participants didn't seem to make any *comparative* value judgements on the basis of accuracy, or indeed any other criteria.

Person 2 had precision but no context, so he/she didn't know if they were measuring something relevant and didn't even seem to understand the basic concept behind the devices within their assessment of 'conceptual art'... and of course, there was no comparison.

Person 3 understood the concept behind the devices and saw that there were differences in accuracy but realised that without a reference point there was no way to determine which was the most mechanically accurate, however this either ignored the question of value, or made a potentially invalid assumption that value only related to accuracy.

When I have occasionally posed this scenario to friends in conversation many of them latch onto Person 2 as being the most scientific due to the precision of their measurements, however if the measurements have no relevance to the question then what is the merit in it?

My point is that labels concerning 'scientific worthiness' only have limited value. In the strange territory of 'spirituality' where we are still getting our minds around the subject, we are perhaps more interested in establishing that the phenomena being described are real before we can hope to really analyse what they represent, due to the lack of gathered evidence that may be relevant.

In this respect we have to judge the persuasiveness of people's testimonies in the context of what is happening. The 'appeal' which keeps the possibilities open, even to sceptics, is that in all of the following topics there have been lots of similar experiences reported across the globe by people who do not seem to be lying, but who are also generally unable to offer anything credible to substantiate their claims that something spiritual was occurring.

Are these all examples of wishful thinking or is it more the case that humanity doesn't yet have precise methods to describe or measure these things in ways that seem relevant?

From either perspective, in order to narrow the possibilities, the methods applied in gathering the evidence will inevitably contribute to people's assessment of its persuasiveness and value.

11.1.1 Hypnotic Regression & Dreams of Past Lives

I like to reminisce with people I don't know. Granted, it takes longer.

Anonymous

For the most part, Hypnotic or Past-Life Regression is where people under hypnosis have been asked to cast their minds back to a time before their birth to see if they have any perception of a prior existence. (I say 'for the most part' because there are some new techniques being offered which supposedly do not require hypnosis).

A significant proportion of 'subjects' who undergo this procedure do seem to have honest recollections of a past life, and are able to talk about them in some detail while they are under hypnosis, (not afterwards)... but are they real, or are these 'memories' unwittingly fabricated in some way?

Although people are not thought to be lying about what they experience, the procedure is **not** generally regarded as 'scientific' because the experiments are rarely conducted under scientific conditions that are intended to test the possibility of a prior life. They are generally being undertaken as part of therapy, or for recreational purposes.

In addition people will be deploying a technique that's not understood, (because we don't know what hypnosis actually does to the mind... specifically).

The criticism is therefore directed towards those who generally conduct these exercises in a casual manner – most commonly using leading questions that undermine the responses given by subjects under hypnosis.

While hypnosis can resemble a dream-like condition, current research does confirm that the subjects are awake, so Hypnosis is probably best described as an altered state of mind which is often thought to increase focus, (by blocking out distractions), yet it also increases suggestibility.

To me it seems fair to refer to an 'altered state of mind' because people clearly do things in this condition that they wouldn't normally do, however this notion has been extended by some people to mean that when under hypnosis the mind is able to do things or to access memories that may be beyond our normal level of consciousness. This may or may not be correct.

I feel it is important to separate the different issues as one aspect doesn't necessarily invalidate the other, (ie. just because someone is susceptible to suggestion doesn't mean that they can't be accessing hidden memories). However, the known suggestibility issues do mean that experiments have to be conducted in very rigorous ways, if anything scientifically meaningful is to be gained from them.

> In one set of experiments by Nicholas Spanos[72], the reactions of 2 groups of people were compared. Members of 'Group 1' were first given a lecture on hypnosis which said that hypnosis always caused

the subject's arms to become rigid, and a large majority **did** display this characteristic when hypnotised. Those in 'Group 2' were ***not*** given this information and they **didn't** show any such trait.

In a similar but separate study conducted by Robert Baker, three groups of 20 people were each given slightly different information:-

- The first group were told that they were part of a study that could help them uncover their past lives. Eighty-five per cent 'remembered' a past life.

- The second group were told that the technique being tested may or may not work to reveal past-life memories. 60% of this group succeeded in doing so.

- The third group were told that ordinary people generally didn't generally experience a past life. Only 10% of this group had that experience.

This is why the process of Past Life Regression has been very vulnerable to the criticism that a subject's mind may have been tainted by external influences, (including that of the hypnotist). People may effectively be role playing when under hypnosis. Yet the alternate view is that if past life memories are normally repressed, then reinforcement of that through the prior lectures may have further suppressed the memories under hypnosis.

We should remember that hypnosis was first used in therapy to unlock suppressed memories in order to help people face the past and thereby cope with their current lives,

So there's a valid judgement to be made in determining where fact ends and fiction begins, when people are asked to cast their minds back to a moment before they were born. How can we tell?

We saw in section 10.1.3 that Cryptomnesia, (the subconscious accumulation of information), is real and can be used by the mind when creating imaginary characters in an imaginary past, as in the case of Mrs. Tighe[67] who imagined herself as Bridey Murphy in a previous life, but the memories were traced to a childhood neighbour, a Bridie Murphy Corkell, (a person whom she had long forgotten in her day to day life).

Cryptomnesia is clearly something that we have to be wary of, especially when there is no prospect of the subject having come into contact with their 'past life' character – eg. if you were to portray yourself as a citizen of ancient Rome. Researchers would have to consider that accurate details attached to this persona had been gleaned from text books, documentaries, etc. However there are very few cases where there doesn't seem to be any such possibility. We will look at one in a few paragraphs time, (Guiseppe Costa), which didn't arise through hypnosis which, if true, couldn't be Cryptomnesia, and could only be explained though other factors.

One significant feature of the testimonies is that I have not heard of anyone who seems to remember themselves as anybody famous, which is both a blessing and a curse. It is persuasive as very few people do actually achieve any historical fame. The downside is that it becomes very hard to validate the claims. Yet there are some cases where very detailed recollections have been made and these have eventually been traced to real but obscure lives in history (see Jenny Cockell & Guiseppe Costa below).

As it is so hard to prove the validity of testimonies it is perhaps understandable that the less credible cases are better known, which can make the field of Hypnotic Regression seem like it is dominated by sub-conscious fantasy rather than reality. For instance, the subject's narratives & reactions may appear limited by the person's current-life knowledge:-

> Subjects who imagine their former selves as living in ancient times, or in different cultures, can put on false dialects, or exhibit very crude forms of a foreign language rather than real fluency. For instance, people have been described as putting on 'movie dialects' of Old English rather than the language as it would truly have been spoken at the time.
>
> In another case, Spanos[72] reports that a subject believed himself to be a Japanese pilot of the 2nd World War but he couldn't give the name of the Emperor of Japan.

Yet such doubts may be based on a false assumption: that because we're dealing with adults who are very articulate, their memories should be complete. In fact, that wouldn't be consistent with what we have learned from studies into childhood reincarnation. If the memories truly reflected past lives, we might expect that most cases *would* be fragmented.

An interesting factor is that if subjects glean new information about their supposed past life through research, their story under hypnosis may be enhanced or modified to 'retro-fit' the realities to their vision of the past. We have to ask whether it's possible for a person's mind to mix real memories with some fantasy?

One of the more compelling cases where Cryptomnesia has <u>not</u> been demonstrated is that of Jenny Cockell, a British housewife and mother who went to a regression therapist in 1988 having claimed to have originally had memories of a past life during her childhood. (Unfortunately there was no evidence of this childhood experience other than her testimony, which is possibly why Ian Stevenson didn't pursue this as one of his European cases).

According to the book which she wrote about her experiences[73] the hypnotic regressions caused her to recount the experiences of her Irish character "Mary" however in some key respects these 'memories' lacked significant detail. By way of example she couldn't recall Mary's surname or the name of the place in which she lived. It was only after research that such details and even the name of her husband were 'identified'.

So is this all fabrication? Well the claims were **not** so easily dismissed. There were a number of other facts about her 'previous family' and particularly her 8 children which did match the circumstances of a "Mary Sutton" of Malahide near Dublin. More surprisingly these children were still alive and despite the fact that they remain Catholics and were originally highly sceptical, several became persuaded that Jenny was indeed their mother Mary, while others were deeply unsettled by the accuracy of the details provided. (Mary had died 21 years before the birth of Jenny in 1953).

Skeptics argue that this is a case of retro-fitting facts to a storyline. It is not Cryptomnesia where facts are declared up front through the early regression sessions.

In broad terms the challenge of Cryptomnesia is less credible where obscure facts are revealed that could only come from sources which have never been published, or to which the subject had no access, eg:-

- where details of an obscure battle is verified by ancient one-off texts found in the archives of a castle, and written in an ancient version of a foreign language, (compared to the language of the subject), or
- the layout of an ancient building that was dramatically changed in subsequent centuries; the original layout only being verified by archaeological evidence held by academic institutions, (which the subject had no access to – as they lived in a different country).

Sadly there seem to be virtually no cases of **hypnotic regression** where this applies in such a unique and persuasive manner. On the other hand, there *is* more compelling evidence from cases which claim **recurrent dreams or visions** which have provided astonishing levels of detail.

> Stevenson[65] reports the case of Guiseppe Costa, who wrote a book about his experiences in 1923 ("Di la dalla vita" – ie. "From the Beyond to this Life" – which was only published in Italian).
>
> Costa claimed that odd feelings and recurrent dreams which he had experienced up to the age of 10 had given him a strong impression of a previous life in which he took part in a small medieval military campaign through Venice and then on to Constantinople. The recollections provided considerable detail about methods of transport, uniforms, and the look of places visited.
>
> Later as an adult on a tourist visit he also felt very powerful associations with a ruined medieval castle at Verres. Caught there in a storm he stayed the night and had a dream about a woman approaching him with love, calling him 'Ibleto', and suggesting that he should read about their past lives in a tower near Albenga.
>
> Costa discovered that among several towers near Albenga, one was owned by a descendant of Ibleto di Challant who had actually built the castle at Verres in 1380.

Guiseppe approached the descendant, asking permission to research the family archives for material related to the exploits of Ibleto. It was there that he uncovered the extraordinary story of a man who was a military commander to Amadeus VI, Count of Savoy, whose modest force conducted a 'belated' crusade against the Turks near Constantinople in 1366. In short, the *details* matched, even to the extent that his true love was the Count's sister, Blanche of Savoy, who wasn't allowed to marry him as she had been promised, (for reasons of state), to Galeazzo Visconti, Lord of Milan.

The only reference to these exploits beyond the family archives are an unpublished manuscript written in French about the exploits of Ibleto di Challant by Boniface II, Lord of Fenis – not a work that has had much exposure! (Within historical works by Anglo-Saxon authors there are very few mentions of this expedition, although it does feature as 4 lines in a history of Venice by Hodgson, 1910).

The major failings of this case are that Costa identified the 'previous life' from his own research, and there is also no evidence to substantiate his claims that he had such dreams, feelings and visions in his childhood. Family members, friends and acquaintances are no longer around to give testimony and to my knowledge there are no written statements from them either. In short, there is nothing to prove that the story wasn't made up after the research had been done.

The case of Georg Neidhart[65] was different in that he *did* tell people of his dreams before he was able to intensively research the details he had recounted. His main visions in 1924 (at the age of 26), were so vivid that he immediately wrote them down – which apparently took several days given the intricacies of what he had seen. His father also recalled some strange childhood stories.

Neidhart both described and drew a castle which he believed to date from ad1150 (775 years earlier), perceiving it to exist in deep forests north east of Munich, across the Danube. The structure was distinctive in that the tower wasn't round but had 4 sides plus a quadrangle, while being sited on the edge of a craggy mountain.

He imagined himself to be a noble named Kuhnenberg who'd first had an argument then a duel with another aggressive noble called von Falkenstein whom he accused of forcing the people to pay unjust taxes as a lackey for the clergy, and also making advances to the woman he intended to marry. Falkenstein died in the fight, which strengthened Kuhnenberg's determination to take the battle to his enemies, the clerics. As a result he became a robber-baron, intercepting any traffic for the local bishop that used the roads through the forest.

Neidhart claims to have experienced Kuhnenberg's feelings as well as recalling events, and stated that the rogue baron felt secure in his impregnable castle. But his increasing brutality eventually made his wife and many supporters turn against him. His enemies also lay siege to the castle. Although he crushed a rebellion, the mysterious death of his wife shortly afterwards served to further undermine support for him and he eventually tried to break free from the castle by launching a desperate sortie at the besiegers. He was captured and beheaded.

From many years earlier Neidhart's father remembered his astonishment when 7year old Georg had told him of detailed memories about his own previous beheading!

As an adult Neidhart followed his instincts to search for the castle, using his senses to determine which route and landmarks to follow, and eventually he did find one with a square tower built on a rocky outcrop at a place called Weissenstein nr.Regen, close to the Czech Republic. The castle matched his description even to the extent that he found a secret passageway whose entrance lay hidden, where he had marked it on his drawings. (In fairness however, there were locals who also knew the existence of the passageway). The layout no longer resembled a quadrangle but had been altered in the 17th Century.

Later research did confirm the existence of a Konrad von Falkenstein who had illegally seized some communities within the bishopric of Passau, however there were suggestions that this man had lived in the 13th century not the 12th – not confirmed either way. There was also reference to a monastery at Rinchnach which had been founded in the 12th century.

No records were found of a man called Kuhnenberg and the definitive records from that period belonging to the archbishop were apparently destroyed in a fire many years earlier. The person who built the castle at Weissenstein also remains a mystery. Neidhart was however directed to the archives at a place called Trausnitz Castle where the curator was very helpful but declared himself astonished at the detail Neidhart was providing, as the records of that period were only just beginning to be researched and catalogued.

It remains to be seen whether Georg Neidhart's narratives are further validated by the archives.

Despite his acceptance of dreams and visions, Ian Stevenson was not a great advocate of the hypnotic technique. He said that if all the regressed subjects who claimed to be present at the Crucifixion of Christ were true, there would be no room for Roman soldiers on Golgotha[63].

He also felt that the children who seemed afflicted by reincarnation didn't need hypnosis, and I imagine he was concerned that the technique could undermine his findings.

It would seem that hypnotic regression will only gain credibility if Reincarnation is proven first, not the other way round. *If that happens* then it would seem that while **some** cases of Past Life Regression will be true, **others** may arise from the imagination of the mind, and it will be hard if not impossible to distinguish the two. The difficulty for any research is that it will invariably involve adults who will have a lifetime of influences to potentially contaminate the scenario. (This is partly what makes the study of childhood reincarnation so much more robust).

Yet the undoubted value that <u>has</u> been achieved from this hypnotic technique is that many patients who have sought therapy for problems have actually been greatly helped and even cured by such revelations.

Whether this is fiction or not, it does seem to produce significant benefits, and practitioners often become persuaded that these regressions do represent past life memories because real problems do seem to be resolved by uncovering them. It's also argued that if the memories were fiction brought about by hypnosis they couldn't have caused the problems in the first place.

Being honest, this research needs to be far more disciplined if it is to gain credibility and one aspect of these cases always niggles at the back of my mind. I see no reports of people being hypnotised by anyone other than the original practitioner and I wonder, if the subjects did allow themselves to be 'put under' by someone else, whether the same results would be achieved? No doubt somebody will tell me at some point!

11.1.2   Mediums,   Visitations,   and Communications with the Dead

The spirit continues to evolve after death, but weight gain may be a problem. - Anonymous

In this section I am not really talking about ghosts which can be seen by more than one person, (a subject which I will cover later); I'm primarily dealing with suggestions that people interact with spiritual beings using their minds, (primarily contacts thought to be with the souls of the dead).

If genuine, these are individual encounters which might be achieved by a 'medium' sensing the spirits around them, or an individual claiming to have been visited in a dream by someone deceased. Such spiritual encounters cannot be seen by others so the only real evidence is in the information and dialogue exchanged.

The important characteristic of this type of experience is that the spirits are claimed to be dynamic thinking entities who can respond to questions posed by the living. They are not simple memories or images of past events, so by implication the dead would seem able to genuinely live-on in spiritual form... assuming that it's real. Many are not persuaded.

If any of these reports are correct then they will shine a light on what an afterlife may be like. If not, then we have to explain what is happening.

In the case of dreams or visions sceptics assume that the individual either entered into some sort of wishful thinking or subconscious role play.

In the case of mediums the sceptics' explanation will be that the scenario is being faked and that the targeted person has either been thoroughly researched by the medium in advance; or that they will use tricks of narrative to glean information through the course of the conversation which they can feed back to the subject - thereby appearing to know things about the deceased which would otherwise seem impossible.

On the other hand, if there are true mediums, any communication with the souls of the dead would demonstrate that spirits do indeed hold onto their memories from life, with very clear and complete recollections compared to those who are arguably 'reborn'.

Unfortunately some testimony from these interactions does seem to suggest that these 'encounters' *are* simply wishful thinking. By way of example, people have reported that they have seen their parents restored to health and with their memories returned in full to the position **before** they fell ill and died. More generically they will often describe the deceased as appearing to be at an age approximating to their later years.

To my mind this seems suspect, because if a spirit didn't have to project their state at the exact moment of death, (which would rarely be pretty), then the deceased individuals would presumably select an image as they imagined themselves to be, probably in the prime of their lives rather than in their declining years. In my experience people generally imagine themselves as being young, and are a little surprised in later life when they look in the mirror. They would choose to be in the prime of their lives - fit, healthy and certainly without the beer gut, loss of hair, wrinkles and deformities brought on by age or illness. I know I would!

I can't help feeling that those who see images of the dead in their later years are more likely to be projecting their own desires, not observing what the deceased spirit may envisage for itself. If not, you would have to ask what perverse mechanism deliberately kept you old.

It is also suspicious or even worrying that in séances the dead often appear to communicate in cryptic ways. They do not clearly say their own names or those of others they wish to speak to, and they generally seem to give clues to things rather than give a straightforward message. Apparently, this is often portrayed as weaknesses in the channel of communication, (the equivalent of a poor telephone line), but instead of people getting missing words in a sentence, they seem to get riddles and hints!

The public is therefore faced with a choice to either believe that the dead always have a bad connection and lose their powers of reasoning, as well as their interest in a decent conversation, or to believe that the exercise may be less than it's portrayed to be.

It's interesting that in the film Ghost, the characters are not simply persuaded by information which the spirits provide, they also require a physical effect or manifestation before they will fully believe the medium. This also seems to be generally true of many real séances. The supposed ability of spirits to manipulate physical things and not just the mind is highly contentious, as I am not aware that any medium has subjected themselves to scientific scrutiny when demonstrating any such ability.

James Randi the well-known magician, spent much of his life searching for genuine examples of mediums and mystical powers, but found none. He established a Foundation that continues his work and offers a $1m prize to anyone who can demonstrate any paranormal, supernatural, or occult power or event. The applicants will be asked to perform a relatively simple preliminary test of the claim, which if successful, will be followed by the formal test conducted by people independent of the Foundation. To date, no one has passed the preliminary tests.

In contrast, we also see that there are people who are very adept at manipulating people's thinking **without** making any claims of spirituality or real psychic abilities, (eg. the British entertainer, Derren Brown). These are honest and open demonstrations of 'suggestion' or mental manipulation which reveal how people think, so it's understandable why the general public in the West are largely **un**-persuaded by the evidence for spiritual mediums, to date.

However there is another side to these possibilities as portrayed by the so-called psychic detectives who investigate murders.

These people claim to get visions of what has occurred at a crime scene, and sometimes supposedly the feelings and experiences of either the victim or the perpetrators. The testimonies here do not form part of the evidence presented in court against a criminal, but they do seem to lead investigators to new clues or more positive lines of enquiry which have led to convictions.

The visions are described like snapshots from particular moments in time. They are not dynamic interactions with a spirit, so in this case there's no possibility of any dialogue with a murder victim who experienced life after death and who retains memory and thought. If there were, you could simply ask the victim, 'Who did it'?

If the TV programmes are to be believed and the interviews with the police are genuine, then it would appear that investigations have been successfully driven in new directions by clues received from psychics. Again, it is up to each person to decide whether the psychic was genuinely receiving visions from the past or whether in reality they had inside information. There's no doubt that in some cases the convictions are very real[74].

Unfortunately, despite the televised claims from detectives involved who did gain benefit from the new information, several studies into this phenomenon have failed to show that it provides any practical advantage. Numerous tests comparing the performance of ordinary people to psychics, have **not** shown any difference in performance between the groups[75].

In short, there seems to be no definitive evidence to prove either the transfer of memories, or a life after death based on this type of testimony. While the convictions do seem real, the evidence which supports 'pro' or 'anti' opinion about psychic activity is light. In short, the jury is still out!

The final topic which I feel should be included in this section relates to the visitations, visions, and interactions that people claim to have received from personalities within their religious beliefs.

Across the globe there are many powerful claims, such as :

- people in India who commit themselves annually to painful rituals, (such as swinging for hours from hooks gouged into their backs), because of visions received, and promises they have made to their preferred deity to get them out of trouble.

- the huge shrines in Europe (at Banneux and Lourdes) which commemorate the sacred healing waters - revealed by the mother of God to children who lived at these places.

In the more prominent cases we find that the claims refer to an interaction with the spiritual characters involved, and not just a vision which might spark a feeling of awe.

In the case of the Christian beliefs there can also be physical evidence that something unique happened, such as the appearance of a spring where the child was told to dig, and which locals confirm did not exist before.

However at their core, the challenge to such claims concern prior knowledge and a vivid imagination, and of course, there is no historical reference to obscure information which can be researched and checked. These claims are based in faith.

11.1.3   Predictions & Premonitions

Those who have knowledge, don't predict.
Those who predict, don't have knowledge. "   Lao Tzu

The significance of this subject area is that if they are real, premonitions may either imply that :-

- events can be seen across time and therefore they must exist somewhere in order to allow an unknown mechanism to accurately portray the future, or
- they represent some sort of spiritual warning of what may be about to happen, in which case we have to ask what provided that warning.

Whether we are talking about Nostradamous or the Biblical story of Joseph interpreting the dreams of the Pharaoh, true predictions imply that the future can be linked to the present, (a structural 'feature' of the Universe), but they do not imply that life exists after death.

In the West today, few people will give any real credence to the ability of dreams to *predict the future*. The vast majority of dreams clearly do not predict anything and seem to be stories concocted by the Mind, whose prime usefulness may only be to reflect our fears, concerns, or hopes.

Yet the conceptual implications and difficulties start to rise where we consider those occasions where people have changed their actions as a result of premonitions which they take seriously, such as the occasional passenger who refuses to board a flight because of a premonition that it will crash, and the plane subsequently does crash on that particular flight.

From what I gather, people do not see themselves dying aboard the plane. Instead they apparently experience a great sense of dread about the flight. If they did see themselves die then the premonition *could not* reflect the actual future because the person didn't subsequently board the plane and therefore survived. At best the vision could have been of 'one possible future', which would again have implications for the way that the Universe was arranged / structured.

For those looking to provide materialist explanations for these 'aircraft disaster premonitions' (by avoiding 'future gazing'), the primary argument seems to be that a proportion of passengers will always have a sudden fear and refuse to join a flight. Although the vast majority will be wrong and will often not talk openly about their choice, some will inevitably be right when a flight does crash by coincidence. This is what people will remember – but I'm not aware that any airline has produced stats to verify this claim.

An alternative is that some sort of extrasensory perception kicks-in which allows the person to realise that something is wrong... either sensing a malfunction or 'wrong mental attitude' by someone. As far as I'm aware, nobody seems to report any direct feelings of a divine or spiritual presence **at the time** even if they may speculate later that God saved them.

11.1.4 Positive Thinking & Telekinesis

If you can't be a good example, be a terrible warning.
Anonymous

I link these two subjects because they both suggest that the Mind can directly influence the wider Universe. These continue themes from section 8.1.1 and the Global Consciousness Project, but they are much more direct in trying to demonstrate mental effects without a link to the body:-

- Advocates of Positive Thinking suggest that by adopting a mindset where you visualise the circumstances you <u>want</u> to come about, ***and also*** have the <u>expectation</u> that they will indeed arise, the Universe will mysteriously arrange itself to enable those circumstances to occur. This rearrangement may take a short or a long time to emerge depending on the complexity of the desired outcome. According to theory you should always try to believe in a positive outcome as people who are 'on a downer' will inevitably cause the universe to bring about the negative circumstances which they expect.

- People who believe in Telekinesis (or Psychokinesis) suggest that some individuals have the ability to directly move or influence physical objects which they are not physically connected to, simply through the use of their minds. The range of examples I have seen quoted (and sometimes even put on film), include watches being sent into reverse and objects moved across tables, all the way to levitation, distortions, and more dramatic actions.

The attractions of such possibilities are obvious but I consider them to be quite different to the question of life after death. They are 'of the moment' and do not point to 'survivability' in any way. Nor should they be confused with the supposed power of spirits to move objects.

The reputation of Telekinesis has suffered because there are no repeatable examples which have been proven to exist under controlled conditions. The standard of proof required by science is understandably high as the phenomenon would overturn basic scientific laws such as the 2nd Law of Thermodynamics; Inverse Square Law; and Conservation of Momentum.

A serious study of all available Psychokinetic activity was conducted on behalf of the US Military[76] between 1984 and 1987 concluding that there was no scientific evidence for it, and that the experiments which had been conducted were unscientific and open to deception. A 2006 review of 360 other studies into Psychokinesis concluded that a small effect did seem to register but that this might be explained by 'publication bias'[77].

Positive Thinking makes a deeper claim, suggesting that our Minds must be linked to some sort of force which permeates through and shapes all of existence; responding to our desires. Of course, this would tie-in very well with the Idealist philosophy where all reality is based in Mind & Thought.

I have to confess that I am less sceptical about this 'phenomenon' than I was. There is no doubt in my mind that a person with a positive outlook will do better and have a happier life than those with a negative outlook.

It's easy to believe that a negative or downbeat impression of ourselves might lead us to present ourselves in the wrong way, when a positive outlook could be much more upbeat and successful. There might also be other unknown but very down-to-Earth factors, which cause events to turn out better for those who are optimistic and enthusiastic. If you are prepared to 'have a go', people will generally 'rally round'.

These factors can all be seen as 'tactical or local', however the philosophy of positive thinking implies that there's a much more strategic mechanism at work. Although I hesitate to say this, our family experience is that positive thinking may be real because our tests turn out to be successful more than 75% of the time. You will laugh, but we follow the instructions that we heard on a radio programme – and this is what we do :

> Our test is to obtain a car parking space in our busy town, in a place that we need it, just as we arrive at our destination, (generally on a busy high street, but also in car parks, or elsewhere – say, at a busy airport drop-off area).

> The instruction is to visualise the empty space in either one or a line of parking slots, and then to *believe/expect* a space to come free. The last bit is the tricky part. You truly have to believe according to the theory.

> I have an above-average hit rate which is surprising in itself, but my wife is truly remarkable at this with success of close to 90%. She has even done this in taxis when the drivers were telling us they would have to drop us in an 'unofficial area' as the chances of getting a space were almost nil. She applies positive thinking plus the belief that goes with it and, hey presto, a space appears to the amazement of the taxi driver!

> Sadly this doesn't seem to work on the lottery – but perhaps there are different levels of belief there! We might also suppose that if everyone wanted the same thing at the same time then logistically, even for nature, it couldn't happen – there just aren't enough spaces for everyone. But in terms of tipping the balance when others aren't so focussed... who knows?

I realise that this is entirely unscientific, and the events can be explained in a number of other ways which primarily involve luck, but to a degree our family sees a phenomenon that has produced results for many years. What else can I say... it amuses us without financial risk. Please don't experiment with this on anything serious!

Returning to the more serious side of this debate, I have read management books and seen tv documentaries written by successful people who firmly believe in positive thinking. There is a **serious** level of belief here, because people wonder what else could rationalise it?

Well obviously clever people will create the best opportunities for themselves, but equally we all need a level of luck in our circumstances. Not everything is under our control, and while we might find ways to skew the odds, can we really say that percentages are all that count?

I don't think so. As mentioned before, I truly find that people who want something against the odds may often be successful, because if others sense their enthusiasm and the goal is realistic, they **will** generally rally round and help in little ways to make the dream come true. We may liken this to the way adults feel when they see the innocent wonder of young children, plus their excitement in exploring the new world around them.

Conversely, I'm sure that we have all been on 'downers' where nothing seems to be going right. What turns it around? Perhaps occasional good fortune, but for a significant number of people it begins with a shift in attitude to say that 'positives must be possible' somehow - beginning with small things that gradually build towards larger things.

Whether you are a businessman who wants deals to come about, or simply someone who uses positive thinking to create a parking space when needed, a belief in Positive Thinking can be perceived to work.

Coincidence I am sure plays its part, and it might also be sensibly argued that we'll remember successes much more than we remember the failed attempts. Yet it's a nice idea if it turns out to be true, and we have nothing to lose by trying – so long as we don't gamble seriously on the result!

11.1.5   <u>Ghosts & Spirits</u>

Stories about ghosts and spiritual contacts have existed for thousands of years, and in virtually all cultures across the globe, which gives them a degree of credibility even if we lack 'solid' evidence for them. If they were ever shown to exist then they would strongly suggest that some form of continuity does occur after a person's death, but any serious interpretation has to begin with a justification of the reality of their existence.

It is perhaps **un**surprising that ancient cultures with a lack of understanding about the workings of the universe, but which have a deep belief in the mystical, would be a lively breeding ground for such notions. Once such ideas became entrenched in society, it would also be likely that such stories would continue to arise even in the modern world, for a variety of reasons – not least being fun and entertainment.

From the ancient Greek and Roman civilizations, (and probably others before them), hauntings have been reported. Pliny wrote in ancient Greece of a ghost bound by chains which was only stopped when a shackled body was discovered, freed from the chains, and given a proper burial.

Across all cultures, ghosts seem to have the same basic translucent appearance, like 'breath on a cold day, which has been shaped'. That consistency across reports from around the world is an interesting factor.

Ghosts are generally described as the spirits of beings who have died, (primarily human), with an image reflecting what they once were, including the style of clothes that they wore in life. Sightings generally confirm that a ghost will not change its basic appearance, (always wearing the same clothes), which either suggests that the image comes from the ghost and not the observer, or everyone is playing to the same storyline!

Why a specific person/ghost would select a particular set of clothes to be seen-in, out of a presumably larger wardrobe across their lifetime, is unclear, but it may reflect the strongest residual self-image by each person.

Yet there have been stories of Ghost Ships and Trains as well as other objects appearing as apparitions which would seem to break the mould of ghosts being related to living humans. Clothes are inanimate objects, as are books, swords, lamps etc – all ghostly things which a 'dead person's spirit' may be carrying. So perhaps Ghost Ships and Trains are simply a larger extension of the ghostly personas which are seen walking in them?

Of course, this is pure speculation about such effects, which have little if any solid evidence to support them. Yet if they exist and match people's perceptions of them, what can ghosts tell us about the nature of our spirit?

Some ghosts are said to appear like a replayed video of what may have happened in the past, (eg. a figure who is always seen simply walking down the same corridor; or in another example, from England, it was claimed that an entire Roman legion marched through a building on their knees, (it later turned out that a Roman Road lay 18 inches below the solid floor of the building)). Such figures do not seem to communicate, interact, or display any of the attributes (other than image) of the deceased people they are supposed to represent. They simply appear and move about a bit.

While it would be fascinating to demonstrate scientifically that such images of former lives could be drawn from the past and displayed through some sort of 'ectoplasm', or possibly through a distortion in the fabric of space/time, this would **not** represent any sort of continuity for the individual. It would indeed be like a video tape.

In stark contrast, other ghosts/spirits are said to be dynamic forces that can influence objects and people, suggesting that they are something more than an image of a person after death. They retain some of the persona, intent, and dynamic thinking of the person concerned.

Western cinema and literature include many active spirits which have fired people's imaginations, from poltergeists, to wraiths, bogies and possibly banshees. Such interactions require any spirit to have an awareness of things around them, plus a knowledge of facts, language and history, and the existence of dynamic Thought or pre-programming in order to generate interactions.

In these circumstances there would be a much stronger argument for the essence of an individual to continue after death, although it becomes unclear whether the spirit continues to reflect the original nature of the person who once lived, or has been distorted by the process of becoming a ghost.

There is simply no firm information on which to judge, and without any credible evidence, science is unlikely to want to invest serious resources in such investigations.

11.1.6   Intuition and Fringe Experiments about Consciousness

Talk of pre-cognition and extrasensory perception are often sensationalised in the press, because they make good headlines. I tend to find that a majority of commentators will also dismiss such claims as wild nonsense because it doesn't fit in with the natural order of scientific materialism. You can even sense their frustration when yet another story raises its head, and the subject refuses to go away.

Those commentators may be right about such claims, but to dismiss them out of hand may be premature, especially when many of us will have experienced mild forms of this. We often have a 'sense of intuition' about something, and indeed many sportsmen have talked about the feelings they had when they were about to be tackled from behind, or their opponent was about to make a certain move, leading them to take evasive or offensive action.

The standard ways of explaining such things boil down to detecting: subtle changes in sounds; ground vibrations; seeing slight mannerisms ('tells') in the other person which indicate their thinking; or information which doesn't quite seem to stack-up. All perfectly valid explanations if they do apply in the right circumstances.

Yet what if they don't?

As a light-hearted way to round off this chapter, I wanted to see if any credible evidence for intuition or other such effects, had emerged.

The scientific study of consciousness has begun to produce some unexpected findings which do not seem to fit into traditional concepts of how the Mind works.

The first examples which I want to bring to your attention relate to experiments into peoples' feelings that they are being watched. Various experiments have been conducted over the past 100 years or so into this possible phenomenon, (known as Psychic Staring Effect or Scopaesthesia), and collectively they seem to find that there is nothing to the claims, **however** it is also true that different techniques have been deployed in the later methods which have shown positive results.

One experiment conducted in 1983 by L.Williams[103] used closed circuit TV cameras to monitor people in a room to see when they could sense being watched. It reported a 74% success rate, but there were criticisms of some of the analysis. An attempt to re-create the findings, combining the CCTV with sensors to monitor people's skin conductance, only produced a weak result and "failed to demonstrate a clear-cut effect".

However that test also required the **starers** to be immersed in intense computer games when not glancing at the subjects, (to apparently suppress any effect of prolonged thoughts about the subjects). If the main intention was to try and demonstrate a positive effect I don't know why the distractions had to be present, and I haven't seen results of the same experiments without the distractions.

One of the more prominent advocates of psychic staring effect is the parapsychologist and author Rupert Sheldrake[104] who has presented his theory of 'Morphic Resonance' as the cause of various psychic effects.

This has been dismissed as pseudo-science by people such as John Maddox who suggested that Sheldrake's book should be burned[105].

It was more seriously challenged by Professor Steven Rose[106] who presented competing evidence.

Sheldrake has received prominence through his writing and also various appearances on the BBC. In his 2003 book "The Sense of Being Stared At", he claimed that across thousands of tests where a blindfold person was asked to sense when they thought they were being stared at, there has been a 60% hit rate.[107] Elsewhere tables of his stats between 1998 and 2002 were at 54.7%[108] While other reports from 2005 were at 53.1%[109] although they reported that some individuals did show remarkable accuracy - "nearly always right, scoring way above chance levels".

Another experiment, (conducted with the BBC), did show that people attending a quiz show in an auditorium glanced sideways more frequently when they were being scrutinised by testers at the back of the hall.

Daryl Bem[110] has been another researcher in this field. In one set of experiments people were asked to predict whether a computer would randomly show a picture behind one of two curtains. The predicted success rate over many tests was anticipated to be 50% which was largely born out in reality (49.8% success in fact), yet when the images shown were erotic, people in different tests were correct 53.1% of the time.

On such small marginal percentages interpretation is questionable, and I can't help feeling that the issue would be taken more seriously, if there had been more significant and repeatable positive effects.

However there is a degree of consistency in the results, and, perhaps more significantly, there are indications that some people may be attuned in this way while others aren't. I'd be interested to know if the people who had demonstrated such strong abilities had continued to do so in later independent tests.

Equally, if a 5% higher performance continued to be demonstrated when using erotic images, it's interesting to speculate why that should be. Is it because we become more focussed when the subject matter is more appealing, or does eroticism tap into a broader set of abilities?

> A more boring but intriguing possibility is that humans have a natural ability to sense *patterns of activity* and because no computer programme or device is ever truly random we could simply be witnessing our recognition of the inherent patterns that were inadvertently coded into the computer programmes, etc.

Of course, the anecdotal evidence is always present, with surveys indicating that more women feel they can sense staring than men, (81% vs 74%), but without controlled conditions this could all be wishful thinking.

A considerable number of other tests have also been conducted into extrasensory effects, but to my knowledge, none have produced significant results. As an example, in one set of experiments two individuals were sat alone in different closed rooms with a full solid wall between them. They wore head apparatus that would insulate them from any magnetic influences, while it also monitored their brain activities.

> In one room the person experienced a light to one side of them, flashing periodically.

> In the other room there was no flashing light, yet the person's brain activity did rise slightly when the light came on for the *other* person! Many subjects also described sensing a flash of light on the same side as happened in reality to the other person – however in some significant respects the evidence given was still anecdotal, and I'm not aware that the experiments continued.

If such effects could be more robustly demonstrated then it could begin to tie back to suggestions of collective consciousness and even the Global Consciousness Project that I covered in Chapter 8.1.1.

Yet even if global consciousness were real this could not explain how it all began, which is likely to take us back to an initial consciousness that was not human... God?

12   Views about the Mind

If you were a sophisticated robot which had modern scientific knowledge about Matter/Energy, and you were conducting experiments on human beings to see how they work, you might determine that their brains were a form of biological computer but you would have no evidence of the 'Mind' that these deluded creatures referred-to.

All you'd see would be electrical signals flying around their bodies with an impressive degree of co-ordination due to their complex wiring, and the fabulous processor that was sadly underused by the creatures themselves.

With no other physical evidence you might conclude that we function, but that is all. If you believe that there is nothing more that could be detected about how we work this is a logical position, and one that has been taken up by various materialist philosophers such as Daniel Dennett[79] who said that "Conscious minds are more-or-less serial virtual machines implemented inefficiently - on the parallel hardware that evolution has provided for us".

He also suggested that there is no 'self' – a theme taken up by Susan Blackmore[78] when she argued that 'the self' "... does not exist in the way that a physical object (or even a brain process) exists. Like a centre of gravity in physics, it is a useful abstraction."

Richard Rorty[80] provided an overall summary of these views when he said: "Every speech, thought, theory, poem, composition and philosophy will turn out to be completely predictable in purely naturalistic terms."

One of the main purposes of this chapter is to test these claims.

Yet those who are more accepting of Minds will often claim that they are something beyond mere computer functions. But what? A computer can process data, so what's the difference? What is it that makes us believe in this unproven 'fantasy' of our Minds, and where is the evidence for it?

Unlike most scientific analyses, we have the benefit of monitoring the Mind 'from the inside'; not as outside observers; so we know that it is real even if we don't know what it represents. We don't have to prove its effects because we all experience them every waking moment of our lives, so we are potentially drowning in evidence for the Mind.

Indeed, it is the experiences themselves which may distinguish a living being from a robot because, while mechanical computers might recognise something, (using sensors & some pre-programming), they won't *feel* what those things mean to us.

'Qualia' are factors that go beyond fact into the unquantifiable: such as the quality of life - including our likes and dislikes. For instance, robots might distinguish red light from blue by the wavelength, but they will have no idea why we say that we prefer one to the other.

To repeat some earlier examples, we might alternatively refer to the smell of cooking bacon rather than sensing the presence of an airborne chemical; or an appreciation of good music instead of merely recognising sounds.

We also saw in Ch.4.3 that emotion and feeling are **necessary** factors when it comes to making basic decisions in daily life. Hard logic isn't sufficient on its own, especially where there is uncertainty, or no clear objective. Yet beyond this there is the belief that our ideas

- can be creative and able to start things, (spontaneity & randomness)
- do **not** seem inevitable.
- are intangible, rather than physical.

All of these observations challenge the notion that our thoughts are based in Matter/Energy, and suggest that the Mind may be separate from the physical material of our bodies. Yet these claims do not represent proof.

We have seen that it is very difficult to prove whether or not spontaneity and/or randomness truly exist. It is also a logical possibility that an intangible Mind might still be *partly dependent* on the physical body rather than being fully independent of it. Full separation may only be necessary if the Mind is considered to roam away from the body, in order to explain Out of Body Experiences (OBE) and ideas about the Soul, (should the evidence become more robust). We therefore see a range of possibilities.

These options mirror the range of philosophies we encountered in section 2.2 and it's worth reminding ourselves about the different ideas concerning the nature of Thought and the brain:-

- 'Materialists' say that **all** thoughts are entirely based in, and generated by, the physical Matter/Energy of our brain and therefore they are governed by the known Laws of Physics, which in turn are based in 'cause and effect'. For this reason thoughts cannot simply arise from nowhere, they must always have a prior cause, (even if they happened to be a particular combination of many sub-conscious factors); and they can only have one inevitable conclusion/outcome.

- The 'opposite' Idealist perspective is that there is only one type of stuff in existence, but it is the stuff of Thought. It argues that physical matter/energy is not real, just a type of idea/concept that adheres to strict rules, while Thought in general may be free flowing, spontaneous, & random. Idealists believe that the stuff of Thought can still process and rationalise information to generate new ideas.

- Finally, the 'Dualist' perspective is that the brain is a physical *conduit* through which the underlying stuff of Thought, (a separate Mind), can influence both the physical Matter/Energy of our bodies and other physical beings. It would be the underlying stuff of Thought which actually **generates** our ideas, **not** the physical brain, (although there are permutations on a theme which suggest that memory storage and the generation of Thought might be shared between physical and non-physical 'types of stuff').

The difficulty is that there is no scientific explanation of how brain tissue generates an idea, or achieves understanding & consciousness; so we don't know the true source of Thought. There **are** generalised concepts that brains might work like computer chips, but these don't sit comfortably with some of the biological facts, (as we will see in the coming sections), and they beg a lot of questions about the source of any programming.

In terms of physical mechanics there's speculation that thoughts & ideas may exist within the brain as electrical signals, vibrations, wavelengths, or some other property of Matter/Energy; but could such **effects** directly represent an idea, or does an effect have to be *interpreted*?

For instance, it is easy to equate vibrations with sound, and wavelengths with colour, but how could either of these things represent the idea that (say) Hitler wanted to invade Poland; or a set of programmed instructions?

If a physical effect has to be interpreted, the effect **wouldn't** be the idea; that would have to be something else. As a further example, someone might say the word 'five' but it is only through schooling and interpretation that we translate the sound into the concept of '5'.

A more significant philosophical point can be made if we extend the same argument to **non-physical** effects. For instance, if the gaps between electrical pulses formed a pattern or code, they would in one sense be non-physical but might also convey meaning to a Mind. It might be argued that the gaps are actually defined by the physical material that marks their boundaries, but it might equally be suggested that the gaps are something fundamentally different in their own right.

From this I hope will you see that in debates about the nature of Thought and the Mind we need to distinguish decisions and ideas from the physical ways in which they can be captured, preserved and communicated. The two aspects might amount to the same thing in some rare circumstances, but there are many situations where that wouldn't necessarily be true.

Again, let's not forget that there's a separate need to explain where and how thoughts are generated, not just stored.

In principle if the Mind is purely physical then ideas must arise in mechanical ways **without any real understanding**, because atoms, chemicals, and vibrations do not think; they just react.

Daniel Dennett again caused controversy when he wrote[79]:

> "The trouble with brains is that when you look in them,
> you find that there's nobody home."

The dilemma for Materialist thinking is that everything we experience about our Minds tells us that at some level they **do** think, understand, and reach consciousness. How can physical materials that are not capable of understanding anything, generate awareness and even consciousness?

Even within individual **cells**, chapter 5.3 showed us that a number of dynamic controls can seemingly adapt to 'fluid' situations; go hunting for clues; make guesses; and can generally be **proactive**, (instead of just being **reactive**, as the principle of Causality would seem to demand).

If we therefore see a degree of 'awareness' at the micro level of cells as well as the macro level of brains, it is tempting to think that a common mechanism might be responsible for both.

If so, it would need to be scalable in the same way that tiny computer chips might control small scale activities, while huge computers might even generate consciousness... except of course that they don't. Even if interactions with a massive computer can seem just like a human being in a 'blind test', the device would **not** have achieved true consciousness.

It would still be operating by the fixed rules of its programming, which it had been given by humans. It would not be forming its own opinions, in its own way, against its own objectives. While computer chips may not demonstrate true consciousness, they do show that **control** and **logic** could be scalable, and we will explore this theme in the coming sections.

That said, *could* computers as we know them, achieve consciousness by themselves? It is the stuff of science fiction, but in reality we haven't found a way to create such a machine. What we currently understand as Artificial Intelligence, or the crude mechanisms that we have devised for computers to 'learn by experience', still do not equate with true awareness, although they offer **the hope of a concept**. The bottom line is that current computer chip technology has its limitations and may not be able to take us that far, contrary to many people's original expectations.

However research may lead us to newer technologies which might be more likely to remove the barriers. As a case in point, you may recall from Ch. 3.2.1, that the Blue Brain Project is waiting to see if its computer model of a brain could generate consciousness. Alternately, physics might lead us to new ways of holding and processing data, (eg. based on 'fields of influence' – such as magnets). We will look at some of these ideas shortly.

In the meantime, what else can day-to-day evidence tell us about the nature of Thought and the Mind? Well firstly, they seem to be intangible. We cannot point to a feeling and say, 'here it is'. We also **guess** when other people are having feelings by recognising the circumstances which are likely to generate them and occasionally observing a person's mannerisms; but we do **not** experience *their* feelings, only our own.

This inability to measure feeling casts a degree of interpretation over what is acceptable scientific evidence for the Mind, and what it all represents - but it does reinforce suggestions that Thought is truly/fully intangible. It seems likely that the unique physical effects being generated by the brain **do** have to be interpreted by the individual's Mind. Yet in itself this *doesn't* have to mean that Thought is based in a different type of stuff to Matter/Energy. There **are** aspects of physical reality which lack substance.

For instance, it can be argued that an *intangible* Mind might be based in electrical signals or magnetic fields, because they are not fully tangible in the normal sense that we use the word. Electricity and 'fields of influence' can be detected but they aren't something that we can pick up and hold.

Having said this, it is still unclear how such mechanics would actually work as a Mind. **Neither fields nor electricity actually think**, and they should always adhere to strict causality, which Thought doesn't necessarily do.

In order to judge whether or not the Mind is entirely based in Matter/Energy we need to look at a broader set of evidence, to better frame our analysis.

Traditionally, scientists and clinicians have learned a lot about how the brain seems to work when medical conditions have caused it to malfunction, and we can adopt a similar approach to test some of the philosophical options. We can also see how well each theory might be supported by observations of the working brain using scanners.

As we explore these aspects further, I hope you will see how the issues which emerge draw us ever closer to the debate about what the **essence of Life** itself might be, (not just the Mind), as there are a lot of parallels.

12.1.1   Framing our Ideas about the Mind and the Essence of Life

We probably all realise that at death, something goes from a body. You may know this by common anecdote, but anyone who has actually seen death will tell you that this is very real. You can almost feel it.

All of the physical tissue remains but the thing that was the person is no longer there. It's not just that they've stopped moving. There's a void.

Death isn't just a question of fixing a broken machine. We can't simply swap-out a defective part that was the cause of death, plug in another power source, and then reactivate the corpse.

Within the first few minutes after a body has stopped working it might be resuscitated, and even kept functioning on Life Support to buy time for the body to repair itself, (possibly the brain too in a coma situation); but if the Mind, or possibly even a 'Life Force', are gone, there's no getting them back. If it was just down to physical structures and 'hard wiring', that shouldn't be the case.

Returning to the common analogy which equates living beings with a physical computer, we can easily understand that if programs and data are wiped from the hard drive, without an information backup, there's no way to restore the device to what it once was. The structures and electronics will continue to function at a very basic level, (as long as the power is plugged in), but they won't achieve very much on their own.

The parallels with a body are obvious, and they can help us to see why its implied programming, (eg. the Mind), may be necessary to maintain life.

However, there are important differences with the computer scenario.

Firstly, while subconscious brain activity can be likened to a computer operating system (program) because it co-ordinates the activities of physical components, (in this case muscles & major organs); its direct controlling influence **doesn't** extend to the activities *within* cells.

Indeed, individual cells can remain alive in isolation, so the Materialist scenario is that internal cellular activity should be entirely chemical, but in reality we've seen that the 'dynamic functions' of cells, (per section 5.3), seem to go well beyond basic levels of mechanical/chemical reaction.

While we don't perceive that the **Mind** influences each individual cell either, Idealist belief suggests that the 'underlying stuff of Thought' may be a common factor that drives both cellular control & the Mind.

Secondly, the essence of Life may be more than just programming & control. It may include the *drive* or pro-activeness which makes Life self-sustaining. Let me illustrate what I mean.

When bodies are on Life Support, the machinery isn't just acting as a power source by providing air and nutrient, it is also partially acting as a driving force. In those cases where the main organs are healthy but (say) there has been some brain damage and the body would quickly die if the machine was switched-off, the individual cells in the body remain alive and the metabolism still functions, but these parts lack the co-ordination and drive to sustain themselves as a collective living body on their own.

You can hopefully see why ideas about a Life Force and the Mind persist, (above the purely physical aspects of our bodies), especially if we equate them to that elusive self-sustaining element.

When we consider the nature of Life, and try to determine the boundary or tipping points where physical mechanisms might become alive/conscious, the latter scenario begins to reveal some of the core aspects of Life that we need to address; not only in terms of capability, and drive, but in the different **levels** of life that we observe, (cells vs bodies).

Put another way, we may find clues about the essential nature of Life and the Mind by exploring them through the prism of scalability.

Despite the fact that we are all made from a vast number of living cells, in *physical* terms Life **doesn't** seem to reflect a single mechanism that is truly scalable because it requires very different types of cell for different organs/components in our bodies, as well as the different forms of Life.

However, *could* it be argued that the **brain** is truly scalable? The computer analogy suggests that the bigger the computer chip the greater the capability, yet it isn't clear to scientists that a bigger brain, (whether measured by weight or volume), necessarily generates greater intelligence. The largest brains are found in some of the largest creatures, (such as sperm whales, killer whales, and elephants), but that may simply reflect the need to control a much larger body, rather than providing intelligence.

Even within the human population very similar sized brains can produce very different levels of intelligence. So the number of neurons **doesn't** seem to provide a scalable factor of capability; reinforcing the suggestion that **physical** life cannot be scaled-up using a single common mechanism.

Intelligence may therefore either relate to the better ways in which we each use our neurons, or may possibly reflect the presence or absence of other factors, (eg. other types of stuff), required to exploit the neurons – ie. the dualist and idealist positions.

An extension of the latter point suggests that the universal *nature* of logic & awareness, also indicates that *intangible* factors may be the only things that are truly scalable - and able to produce ever-more sophisticated controls/Minds. In support of this we might draw parallels with a termite colony which is formed of creatures that are largely the same, but which seem to generate a *collective intelligence* (per Ch. 8) - a form of life that has been 'scaled-up'.

Clearly these are generalisations which include big assumptions about what any intangible factor could achieve; but if such observations hold true, scalability could be another useful pointer to the essential nature of Life. So what does other evidence reveal?

Let's begin with the dominant belief in most societies that we each have a single Mind, (and possibly a single Soul), which will attach to one entire body – ie. there will **not** be a separate Mind for each individual living cell. As far as I can tell, this reflects most people's experience of the Mind.

Even though our brains have many billions of cells our conscious Minds tend to work through many potential options in a scenario one after the other, (sequentially). We may do so quite quickly, but we do not consider **all** options at the exactly same moment, (in parallel), by a myriad of different Minds in our heads. Despite the fact that neurons are individual brain cells they appear to somehow *co-ordinate* their actions to form a single cohesive whole. But what allows that to happen?

In basic terms, something either has to control the individual neurons, or they must control themselves.

In terms of the scientific monitoring of brain activity we have **not** identified a control or programming centre within the brain, (or elsewhere), which appears to tell each brain cell what to do at each stage of a process; then constantly gets feedback from them after each calculation, in order to determine a next step.

Yet if we consider the alternative: that the neurons control themselves - the implication would be that each of these miniscule cells is achieving a level of 'understanding' - which is **not** what materialism generally accepts.

It believes that atoms and molecules are incapable of any thought, and everything they do must be down to inevitable physical mechanics that somehow emerged from 'evolution'.

This is one of the core dilemmas for Materialist thinking. Despite brains being the accepted centre of our thoughts, the individual components within the brain are not allowed to think – just react. More importantly, the physical neuron is a full cell; and if these things are the base level of brain processing they cannot explain any logic or awareness at a smaller level *within* a cell. That would have to come from something else.

So we now have to look inside neurons to determine whether their internal hard wiring and chemistry can not only explain their internal control mechanisms, but also the broader thought processes of the Mind.

All computer chips work by flicking a myriad of switches that turn different circuits on or off, with different combinations resulting in different outcomes as determined by the programming.

If we consider the scaling-down of the computer chip analogy, is there a limit to the miniaturisation of the circuitry that could occur? Could even molecular level 'nano-technology' perform the observed cellular activities at that scale? It's **not** clear that it could – which again hints that the core functions of control and thought maybe based in a 'different mechanism'.

As another indication that neurons do more than just flick a single switch, we should recognise that the networks in the brain do change over time. Each of the 100 billion neurons (10^{11}) in our brains forms long-term 'wiring' links to approx. 1000 others[12] and these connections seemingly adapt in response to greater 'traffic' flow between areas of the brain.

The general theory has been that new connections to other neurons may be sought where new forms of idea arise, or where the level of traffic being generated between specific neurons encourages the forging of new short cuts, or the strengthening of old links. Conversely, underused connections may break down and not be renewed. There is even some evidence to suggest that drinking coffee or other stimulants causes more connections to **break**, stimulating the formation of new connections and new ideas.

It is probably for this reason that David Eagleman says that human "culture does leave its signature in the circuitry of the individual brain."[85] but it also shows that brain cells have advanced levels of sophistication.

An interesting question is whether a neuron puts out new 'wires' in the **hope** of finding new useful connections, or whether other neurons are specifically **targeted** for a new link. If the latter, it would strongly suggest that an analysis of traffic flow is being conducted by the brain cells themselves – with profound implications for all philosophies.

At present we don't yet know how purposeful this search is, but we might draw some clues from the way in which neurons seem to communicate.

If the electricity generated by neurons flowed through an unbroken net of intricate 'wires' that formed one seamless and extensive circuit inside your head, you might expect that electrons would carry on travelling around the brain until the energy was exhausted; but again, that doesn't seem to be the case. In broad terms ideas seem to end quite abruptly once the brain has 'come to a decision'. We therefore have to ask what stops the signals?

To a degree, this will be because the neurons **don't** have a full electrical link between each other. Each neuron cell puts out a series of 'dendrite' strands to *receive* signals from other cells nearby, and puts out other 'axon' strands to *send* signals out. Axons from one cell may therefore align with dendrites from other cells, however while the different sets of strands come very close to each other **they don't touch**, and actually communicate by sending chemical signals across the gap, known as 'neurotransmitters'[12].

This physical separation of the wires means that electrical signals don't immediately flow through a neuron and straight out again. So there is a possibility that each neuron may choose to **not** pass on the signal. But this would suggest that a neuron may be doing more than just processing the signal information it receives. It may be thinking and making a decision.

When a neuron fires it is also unclear whether every one of its live axon connections passes the signal on, or whether it is just some of them – the latter implying that specific neurons are being targeted to receive them.

One way or another, however, a degree of targeting does seem to be occurring, because in processing an idea we only see some specific **areas** of the brain conducting onward processing of an idea. So whether neuron cells are making a judgement to pass information onwards, or hard wiring automatically routes communications to those specific destinations; a level of control and even decision-making **does** seem to be in operation.

Having considered all of these points related to scalability let's now return to the way in which different theories might explain the difference between a dead body, and its cells which may continue to live. The notions of 'Life Force', the 'Mind', and 'Matter/Energy acting alone' all place emphasis on different things.

Those who believe in a Life Force essentially argue that new levels of Life require new levels of energy; while those who believe in the power of the Mind effectively seek an explanation based in different levels of programming, ie. inside and outside a cell. In contrast, Materialists might argue that it relates to the different levels at which entire systems are enclosed: one level of system is contained within a cell, while the other is contained in a much larger 'body'. Each level of containment would be subject to different levels of physical breakdown.

Let's look at each of these in turn.

In Chapters 5-7 we looked at the functions of living cells and saw how they appear to gather/store their own energy from nutrients, and operate largely on the basis of chemical activity. We also know that bodies seem to gain all of their energy from the foods that they eat. In other words, to this extent, there is **no** evidence, or requirement, for a separate source of energy that would equate with a 'Life Force'.

While there is nothing to say that a distinct Life Force has to be noticeably powerful, or in a form that we could necessarily detect with current technology, the lack of evidence for additional power sources beyond a chemical metabolism, probably leaves us needing more justifications to believe that the notion of a distinct Life Force is a strong possibility.

Yet there **is** a need for a mechanism of control and direction between physical components, even within a cell. This puts emphasis on the Mind.

Could it be that the Mind **is** the Life Force, (especially as many of us will be familiar with the idea of classifying death as 'brain death')? Possibly.

More accurately we could say that the 'underlying stuff of Thought' might be the source of both cellular control (programming) and the Mind, if it operates at different levels of sophistication within the different levels of Life. If true, it might indeed be the elusive driving force for Life.

In contrast, the Materialist interpretation looks for physical breakdowns between the different technical elements of our bodies. From one perspective Materialists can say that the different levels of Life reflect different levels of physical programming, (ie. cause & effect chemical reactions that were assembled/coded through evolution).

A different tack is to argue that cells are purely mechanical, while bodies require a functioning brain. In support of this some people have pointed out that individual cells can be stored in 'suspended animation' within a lab, and restarted when needed – the implication being that they are purely mechanical. Yet, the reality is less straightforward.

Only a proportion of stored cells in the lab will actually be successfully restarted. The key question is *why* do some cells in suspended animation fail to live again? Is it due to physical deterioration; or because their programming has been wiped; or has the Life Force gone? As things stand we cannot say.

There is also the question of how software could evolve in an evolutionary manner. At one level of life we can see that conscious thought can grow by experience, but that can only happen because of the huge amount of subconscious programming that runs our bodies – which we are born with in our brains. This pre-programming needs an explanation.

We also need an explanation for the dynamic arrangements within a cell listed in section 5.3. There is no known controlling mechanism yet they still seem to display a lot of high end logic.

While every cell **is** known to handle information in the form of a central 'DNA manual' which has non-coding genes to guide operation, it is hard to imagine that electronic software could follow the same evolutionary path, as software development generally requires understanding of purpose & probably design. We considered the difficulties for evolution in capturing intangible process steps, in Ch.7, but we can also say software is unlikely to be developed before the appropriate components are already proven.

DNA represents the long-term storage of static information, not the dynamic circumstances/responses that we have identified, or indeed the differences between the logical and emotional networks of our brains.

How could physical attributes provide that responsiveness? The programming for any computer chip analogy may perhaps be easier to rationalise within logical networks because equations, hard logic, and even chemistry are all firmly based in precise 'cause & effect' principles.

Yet there are many things in life which are imprecise & distinctly uncertain, and these will be challenging to any mechanism that requires precision – as we saw in section 4.3. We can also say that emotions and feelings can seem infinitely varied and not really precise like 'switch-flicking'.

You might argue that this depends on the number of switches, and that a huge number of switches might give us a very fine grading of emotion, but if there is a requirement to consider many imprecise/fuzzy possibilities our Minds are much more effective at this than modern computers, so we can see why something other than 'hard wiring' and therefore 'hard evolution' may be involved.

We will consider some 'radical' ideas for these other mechanisms later, but while physical science has been seeking a physical solution for the brain and Mind, we should remember that alternate philosophies suggest that the brain may simply be a **conduit** for thoughts and memories that have been generated in another type of stuff.

Is it realistic to suppose that a different type of underlying stuff might be involved, (which provides capabilities that go beyond Matter/Energy)?

Once again we return to notions such as 'Dark Energy' and Gravity – which are accepted by most scientists as a potential/likely reality everywhere in the Universe; but which we cannot detect. They represent a clear example of hidden influences, and possibly another type of stuff.

However if the Mind was wholly or partly separate from the physical material of our brain we might expect to find some clues to this in the medical conditions associated with mental health.

In some forms of mental disorder we might argue that some parts of the brain which had originally been constructed normally, have now become badly 're-wired' leading to confusion. This could potentially happen due to damage, or if new connections in brain tissue had not been done properly. Bad 'physical wiring' could also fit the dualist and idealist models if (say):

the brain sent confused messages back to a non-physical Mind; or confused wiring represented a breakdown in the strict rules of Thought.

However the notion of a non-physical Mind **doesn't** seem to readily fit with Dementia. Even deeply held long-term memories can be truly lost - to the point where parents can no longer recognise their children.

Awareness can also be affected, so that only *some* facts are taken into account for decision-making, but not others. For instance someone may still be able to read a clock, but it may not occur to them to check whether 12:00 is midnight or noon. They will just make an assumption - often wrong. In more extreme cases logic and reasoning can break down altogether.

If the brain was a mere conduit to translate the thoughts of a non-physical Mind into physical actions, we might expect that any physical condition should still leave the background Mind able to understand the need to check for night and day, and presumably to recognise children.

We diagnose dementia from the symptoms and can sometimes associate the condition with physical problems in the brain, but it is not proven that all dementia cases are related to physical damage. What we can say is that there are no cures for dementia and that it generally seems to worsen.

How can theories about the non-physical Mind explain dementia? Much seems to depend on what you believe a non-physical Mind might be capable of. Would they hold information? Could they compute/think?

What we *can* say is that as the condition develops many patients show signs that their symptoms can fluctuate; with moments when they seem relatively normal and others when they are less lucid/rational. To this extent there might still be a case to argue that confused physical wiring might be scrambling messages back to the non-physical Mind which then struggles to know how to respond. But this notion doesn't quite work in the example above, where there is a recognition of a time but no logic to cross-check.

One tentative suggestion is that the Mind might be working fine, but the brain might be unable to receive messages back from the Mind. However if the non-physical Mind was working but the brain wasn't, you might expect a level of frustration to show, along the lines of – 'I want my body to check this fact but it isn't doing it'. Yet as I understand things, in dementia, the Mind simply doesn't appear to recognise the need to check.

This 'symptomatic' evidence may therefore be pointing us towards two other possibilities: either

- The physical brain does a lot of logical processing, **alongside** a non-physical Mind which does more creative / spontaneous activities, (which aligns most closely with the Dualist position), or

- the non-physical Mind may itself have a problem; possibly *because* a long period of exposure to false/disrupted signals from the brain might alter its thinking processes.

If the physical brain did do some processing, the non-physical Mind would be more dependent on what the physical brain concluded. For instance the brain may say that it had checked something, when it hadn't, (eg. whether it was night or day). Alternatively, there may be a division of duties in the information which is held by the physical brain rather than the Mind. For instance it may be that physical tissues hold images (of children) while the Mind holds concepts. In that way it may be that the brain says it has failed to recognise someone, and the Mind reacts accordingly.

However, without more evidence it is easy to dismiss such speculation as wishful thinking, or even clutching at straws. Dementia does seem to pose a problem for Dualist and Idealist thinking. Yet in contrast, there are other medical issues in the arena of language (section 12.2.2 below) which go the opposite way.

It seems that all perspectives on the nature of the Mind have their problems. While Materialism still has an ***advantage*** by being able to demonstrate that physical abilities **do** fit within the 'physical model', it still cannot explain how the brain works to match our proven experiences within its principles.

12.2 <u>Evidence to Refine our Thinking about the Mind</u>

Regardless of your philosophical preference, (Materialist, Dualist, or Idealist, per Chapter 2), our sense of survival is dependent on keeping our bodies alive, not just our Minds. Put another way, even in an Idealist interpretation of Life, we still seem to die if the body ceases to function.

To this end, it's understandable that doctors and other scientists should look into the mechanics of our bodies to understand how they work.

In doing so, many expected the research to show that we are entirely based in physical mechanics and chemistry. Yet many aspects of living beings have retained their secrets, as we have seen.

Perhaps this is why surveys have shown that approx. 76% of doctors and medical scientists[81] have religious or spiritual beliefs, in marked contrast[82] to other scientific disciplines such as mathematics (45%) & physics (22%).

The difficulty for science is that the workings of the human brain cannot be easily observed as the person has to be alive for it to function. There are limits to how much we can physically open it up and scrutinise its component parts while the patient is conscious. Neurosurgeons essentially tinker at the edges or very carefully move between working parts to access tumours, but on the whole they don't interfere with the wiring or components of the brain.

In order to try to understand how the brain works science has had to work obliquely. The traditional technique was to use observations about how a person's behaviour changed after a known brain trauma, to roughly equate some areas of the brain with certain abilities, however in recent years this has been enhanced by modern scanning devices that can reveal which parts of the brain seem to be active when people are doing certain things, or thinking about certain subjects.

Neurons are the cells in the brain that generate the electrical signals which appear to represent our thoughts, and which control our bodies. However modern Functional Magnetic Resonance Imaging (fMRI) scanners do **not** detect those electrical fields which the signals generate. They detect increases in **blood flow** to areas of the brain which are in use. (The alternate 'CT scanners' build up a picture of the brain through a series of X-Rays in different layers through the head).

So none of these techniques are precise enough to explain what is really happening in detail. Even the best scanners cannot see individual neurons firing, and the speed of brain activity is so fast that we can only interpret which areas are active from a series of snapshots, even if those are gathered thousands of times per second.

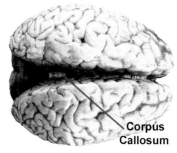

As most people will know even from basic images of a human brain, it is divided into two 'hemispheres'. These are linked at the bottom of the central cavity by a mass of interconnecting nerves, called the **corpus callosum**, through which all communications between the two halves must pass[83]. Each hemisphere is also divided into four lobes that have a number of more detailed operational areas within them:-

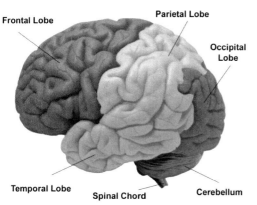

- **frontal lobe**, (front of skull), provides control, problem solving, planning, organizing, short-term memory, and movement.
- **temporal lobe**, (lower middle), plays a role in memory storage but also processes information about smell, taste, and sound.
- **occipital lobe**, (rear of skull), constructs mental images from our eyes and links that information to images stored in memory.
- **parietal lobe**, (top middle), seems to deal with temperature, taste, and touch.

The reason for pointing all of this out is because of the strange findings that emerged from early scans, which began to test some of the Materialist explanations of the brain. So with this introduction we finally get to the factors which might help us to judge whether the Mind is both real and separate from the physical brain.

Activation of Distinct Areas in the Brain

It soon became apparent to early researchers that a large proportion of brain activity relates to unconscious tasks[85] which are thought to monitor and maintain bodily functions, (running continually). These effectively provide a lot of 'background noise' on brain scans, so it is important for researchers to identify the *additional* brain activity that relates to **conscious** thought.

In order to see which areas of the brain were active during different sorts of conscious activity scientists calmed people down and asked them to clear their minds so that brain activity was reduced to a background minimum. The subjects were then given an idea, and the scanners detected which areas of the brain were stimulated above the background activity.

New conscious thoughts would appear to immediately spark a number of brain activities, at the same time, but in quite separate parts of the brain. They initially didn't seem to be connected or talking to each other – which appeared to go against the principle of physical causality. But of course, the scanners are detecting significant blood flow not electrical signals.

One thing is clear, an idea doesn't create a broad sweeping wave that spreads from a starting point across all the rest of the brain, as it explores the possibilities. Activity is focussed on discreet areas appropriate to a task.

The same active areas are always triggered for the same types of task, so it is assumed that these areas work collaboratively even if they are in different halves of the brain. It is further assumed that the activity is co-ordinated by the background 'unconscious' functions of the brain, which may also trigger those different areas into action.

Yet we can't prove this as we can't track the electrical signals; so while this isn't an unreasonable assumption, the possibility of a non-physical Mind controlling the brain remains open for philosophers to debate.

An explanation of how ideas develop in the brain remains one of the 'Holy Grails' of neuroscience, however, as we saw earlier, the more immediate underlying question is whether the neurons themselves are making choices about which other areas of the brain to engage in a given situation.

Areas of the Brain Handle Multiple Issues not just One

If you recall, one of the dilemmas for materialism is that atoms, molecules and waves shouldn't be able to think, and therefore all control and decision-making should be based on unthinking chemical reactions. Yet we know that brains/Minds do achieve understanding.

We also saw that neurons seem to control the flow of electrical signals around the brain by either appearing to choose when to pass them on, or potentially targeting other neurons for onward processing of an idea.

One way to avoid the need for neurons making considered choices was to argue that they operate within a structure that gives them a 'one-for-one alignment' with the issues and body parts they were handling. Put another way, there were so many brain cells that individual neurons might only handle one type of issue that could only influence one area of the body. However there is now direct evidence to counter that view

It is now strongly believed that **each** area of the 'Motor Cortex', (which decides our movements), sends signals out to **many** different muscles[117] across our body – telling them how to act. Individual brain cells would therefore need a means of choosing where to send signals, and ensuring that they were routed there correctly, across many complex junctions.

Assembling an Image or an Impression of Something

In basic terms we can say that eyes have millions of sensors which form an image made up of dots in a similar way to a modern digital camera, (or should I say that digital cameras mimic the eye). Each sensor sends signals, via the optic nerve, to an equal number of cells (neurons) in the brain which interpret each dot. What is unclear is how these dots are then assembled into an image in the mind, if each cell can only handle one dot.

We do know that different parts of the 'Visual System': from the retina via the 'Lateral Geniculate Nucleus' (LGN) through to the 'Primary Visual Cortex'; break down the images into a number of elements:

depth, colour, lightness, shape/outline, movement,
orientation & distance, plus recognition/identification

Yet each of the different parts of the brain still has vast numbers of neurons, and they do not project the image onto an internal screen. Some mechanism has to assemble all of those dots to form a complete image, yet we don't know what that is. It doesn't seem to be a single neuron or a discreet organ. Is this further evidence for a separate Mind?

Some experiments are beginning to show that individual ideas may be stored in some neurons, but in a similar way to vision, millions of neurons may be involved in processing a thought or idea. Something needs to assemble the individual elements into a concept and/or a set of options.

As these processing areas of the brain get reused is seems unlikely that every single pixel or every preliminary notion that led to a concept is stored, so is it possible that a combined image or concept can be stored in a single neuron? While each neuron may have a link to 1000 other neurons, we know that this wouldn't be enough for a digital camera image made up of millions of pixels, so the basis of storing an image/idea is challenging.

Traditional 'cause and effect' logic says that a new idea cannot simply emerge from nowhere. Every thought must have a prior cause or trigger: such as signals received via our senses; or feedback from the internal workings of our bodies. Both of these may trigger some thoughts and **un**conscious brain processing.

Sometimes in our **conscious** thoughts, we can just think and play around with concepts, so all of *that* brain activity would be internally generated.

Yet many of us, if not all, are likely to have experienced an odd idea that just seems to pop into our Minds, without us thinking about the subject, and which doesn't relate to current events around us, in any way.

Where does it come from if we haven't been thinking about that subject in months or even years? We may have stored memories and facts, but like a computer program accessing files on a hard drive, there needs to be a reason for accessing such memories. So what was the need?

Materialists may argue that some sub-conscious thing happening around us which prompted the thought; or possibly that the large amount of background processing which our brains seem to do[85], might inadvertently trigger a stored memory. Others suggest that our Minds constantly try to *anticipate* dynamic events that are happening around us, but in my experience such short-range future gazing always relates to current events.

Yet on a quiet day, in the peace of our homes, ideas can just come; 'out of the blue'; on subjects that you could never have expected. I have experienced it myself and I know it to be true. But is it due to hidden physical causes per materialism, or potential acts of spontaneity?

Few people deny that ideas do pop into people's heads, and to this extent the evidence may incline towards spontaneity, but neither explanation is likely to be provable. We would need a large number of monitored examples – which is unlikely in itself. Yet even if scanners today were sophisticated enough to monitor all of the individual neurons in the brain, (and we are not even close to that), it would seem almost impossible to distinguish a single neuron that fires without cause, from all others that were triggered by unconscious background processing by the brain.

All philosophical options are therefore 'still on the table'.

Control without physical wiring

One bizarre finding in respect of brain vs Mind, is that people born **without** a corpus callosum, (a condition known as callosal dysgenesis (CD), or agenesis of the corpus callosum, (AgCC)), do **not** seem to suffer from a lack of co-ordination despite the normal nerves between the two halves of the brain being absent, possibly due to an inactive/missing gene. Yet people whose corpus callosum connections have been severed in later life[84] through accident or surgery, **do** suffer co-ordination problems.

The first group must have developed novel ways to function, because CD patients **do** use areas on both sides of the brain in the same way as **normal** brains – but how they do it remains unknown. There are indications that other channels between the brain hemispheres may have been adapted to carry signals for this purpose, and possibly that the brain has adapted to form new nerves that jump the gap between the hemispheres. Yet the corpus callosum remains absent, and the full explanation is not yet known.

Even if these explanations are verified it seems remarkable that an unthinking set of neurons should go looking to establish a connection that they are not genetically programmed to know – even adapting/changing existing structures to accommodate this ability.

Speculation that this co-ordination has arisen from the interaction of electromagnetic fields **doesn't** seem to be born out[84].

Alternatively, could these facts point to the possibility that thought may actually be conducted by a non-physical Mind which can direct activity to different parts of the brain as required? If so, the evidence seems less like a *direct* pointer and more like an *indirect* pointer.

One way or another it has all added to the mystery.

Decisions on When to Use Energy

If our conscious minds are active then the number of electrical signals flying around our brain will increase; but we can also consciously clear our minds and reduce that activity.

Neurons in our brains do not fire like clockwork producing (say) a new thought every 100th of a second. Conscious brain activity is targeted, and apparently activated only when necessary.

Not only are there questions about the origin of any idea, but we also have to consider where the brain gets access to instant power when necessary – and the obvious answer lies in the 'universal energy currency' of the body, ATP, that we saw in Chapter 5.2, (cell metabolism). ATP can be used in different ways and can be converted to other things, but for simplicity let's stay with the basic notion.

ATP is like a tiny battery pack, and when we see it powering motion in a motor protein, it attaches and instantly discharges, causing the protein to twitch in one or other way. Enzymes and other catalysts may also use the power in ATP to undertake certain reactions, generally instantly as well.

The point here is that each neuron needs energy to operate, (to do its processing), as well as requiring additional energy to send out a signal, but only when it deems that appropriate. This conditional use introduces a timing delay because a neuron cell would have ATP molecules available within or around it but we have no idea what suddenly causes them to be used. It is not like an enzyme which triggers automatically when it bumps into a suitable molecule.

This is another aspect of the apparent 'decision process' that we suspect from a neuron when it either chooses to fire a signal at other cells... or not. However our theories now require them to have even more sophistication, in order to control the additional power usage.

A Challenge to the Notion of Mind: based on Energy

Daniel Dennett and John Searle have argued that the Mind is no more than a concept, and that it's not even a scientific one.

The basis of their argument is that there's nothing to explain how the physical brain could be forced to do something by the non-physical Mind, **because this would require an exchange of energy**, which we do not see.

The underlying point is a good one because the whole of physical matter does work on exchanges of energy, so a non-physical Mind would indeed have to deploy power in some way to activate/trigger the physical tissues – the neurons. The failing lies in the presumption that it doesn't happen.

While it is true that we haven't seen 'energy emerging out of nowhere' in a neuron, or mysteriously disappearing from there into a 'non-physical realm', we haven't actually looked!

More specifically scientists haven't done the precise measurements to find out if it is happening in a living subject. At this stage in our technology such an exercise would be virtually impossible to do, and it might also be a very subtle effect. So the presumption that there is **no** exchange of energy with a non-physical realm is premature.

At headline level it might seem fair/balanced that if Idealists & Dualists wish us to believe in other types of stuff to explain the operations of the body's metabolism and brain, Materialists should be allowed to claim unproven things as well. I'd probably agree, in terms of fairness, but it doesn't really help us to determine the underlying truth of the situation.

However there are subtle differences in these positions. While the main challenges to the Materialist view are based on real observations/effects that appear to contradict its **principles**, the absence of proof for an energy exchange doesn't contradict the principles of Idealism or Dualism - it only extends the basic premise a little further. Yet in fairness to the Materialist cause, the other philosophies haven't defined what's possible in their non-physical realm – which makes it rather hard to either validate or challenge.

So let's be fairer, and look at how Dualism might respond to the initial challenge – that exchanges of energy with a non-physical realm are not happening. As you may have guessed, the first counter-argument is that: energy might be being deployed in some way, but we don't know how.

We know that science acknowledges the strong likelihood of Dark Energy, (which we can't detect), so it is always possible that a non-physical Mind might be utilising this in some way too. In terms of explaining why we can't detect this, it might also be pointed out that this is not unique: there are no detectable exchanges of energy from gravity either.

As already mentioned, it may also be true that the level of energy exchange with a non-physical Mind may be very slight indeed, making it very hard to detect. The Mind isn't required to power a neuron or its signals directly; only to act as a trigger, to encourage its use of ATP when needed.

Equally, in terms of the reverse flow, (where a neuron would pass information back to the non-physical Mind), we can speculate that very little energy would be required to get it working, as there would be no perceived mass or momentum to overcome in a non-physical 'realm'.

One possibility for the more technically minded is that if there are differences between the *types* of energy used in the physical and non-physical realms, some sort of *induction* process may be possible to transfer power between the two.

> Induction basically puts energy from a source object into a separate object, without them touching. It's a prime way in which we generate electricity and it can even transform one type of energy into another type - for instance, in hydro-electric power stations, the energy in flowing water is converted to electricity.

The only methods that we know to generate an induction effect are not precise in the way that we envisage the targeting of a neuron, and we would either have to assume that the brain would be using a highly specialised form of induction, or that the induction process influenced a much broader area of the brain than individual neurons.

While we **do** see that blood flow increases in those areas of the brain which are in use, and also that more electricity is generated from those regions – it wouldn't be easy to determine whether **all** energy came from the blood or whether some of it had another source.

12.2.1   Ideas about How the Brain might Work

It is clear that explanations of the brain based in mechanical/chemical operations have failed, so far, to explain Thought and consciousness in all its forms. So Materialists have increasingly turned to Quantum Mechanics to try to explain various operations of the body in terms of Matter/Energy alone. This has led to the new and interesting field of Quantum Biology.

The term was first coined some 50 years ago, and in that time it has been used to explain the process and efficiency of photosynthesis in plants, and the way in which eyes are sensitive to light. It has also been used to try to explain the efficiency of enzyme reactions through 'quantum tunnelling' - associated with ideas of electron transfers in 'redox reactions'. (Don't worry about the terms just go with the flow).

Before we move on to see how Quantum Mechanics might assist the explanation of brain activity, I wanted to bring one other significant breakthrough to your attention – an explanation of the sense of navigation which is clearly demonstrated in many species from homing pigeons, to animals and fish, (such as salmon returning to the fresh water spawning grounds of their birth in order to breed after many years at sea).

Unlike creatures such as ants, (which seem to use a much more simple scent trail), these different forms of Life use a variety of techniques in order to find their way over large distances: combining a sense of the Earth's magnetic field (Magnetoreception), with the position of the sun over water, geographic features over land, or seemingly even the stars at night.

It was discovered that most birds are sensitive to the **_polarity_** of the Earth's magnetic field, which they sense through the presence of magnetite crystals in their beaks. These in turn send signals to their brains. However it was the work of German researchers Wolfgang and Roswintha Wiltschko in the early 1970s which revealed that the European Robin uses an entirely different technique when migrating.

They were able to demonstrate that these birds were sensitive to the **_angle of inclination_** of the magnetic field and also to changes in its **_intensity_**, but it was the later proposal of 'The Radical Pair Mechanism'[98] which opened the door to **how** this might be achieved, (the leading theory).

> This makes use of a property established by Quantum Physics, that tiny sub-atomic particles, (primarily photons and electrons), can be 'paired'. This establishes an unknown link between the pair which always keeps them spinning in **opposite** directions to each other regardless of how far apart they are in reality. The Radical Pair Mechanism suggests that paired electrons in the right eye of birds, (held within the protein cryptochrome), can be attuned to the Earth's magnetic field, causing them to alter their spins, thereby sending different signals to the brain[99].

Philosophically, what this, and other 'quantum' explanations demonstrate is that subtle physical aspects in the abilities of light particles and electrons, **can** explain how some of our senses operate. We also know that other senses operate through chemical reactions. However **none** of this seems to explain awareness, consciousness, or the experience of life – qualia.

When the brains of these creatures get signals from a variety of sources it is clear that they don't just have a single 'cause & effect' response. They have to process and assess many factors, leading them to a judgement on their circumstances, (eg. direction & location), plus a decision on how to react, (eg. whether to change course).

This clearly suggests consciousness, rather than mechanics or sensory function. So what might explain consciousness?

The highly controversial 'Penrose Hameroff Orch-OR'[86] theory does provide a scientifically-based alternative to physical hard-wiring and mechanical cause and effect, which may explain how brain activity can arise without direct physical connections. It does so, using some of the extended principles of Quantum Mechanics.

Going back to some of the earlier points in this chapter, it is this theory which argues that because people can understand 'non-provable statements' and feel emotions. The body may be using tiny electromagnetic fields within neurons to undertake reasoning.

In the book "The Soul Hypothesis"[88] C.Taliaferro presented the cryptic example of a dentist telling you that the agonising pain in your tooth was merely an illusion because neither electricity nor chemicals can think or feel... yet we do feel such things, and Penrose Hameroff argued that a different mechanism was needed to explain how.

The principles of Quantum Mechanics say how *likely* something is to happen by attaching probabilities to events, without necessarily explaining how those outcomes might be generated.

In this case however many of the effects that are assembled and used in the Orch-OR theory **do** have some substantive proof of their existence, but many scientists consider those 'abilities' to be too weak to generate the outcomes that Penrose & Hameroff want to achieve.

We saw the notion earlier that different parts of a 'magnetic' or other type of field might hold a range of permutations about a single idea, and that overlapping fields could assess any compatibilities quickly. There is no evidence to show that information could be held like this, but if it could, how would that assessment occur in a physical way? As a suggestion...

Wave theory, (think of ripples on a pond), says that where waves from different sources overlap and they are in sync, (a crest meets a crest or a dip meets a dip), the two waves combine and become much bigger, whereas those which are out of sync tend to work against each other - weakening and even completely disappearing.

On this basis, as a general principle, we might speculate that if fields operated like overlapping waves, then those points where the waves became larger would instantly reveal aspect of compatibility between the ideas, that was possibly strong enough to trigger the firing of a neuron.

In similar terms, Karl Pribram[89] and David Bohm suggested an alternate approach to the workings of the Mind which resembles the operation of a hologram but based on particle waves rather than light. (A hologram is a 3D image made from intense beams of light from lasers, that bounce off each other to create a picture you can see from any angle).

This is known as the Holonomic Brain Theory, but it expands the information available to every neuron.

The theory places an emphasis on the dendrite receptors coming out of a neuron, where the authors suggest that information may be held. (Again, if you're struggling, don't worry - just try to get the feel of the notion).

They realised that any **part** of a hologram can store **all** of the information held within it. In the same way they envisaged that any part of the dendrite network could contain all of the information across the entire network – making access to all information very easy anywhere in the brain.

While these two notions, (Orch-OR and Holonomic theory), start to overcome some of the challenges faced by cause and effect 'hard wired' materialism through the use of fields, they **wouldn't** address all of the philosophical issues.

For instance, even if the notion of combining ideas in these ways could be demonstrated, it could only provide a list of options, at best. It wouldn't tell us how those options could be *evaluated* and a *decision* taken.

Aside from these two prominent suggestions, scientists who believe in the Mind have suggested various other theories of how it may arise – for instance, that it could exist within the resonance of sub-atomic particles; or the even deeper levels of existence described by String Theory. One collection of such writings was compiled by Professors Baker and Goetz in their 2011 book "The Soul Hypothesis"[90].

12.2.2 Language as Evidence for a Separate Mind

Another classic example of the Mind being able to make spontaneous or random choices, is suggested through the use of language.

When people talk or write they are free to combine words and phrases in a huge variety of ways. I can probably go further to say that if a subject is more than the simplest of concepts, you would probably be astonished if different people happened to describe the same event using exactly the same words, expressions, and phrases. Accusations of plagiarism would fly!

If a single idea can be communicated in many different ways, then the choice of words deployed by an individual would seem to be spontaneous/random yet also controlled.

The question is, does that spontaneity emerge from something that is entirely physical or does it require another 'spiritual' factor? Can language prove the case for Materialism or Dualism?

Noam Chomsky[91], (founder of modern **linguistics**), identified three components of linguistic use:-
- The lexicon (list of words or dictionary)
- The grammar (set of rules with which to combine words into sentences), and
- Creative Aspect of Language Use or 'CALU'

Through quite separate research and thinking in the field of **psychology** Willem Levelt[92] described 3 'processors' involved in language production, which he called :-

- The 'Conceptualizer', which structures the basic message.
- The Formulator, which accesses vocabulary and grammar to change the concept of the message into an 'inner speech'.
- The 'Articulator' which communicates to the outside world.

It is easy to see the parallels between the CALU and Conceptualizer, and how these might reflect the more spontaneous activities that could identify a Mind beyond the physical brain.

Following this line of thinking, Professor Mark Baker[90] whose specialist field is linguistics, suggested that if our thoughts were entirely based on the physical brain, then there should be medical conditions which would affect the CALU or Conceptualizer.

'Aphasia' is one of the oldest branches of neuroscience. It studies the effects of brain damage on language and it categorises the conditions in 7-10 ways, (3 of the 10 types are combinations of the original 7). As people are diagnosed using these criteria and not the specific effects on the CALU, Baker went looking for cases which suggested such damage. He determined that two types of aphasia, (Wernicke's Aphasia and Broca's Aphasia), could meet the criteria.

He also determined that in the realm of genetics, only one of four 'Specific Language Impairments' (SLI's), ('pragmatic language impairment', otherwise known as Semantic Pragmatic Disorder), could point to a CALU gene that may have gone wrong.

Baker then analysed the conditions using detailed descriptions of the patient symptoms and concluded that in all cases damage only seemed to be done to the 'Formulator' or 'Articulator'. He concluded that there were **no** medical conditions that damaged the Conceptualizer/CALU - which in turn implied that the CALU *could be based in something non-physical.*

It's an interesting finding but we have yet to see whether his conclusions will be supported by the scientific community in the long term. In some respects these are early days for this type of analysis, and if an original patient diagnosis was not specifically looking to investigate the CALU, it's difficult to say how reliable a later retrospective analysis might be in justifying the conclusion. Could it be that there are medical conditions which do affect the Conceptualizer elsewhere in the world, but which have not been identified due to mis-diagnosis?

One of the pioneers of aphasia research, Lichtheim, had proposed a model of language faculties in the brain based on yet another 3 'centres' of activity, and as early as 1885 had proposed that the 'concept centre' was the only one which **didn't** seem to have aphasias linked to it. On this basis

Baker suggests that the assertion seems to have withstood over 100 years of scrutiny, and is still valid. More research is clearly needed but it **is** a very interesting conclusion from the limited evidence available to date.

So can we glean any special features of language from its use by animals or in computers? Can language be seen to break the principles of physical cause & effect?

Mark Baker also points out that even the most modern computers currently assemble language in a formulaic and pre-recorded way due to the nature of their programming, and that this is not the construction of natural language as we understand it. As these are relatively early days for computing it's probably too early to say that technology will never be able to generate natural language, yet it's hard to argue against the fact that

> all programmed code is formulaic so computer-generated language would always be predictable, and would lack spontaneity.

So can we derive any principles from the abilities which **animals** display in communication? Here, we probably have to differentiate between the communications they undertake in the wild, and what they might be capable of doing with human training.

In the wild we see that each particular species of bird does seem to have a distinctive type of song - and although there do seem to be variations in that song it is relatively limited.

Other species, including animals, seem to use clicks, whistles, howls etc, which can all indicate a relatively small range of apparent meanings along the lines of an alert rather than a full concept or sentence.

We seem to observe mating calls; warnings of danger; etc. but nothing really more sophisticated. Yet these creatures do assess the quality of each other's communications, for instance in whether a female shows interest in a male, or rejects his advances.

However, the recognition of potential danger, or the desire to share food, (which have both been clearly demonstrated), do show that animals have concepts based on experience. Whether this extends to more abstract notions is hard to demonstrate.

Who is to say that there isn't a deeper level of communication that we just don't understand at the moment? Could it be, for instance, that some animals could have quite sophisticated thoughts that are communicated telepathically, and that sounds & gestures are just there to give reinforcement/emphasis? Perhaps they achieve long range communication? In all honesty we probably don't know enough to make a real judgement, but the indications so far are that animal communications are quite crude.

Yet, they don't have the same upbringing as us and are not trained in more academic types of communication. People have therefore been fascinated to see whether the larger apes could be trained in a richer use of language to demonstrate spontaneity, creativity, and even abstract concepts.

In such studies, apes such as Kanzi and Lana[93] have effectively been given a child-like upbringing with schooling and high levels of human contact. They have been taught to communicate using basic language abilities through the use of keypads or touch screens which reflect nouns and verbs to create a basic grammatical structure. However it is argued that they have not shown creative abilities equivalent to the CALU... but we are into difficult territory here.

The latest estimate[94] I have seen for the number of words in the English language is 1,025,110. If *we* only had a vocabulary of 200 words wouldn't we all struggle to demonstrate creativity?

When you cross species it becomes hard to establish an agreed meaning when the points become ever more subtle, and the interest and attention span of these creatures is clearly very different to our own. You may also be limited by the number of words/symbols you can display to the animal.

People try to compare the mental development in apes with the average development of a human child but if you don't have the same vocal chords and are forced to communicate by pointing to symbols, doesn't this greatly limit the ability to learn? Put another way, **does a limited vocabulary mean a limited CALU or just a limited ability to demonstrate it**?

People have pointed out that apes **do** have the same physical areas of the brain that we associate with human language, so are the differences boiling down to vocal chords and attention span, or something more fundamental?

The alternate suggestion is that if humans are able to achieve very different levels of ability with the same physical brain equipment, language may not be an entirely physical thing. I suspect that until we know a lot more about the mechanisms of brains it's too early to say whether these areas of the brain are indeed the same.

David Attenborough and other scientific observers have demonstrated that animals clearly do show emotion; feel pain; have preferences; and do communicate through a variety of sounds, signals, and expressions. These all indicate the **experience** of qualia. If animals could associate words with the emotions that they feel, then they would presumably know what we mean, because they seem to feel similar things.

The question is whether they can form a concept of those feelings rather than just remember an experience.

Review and Conclusions

Right now I'm having amnesia and deja vu at the same time.
I think I've forgotten this before.   -   Anonymous

This book has investigated the nature and origin of Life, Mind, & Soul. It has sought to explore the full **range** of opinion, even if it wasn't possible to explore every subtle permutation within that range.

As a result, you are highly likely to have come across views which seem at odds with your personal beliefs. I have tried to indicate why these opinions are held, based on the evidence available, (which can be interpreted in different ways), as well as showing you the gaps that still exist in our understanding, which leave room for speculation.

Such gaps do **not** imply that an alternate view is automatically correct, but they do pose questions - about whether a solution is likely to come from established principles, or whether something else may be required.

Science has made great progress in explaining how our bodies work through the actions of Matter/Energy alone; including the rules which govern its behaviour:- the Laws of Physics and the principle of causality, (cause & effect). This approach is taken because Matter/Energy is the only 'stuff' we can identify and test, and the results have been very successful in *predicting* how the physical/chemical aspects of our bodies will operate.

The question is: can scientific materialism explain **everything** about Life?

On the one hand, it's not unreasonable to expect that physical answers will be found to physical things, but we seem to have uncovered a number of unexplained factors which challenge the *principles* by which Matter/Energy should operate, and these all relate to **intangible** things.

Some may try to argue that intangible things do not exist, and are an illusion; yet many will feel from our experience of Life, that they are not only very real but also get to the *essence* of life – demonstrating why it is more than the mechanics of our physical bodies. In one way or another, those unresolved issues seem to boil down to five interlinked factors:-

1) the nature of awareness, thought, and consciousness.
2) Life's apparent ability to assemble, grow, and become ever more sophisticated, (assuming that you believe in the Theory of Evolution), bucking the normal trend of physical matter to constantly degrade.
3) the **proactive** nature of life rather than the **reactive** nature of causality and physical Matter/Energy.
4) special abilities/characteristics, (eg. spontaneity or randomness), that seem necessary to explain the actions/events we observe.
5) a fundamental question about which types of stuff underpin reality.

Thought is real - we use it every waking moment. It's just that we don't know **how** it is generated – (ie. what it represents).

People have commonly associated Thought with logic, not only because it's an important factor in our reasoning, but also because it is very formulaic and could be described in mathematical terms – a manifestation of 'strict causality'. Mechanical computers are also based on this principle, and they require precise bits of information that they can manipulate.

Yet the puzzle about how our brains and minds operate, deepened when we found that precise facts and hard logic were insufficient, on their own, to enable us to take basic everyday decisions.

It has been shown that the parts of our brains which handle emotion are vital to human decision-making. We instinctively know that emotions are fuzzy, but it seems that this part of the brain also helps us to deal with uncertainty; our ability to set objectives & prioritise; and probably be creative – all factors which seem to go beyond cause & effect precision.

These are the abilities that have eluded a 'mechanical' explanation of our brains; and may also explain why even the latest supercomputers cannot generate consciousness and emotion.

Philosophically, it is also compelling to suggest that:

Thought may be the **only** thing which can cause
Matter/Energy to deviate from its inevitable chemical path.

Our thoughts **can** influence the physical matter in our bodies to produce physical effects, and through the communication of ideas, our thoughts can also influence physical events that are separate from us and far away, by prompting other people to act upon them. *Yet* Materialists will argue that Thoughts are mere physical effects in themselves. If true, Matter/Energy would be influencing itself without any need for another type of stuff.

Chapter 2 therefore tested whether Thought demonstrated true spontaneity or randomness; characteristics which would break the principle of strict cause & effect, (indicating that it might not originate in Matter/Energy).

The example of 'ending a deliberate pause in conversation' not only appeared to show those elements, but also demonstrated something which is not normally possible for raw chemicals – a pause. Atoms and molecules always react immediately.

The mystery over the nature of thought and awareness deepens when we consider that many other aspects of life are **not** associated with a brain yet they still seem to display similar properties, all-be-it with different strength settings in different contexts. Let's remind ourselves of some.

Firstly, we have seen that any evolutionary process must have a 'sense of direction' and the only known mechanism which we have relies on 'survival' and elements of thought/awareness, to provide that direction – but it's hard to see how those could apply before the first cell existed.

Although early evolution may have only been driven by 'survival issues' for the first basic living cells, we have seen that today's single celled organisms such as 'Didinium' display proactive and even aggressive behaviour... even though they have no brain. This miniscule creature 'swims around' looking for prey which it then attacks with poison darts before eating them... a sign of crude awareness, or pure mechanics?

Quite apart from the actions of Didinium, the core operations of cells in our bodies also have abilities which suggest crude levels of awareness in a number of their amazing functions, such as:-

- the self assembly of complex units such as ribosomes and viruses.
- the astonishing motor proteins which walk along roadways carrying cargo to a variety of 'user destinations', with abilities to plan routes.
- complex programmable assembly machines which construct the functioning components of cells, eg. Ribosomes and Enzymes.
- 'quality control' mechanisms which correct malformed components.
- recycling mechanisms for when repairs fail or components are used.

and perhaps most amazingly of all,

- elaborate mechanisms such as Homologous Recombination which undertake DNA repairs - investigating problems and providing tailored responses, using a number of devices in combination!

Again – there is no brain and no known equivalent of a computer chip within a cell; just a small number of molecules that do appear to show: purpose; objectives; and seem able to make choices & guesses. Several of these elements may also have been necessary for the first cell.

Whether these functions just give an *illusion* of awareness brought about by the way we rationalise them, has yet to be demonstrated – but in the meantime it seems wrong to deny their appearance on the basis of faith.

Some scientists have recognised the dilemma surrounding Didinium and the cell functions above, by suggesting that their complex chemical signalling mechanisms all operate like 'on-off switches', which if used in combination could potentially act as a crude computer processor... possibly. Yet, even if these did amount to invisible chips within each cell:

- could they exist *before* the first cell, with nothing to control?
- something would still need to program them... especially before the first cell came into existence.

DNA is an information store, not a computer. Its reproductive mechanism, (common to all cells), represents the single evolutionary mechanism that we know of, which may well explain the increasing sophistication of Life once the first cell existed, and might even provide a 'sense of direction' through survival, but it could **not** explain any development that would bring the first cell into existence. We need a 2nd evolutionary mechanism.

Abiogenesis research is seeking another unthinking mechanism which could to this, but scientists only have a vague idea of what that could be. Experiments are being conducted into 'designer' forms of RNA that may be able to replicate both themselves & proteins - but these are early days.

Returning to the question of how 'crude awareness' might be explained without a brain, the possibility that thought is based in another type of stuff might offer a solution; but is there any reasonable prospect of other 'external influences' emerging into the limelight? Well yes, there might be.

Materialists increasingly sense that the mysteries of Life may lie in the inner recesses of sub-atomic particles and raw energy – the realm of Quantum Mechanics. This is because it is becoming harder to deny the that randomness may truly exist in the 'quantum zone', while at the same time it still offers ways to contain it through different rules of physics - keeping things 'within the materialist house' so to speak.

The difficulty here, (and the source of profound and passionate debates), is whether this quantum realm truly provides a source of randomness. It reveals effects which *do not seem to be explained by known factors*, but we cannot be sure why. The fundamental problem is that we **cannot** directly see what's going on at that level of reality, and so we cannot say precisely what's involved in each event. This is why the techniques of Quantum Mechanics rely so heavily on the use of probability.

For many decades, senior scientists argued that explanations based in causality would ultimately be found in these murky realms: it's just that we couldn't see them. Yet younger scientists are increasingly considering that the evidence may reflect true randomness and possibly spontaneity.

If the modern view is correct, then there is a second question – what allows randomness and spontaneity to occur? Is it Matter/Energy itself, (breaking all of our normal perceptions about it), or is it down to something else?

Book 1 showed that mainstream science is increasingly relying on ideas about 'hidden types of stuff' to explain phenomena which can no longer be denied. A good example of this is the notion of Dark Energy.

Could such things, (which we cannot detect), be an explanation for life and its extraordinary abilities – the source of capabilities that seem to go beyond Matter/Energy? Perhaps, but it has not yet been demonstrated.

It may yet be shown that we *don't* have to resort to things such as Dark Energy, and that the inner workings of atoms could explain the randomness we perceive. Yet philosophically, I see little difference between the two possibilities, other than 'clarity of vision' on an academic nuance. All of the **real world** discussion is about capability & the clear separation that exists between the realms of causality, and spontaneity/randomness.

If these things do exist in a largely separate way, then all Dualist and most Idealist suggestions are likely to be validated. The precise means of delivery, and abstract points about dualism vs. monism, are side issues.

The unspecific/imprecise nature of qualia, (feelings and emotions), **plus** our ability to handle uncertainty, **and** the speed with which our brains consider a myriad of possibilities, all seem to suggest that our Minds work on a different basis to that of computer chips, (which essentially flick lots of switches 'on or off'). Ideas are shifting to the possibility that Thought may come from the interaction of 'fields of influence', from magnetism to holograms, (materialistic), or based in another type of hidden stuff.

The notion is that if a 'field of influence' can incorporate all the **permutations** of an idea within it, and different fields can also overlap with each other, then areas of compatibility could be identified very quickly – producing a set of practical options that could lead to a choice, etc.

The purpose of mentioning this is **not** to prescribe a solution, but to show that 'physical' solutions might overcome many current objections if we start to view things in a less mechanistic and more fluid way.

If fields were shown to be active in control and memory, then there may be ways in which crude awareness might emerge in cells without a full brain. They might also help Abiogenesis to find the elusive 'sense of direction' that it needs for its alternate evolutionary process. We should remember that this direction is considered necessary to allow unthinking processes to achieve life in the timescales available, (avoiding many backwards steps).

On a similar theme, I return again to the **proactive** nature of life's actions, rather than the **reactive** nature that is demanded by causality. The processes of Homologous Recombination, and also the routing of vesicles to end destinations, are both good examples which suggest that molecules *go looking* for solutions. These functions illustrate why people suspect that crude levels of understanding may be involved, that go beyond simple chemical detection producing a single response, (ie. the mechanical senses).

There appear to be choices being made within a single living cell, plus judgements, and even guesses – however, as mentioned before, could that simply be the way that our brains rationalise what's going-on in the absence of inevitable chemical mechanisms *which we may yet find*. Perhaps, but it's still surprising that intense scientific scrutiny hasn't yet revealed them, even if these things were not easily observed due to their miniscule nature.

Even if the logic which seems to be displayed in these cellular functions isn't as dynamic as it first appears, it would still imply that it had to be 'hard-coded' within molecules. Can logic also be the result of evolution? We wait to see if chemistry; other atomic codes; or even fields of influence can resolve the dilemma.

In many ways the philosophy of Dualism offers a very similar approach to the notion of 'fields of influence', but it differs in some significant ways.

By arguing that such fields come from another type of stuff, it offers the possibility that the Mind is separate from the body. Dualism argues that the Mind does some if not all of the processing – not necessarily the brain; and the primary purpose of the brain would be to act as a conduit for the Mind, allowing it to interact with physical reality.

That potential separation is interesting because in a purely physical body we might suppose that all electromagnetic influences would stop when the body dies, (ie. all thought, awareness, and life would end). However Dualism opens the possibility that a separate Mind may be preserved in a Soul, and would therefore be able to transfer to another life.

The Soul is not an inevitable outcome from this type of Mind, but it could be a possibility. However, in order to believe in an invisible and undetectable Soul, there has to be some evidence for it.

It is only in the past 50 years or so that scientifically gathered evidence has started to emerge which may support ideas about the Soul – through studies into 'Near-Death' and 'Out of Body' experiences, plus the more contentious study of Reincarnation.

Such research has not been conclusive by any means, but the possibility of a soul can no longer be reasonably dismissed out of hand.

Most significantly the main evidence has **not** been **disproven**, and it seems to point to genuine experiences. The point at issue is whether the evidence is truly pointing to the Soul, or to something more mundane.

One surprise is the sheer number of cases which, although still rare, are still occurring on a regular basis. These have allowed clear patterns to emerge in the way that cases seem to pan-out – reinforcing the notion that they may indeed be based in an underlying mechanism, rather than them just being a figment of people's Minds when they are under stress etc..

A number of prominent Materialists have been affected by 'Near-Death' and 'Out of Body' experiences – persuading them that it is a real phenomenon – but also setting them looking for a physical mechanism.

There is much greater philosophical difficulty with the possibility of Reincarnation, because although it is harder to prove, there is no other mechanism than a Soul which could enable it to happen. Again, there is nothing to stop atheists believing in the Soul, and indeed there are some religions which do exactly that, such as Jainism.

However we should be clear, that while large parts of the world community believe Reincarnation to be a fact of life, the phenomenon has not been proven scientifically. If it is real, there is nothing to make it incompatible with other beliefs such as Resurrection. Indeed, Resurrection could be seen as one way to end the cycle of birth, life, death and rebirth.

There are clear statistics from various surveys[61] which indicate that a significant number of people do have 'combined views', yet this is not the way that any of the main faiths perceive it.

So where does this leave us?

Conclusions

We all know that there is something fundamentally different about Life compared to the sterile rocks and chemicals of our environment. This has been loosely referred to as the "Essence of Life", yet it has been very hard to identify and define what that may be; or even the factors that may characterise it. Despite there being over 280 attempts at a definition of Life there is no consensus, so this book has sought out the core physical aspects of life which remain unexplained, to identify possible characteristics.

Having briefly looked at the diversity of species on the planet we quickly came to recognise that, in one form or another, life can survive in virtually all types of environment the Earth has to offer: occupying almost every crevice in the earth's crust; plus water; ice; the air; and even the waste from atomic reactors. Some organisms may not need light; others can survive in extremes of temperature and radiation. Life is very adaptable.

Yet they are all based on a common 'technology' – the reproductive ability of the living cell. The universal nature of that mechanism is such that if you take a section of gene code from any creature and put it into the DNA of another, that code will be recognised and duplicated as before, even if the new host creature itself cannot make use of the gene, or worse, the protein it produces turns out to be incompatible with others that the creature needs[12].

> By way of example, the so-called 'spider goats' had genes transplanted from a particular type of spider that made incredibly tough silk, and this now grows within the milk of the goats which can be filtered to extract industrial quantities of that silk while being totally functional for the normal rearing of its young[100] . At the time of writing there are now over 30 of these goats in the herd.

It is also very interesting that the DNA of each species is filled with lots of genetic code that's unused. Within humans this seems to include old abilities such as enhanced levels of smell, (similar to animals), which is no longer activated; plus others which may be useless code from bacteria; or failed evolutionary 'experiments' from the past.

All of this seems to be good evidence for two things:

- How vital it is that the mechanism which selects the genes to use for each individual, operates properly - ensuring they are compatible with each other, while enabling each living thing to conform to the basic profile of its species. We just don't know how it does so.

- There is strong evidence to show that the known mechanism of genetic evolution in cells is part, if not all, of the explanation for the increasing complexity of life **once the first cell had emerged**.

However it is impossible for the known mechanism of evolution to account for the origin of the first cell. There either had to be a different mechanism that was based in Matter/Energy which has seemingly left no trace of itself, or there were other factors involved – which may include other types of stuff, and/or God.

From all of this, people have speculated that Life only arose **once** on this planet: a likelihood reinforced by the complexity of what had to happen to even produce basic building blocks such as proteins, let alone the first cell.

The odds of it happening without a clear process to steer it are so vast that it could even be a unique event in history of the Universe; however it seems much more likely that there <u>was</u> a process to guide it.

Yet the nature of that process is very puzzling when you think that sterile chemicals should have no interest in creating Life, or even a reproductive capability; **but also** that they seem to have utilised elaborate sets of **codes** in order to do it – all working together in perfect harmony. Codes tend to imply purpose and understanding, even if only at a crude level.

One of the fundamental characteristics of Life is that it seems to buck the trend of 2nd Law of Thermodynamics which says that everything physical is in a constant process of degradation: losing form and structure.

The principle that everything constantly degrades ignores 2 facts :

- structure has to be assembled before it can deteriorate.
- science believes that the totality of existence doesn't change, therefore we may well be in a constant cycle where some parts are being created while others are degrading – the traffic doesn't all have to be one way – as Big Bang theory has previously indicated.

Gravity has long been held out by physicists as the primary assembling force because it gathers the most distributed & basic forms of physical material before assembling them into clear structures, (suns and planets).

Yet Life also assembles. Bacteria and plants have been gathering the most basic form of radiated energy from the sun and using it to construct living structures for millions of years. Human beings have only recently learned how to use solar power, but we also use it now to create tangible things.

This has been recognised by prominent scientists such as Erwin Schrödinger[5], when he said that Life is:

" That which avoids the decay into equilibrium."

While this is not a universally accepted view, it does seem to have a ring of truth about it and in this respect it is interesting that Gravity and Life are the two things whose essential essence have not been identified.

Normal chemical reactions will slow down and stabilise at an equilibrium point unless some external factor like an external power house, or a human being, keeps them going. But individual living cells are unlike a bag of chemicals because, (as the biological text books acknowledge[12]), they sustain their chemical activity well above equilibrium by relying on a remarkable set of elaborate components.

Some may try to dismiss cell functions as mere chemical reactions as well, but anyone can see that they are far more than that. They are highly sophisticated and, from enzymes to ribosome, their secrets have not been fully explained - including their origin as part of an extremely elaborate and co-ordinated mechanism... which has been put down to an evolutionary process that could **not** have existed before the first cell.

Another remarkable element of Life is the ability of viruses and some elaborate components such as Ribosomes to self-assemble! Scientists can describe a sequence of events in which these things come together, (sometimes using tools such as scaffolding to assist the process), and there is talk of the energies within molecules to help shape the structures, but this is nothing like a proper explanation.

A full answer to this amazing ability may take us a long way towards an explanation of Life.

In trying to focus on some key abilities for living cells I drew a distinction between 'structural elements' that were reliant on a past evolutionary process, and 'dynamic factors' that seemed to be respond in variable ways to issues and 'information' of the moment.

As mentioned earlier, two clear examples of this were the DNA Repair mechanism of Homologous Recombination, and the routing of vesicles to their many potential end destinations, using a **variety** of walking transporters, across an ever-changing 'road' network.

The former seems to go well beyond 'simple detection' by one molecule or another, by **looking for** other DNA code which might be used to fill-in gaps; apparently making **choices** on how to conduct repairs; and then **deciding** how much code to copy as an in-fill! That's easy for us to rationalise with a brain – but for a bunch of molecules without a brain?

In respect of the other example, how do the motor proteins read a destination code, and understand what it means, (ie. where that location might be found), before working out a route on an ever changing network?

Routing may also be a factor within the larger scale activity of brain signalling because it appears that particular areas of the brain which generate instructions, can send signals to a **variety** of delivery points. (arms, fingers, mouth, tongue etc), In other words they are not aligned on a one-for one basis with muscles/organs, and must presumably engage in some form of routing and decision-making at various junction points.

Again, some will argue that all 3 examples represent a form of chemical 'hard wiring' yet to be found, but there are reasonable grounds to suspect 'awareness'. It will be interesting to see what future research reveals.

However, talk of codes, self-assembly, control, and even crude awareness all point us back to the underlying nature of qualia, Thought, understanding, and ultimately full proactive consciousness.

The research done by Professor Mark Baker into possible diseases of the CALU (the 'mechanism' believed to lie within the Mind which generates the creative use of language), seems to indicate that in over 100 years of searching, no diseases have ever been found, (although diseases have been identified for all other aspects of language generation). One implication from this is that this creative element of the Mind may be non-physical.

When we add to this the findings from neuroscience that the logical mind is insufficient to make every-day decisions on issues which have elements of uncertainty, where the *emotional* parts of our brain are necessary, there is another potential reason for considering that the **Mind** is not a physical thing based entirely on rigid 'mechanical, cause and effect, principles.

A non-physical Mind certainly opens up a stronger avenue to consider the Soul, but these things may still relate to Materialist factors such as interacting fields of influence. However at this stage it is too early to say what any of the scientifically gathered evidence might represent, from the study of 'Out of Body' experiences and possible reincarnation.

There are good reasons to believe that these events are real phenomena even if they do not represent a Soul, so they should therefore be explained.

The results of the AWARE II project across many major hospitals in different countries may be particularly interesting in this respect.

Yet persistent claims about other fringe beliefs, such as past life regression, that **do not have** scientifically gathered evidence, either have to become much more disciplined in their techniques, or they will only gain credibility if more rigorous investigations demonstrate the Soul by other means.

In the meantime we will continue to live our lives on the basis of our normal perceptions, but hopefully if we have a better understanding of what Life is, we can make better choices about how we wish to live them.

The mechanism of Evolution through genetic mutation is likely to persist, but interestingly, humans may now be in the process of moving our evolutionary development **away** from basic survival as we are **consciously** providing healthcare and support for others in need. Is this an example of Free Will finally becoming a strategic influence in Life?

What we can say however is that evolution doesn't seem to be making much headway on the process of ageing. Almost all the improvements in longevity seem to have come from improved healthcare. It seems that Evolution is determined to keep us in a cycle of 2 overlapping generations, like tiles on a roof. It is probably necessary in order for us to live within the resources that the Earth has to offer.

Death may mark a physical boundary, but not necessarily an end to Life itself. An eternal Soul would mean that we have a long time yet to come. Whether Life represents a single 'bite of the cherry'; a series of fresh starts; or a continuing single consciousness is a matter for personal belief.

A Short Glossary of Key Terms Used

Strict Causality — 'cause & effect' - a precise set of starting conditions can only lead to one inevitable outcome.

Logic & Equations — the formulaic application of strict causality.

Spontaneity — something happens without a cause.

Randomness — more than one outcome can arise from a precise start point.

Awareness — any level of understanding that can interpret a sense, which may be very crude or very sophisticated.

Control — the regulation of a system to produce an objective.

Thought — the mechanism and capabilities that generate ideas and concepts which might lead to decision-making.

Soul — the means by which the essence of an individual can be preserved, possibly allowing it to transfer to a new life after physical death.

Resuscitation — the revival of somebody on the brink of death, but who has not fully died.

Resurrection — the restoration of life to the same individual who has physically died: either in the same body or in a new spiritual form reflective of the soul.

Reincarnation — the transfer of an existing life to a new physical body with a new identity, through rebirth.

<u>Appendix A</u> – the Purpose & Structure of DNA

This appendix provides a fuller description of the processes involved in the special mechanisms of life dealing with reproduction, for those who wish to gain a more complete picture of the steps in the process.

The 'nucleus' of every cell contains a full 'instruction manual' on how to build an entire body. In broad terms it does so by :-

1. providing a 'design template' for every cell component, **and**
2. providing the sequence in which they should be produced, in order to assemble them into a full working copy of that cell; **before**
3. 'saying' how each subsequent generation of cell should be adapted and linked together to create an entire body.

That manual is known as DNA.

Deoxyribo Nucleic Acid (DNA) is a polymer, and as we know from earlier chapters, such things are made by stringing together a long chain of standard building blocks known as Monomers. There are different types of monomer, and in the case of DNA, there are just 4 versions of one monomer 'family' being used, (the type known as **Nucleotides**). It is the *sequence* of those 4 nucleotides copied many times along that enormous chain which acts as the coded language of the manual.

The DNA inside a cell is split into sections known as 'Chromosomes', which provide separate sets of templates for things that need to be constructed, or which describe different activities . There are 23 pairs, (46 strands of 'double helix' DNA), in the human genome. Each of the 23 pairs of chromosomes has one DNA strand from the mother and one from the father. These pairs are matched because their code basically describes the same sorts of instructions, but there will be slight differences between the two as each person is different. Across the 23 pairs we each have a complete set of DNA from both parents.

Like other multi-celled organisms, (Eukaryotes), our chromosomes are all linear, *unlike* the 1 or 2 chromosomes which exist in Bacteria & Archaea, (the single celled Prokaryote species), that are circular[21].

Other Eukaryote species have different numbers of chromosomes. For instance, fruit flies have 4 pairs, while a rice plant has 12 pairs, and a dog has 39 pairs. So the size or complexity of the organism does not determine the number of chromosomes – and the size of each chromosome will vary.

How the DNA code is divided between chromosomes is not yet understood. Although the human genome has been mapped it has not been fully analysed, so we cannot say whether there is a logical grouping of code inside each section. Having said that, we do know that just one of the 23 pairs is dedicated to sexual reproduction.

We also know that each chromosome is sub-divided into a number of '**genes**'. Each gene is an instruction that either describes how to build a cell component, (a '*coding gene*'), or a molecule that will help to regulate cell activities, (*non-coding genes*).

Gene codes are flagged at the beginning with a 'start marker', and at the end with a 'stop' marker, which are used when the gene is copied. Those markers also help scientists to identify them, even though we don't always know what they do.

In normal circumstances, each **pair** of linear chromosomes lie side by side and are joined at a 'pinch point' known as a Centromere, (although this is **not** positioned in the middle of a strand as its name might suggest, but close to one end). On one side of the pinch point it looks as if there are two short arms, while on the other side there are two very long arms. The Centromere holds the paired chromosomes together, during reproduction.

There are 'end stops' to each arm which are known as Telomeres. In normal cells, a bit of the Telomere coding seems to be lost each time the cell reproduces, until there is insufficient to reproduce again and the cell dies. It is tempting to think that this mechanism helps to prevent errors through 'wearing out' and excessive reproduction, yet some cancers are very aggressive because their Telomeres do not degrade[21].

Linear chromosomes are wound around proteins known as 'Histone particles'. This tight packaging helps them to fit into the nucleus in an orderly way. However it also means that the incredibly long and tightly curled DNA strand, (which holds the information in a very stable form), has to be uncurled before specific instructions inside it can be used/copied.

This is **not** simply a case of something working its way along that long strand, reading the code from beginning to end on a continuous sequence. New components can often be made in isolation. We need to ask how the triggering molecules, called RNA-Polymerase, know which bit of code they are interested in, as well as *where to find* that particular set of instructions? There is no index and no Thought process to ask the question.

Many of these probing issues remain unanswered. So we can see *what* is happening but don't know everything about **why & how** they are achieved.

As indicated above, the key function of DNA is to act as a preserved instruction manual for every cell that is produced. To achieve this it is made from very stable molecules however the very need to make copies for the purposes of reproduction means that the DNA has to interact with other things – but carefully! This is achieved using the relationships that exist between the 4 nucleotide components.

The core of every nucleotide is a nucleobase. The 4 nucleobases generally operate in 2 distinct pairs. Thymine always matches with Adenine (T-A); while Guamine always matches with Cytosine (G-C).

These base pairings **never change**, and when they are attached to each other the molecules gain a degree of stability, (become less reactive).

One of each pair can also be considered as the '**negative**' of the other.

Nucleobases are quite reactive compounds but they can also be stabilised, or made to react in specific ways, using one or more other 'bolt-on' molecules, (such as a methyl group, and/or a sugar, and/or a phosphate). The least reactive form is DNA but when it is copied as part of the reproductive process, the copy is set into a more reactive form – RNA.

One of the ways in which this is done is through the use of a modified and more reactive form of Thymine known as Uracil, (which has a missing *methyl* group/molecule). Uracil also only pairs with Adenine (U-A).

The term Nucleotide refers to one of these five 'bases' plus a sugar and a phosphate molecule. The less reactive Thymine nucleotide is only used in DNA, while a Uracil nucleotide will only be used in RNA. In this way there will only ever be 4 nucleobases being used in any copy of the genetic code.

As a mere point of interest, another distinguishing feature of DNA, (which makes it makes it less reactive than RNA, and also partly influences its shape), is that it has a missing 'hydroxyl' molecule from its 'ribose' unit – hence the name 'Deoxyribose' – the 'D' in DNA.

In summary we see that both DNA and RNA have the same active elements, the nucleobases, which can be variants of each other, but various chemical additions/removals have made DNA more stable and robust.

DNA is a very long chain of nucleotide pairs set side by side in a line, taking the shape of a twisted ladder. The **rungs** are made by the individual

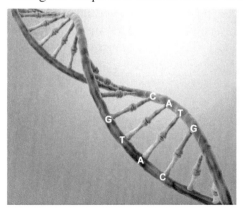

pairs which form a bond between them, (in the middle of the rung), while the sides of the ladder are made by stringing together the nucleotides at the ends of the rungs, (which are not pairs). As mentioned before, it's the **sequence** created by the **4 types** of nucleotide running along either *side* of the ladder which acts as the critical information store/code/instruction manual.

Orig. Image courtesy of FreeImages.com

Due to the pairings**, each side of the ladder represents a full copy of that manual**, but they are

255

'negatives' of each other. Copying, (or 'transcription'), of the DNA sequence to form RNA will normally be undertaken on only one side of the ladder, beginning at the start marker for a gene. It **always** results in a *single* strand of RNA nucleotides, (not a twisted ladder pairing).

Chemicals known as 'Riboswitches' can also be made by a cell, from a **non**-*coding* gene. These can bind to a section of RNA as it is being formed, to either change its shape, (and therefore its effectiveness), or even prevent its use in certain circumstances.

Different types of RNA are used for different purposes. Some have specific functions in their own right, (such as rRNA and tRNA), but a large proportion will be used as working templates, (mRNA), copied from 'coding genes'. This type of RNA is used to produce the main working components of our bodies: another type of polymer known as a protein.

Proteins are long chains as well, but they are assembled from a different family of monomers known as Amino Acids. Unlike nucleobases, there are 20 amino acids that are available for use in a cell.

It is here that we see more clearly why DNA and RNA are regarded as codes. Particular combinations of nucleotide are used to signify different Amino Acids. More specifically, when 'devices' in a cell read an mRNA strand, every **three** nucleotides in the mRNA sequence, (a '**codon**'), will represent an identifier for <u>one</u> type of Amino Acid.

As mentioned, DNA has markers for the start and end of a gene sequence, but it *doesn't* have markers to identify each codon within the gene. Its long sequence of nucleotides must simply be read in groups of 3, in turn.

Put another way, if you were able to insert a single nucleotide anywhere in a gene sequence, or start to read the code from the wrong place, you would change the meaning and the end outcome completely, as each group of 3 nucleotides would seem different after this point!

Mathematically there can be 64 sequence combinations of the 4 types of nucleotide if they are grouped in 3s, but there are only 20 Amino Acids.

However, due to the rigid pairings of nucleotides, one Amino Acid can be described in two ways, ('positive' and 'negative').

> One of the key 'filtering and selection' techniques which nature uses, is to match codons with their paired negative form, known as an '**anticodon**'. This works because the pairings are chemically drawn together, (*unlike* the <u>same</u> codons).

Positive and negative descriptions use up twice as many of the 64 potential combinations, effectively giving us a distinct purpose for 40 of them. A few of the other 24 can be used as marker points for the start and end of the reading process, but the rest seem to have led to some duplications in Amino Acid identification. Yet, overall, the process works well.

An Overview of How Cells Normally Use their Genetic Code

There are many processes in a cell. Some can be thought of as cyclical: for instance, where things are produced, used, and then recycled. Other processes are linear - generating things that have an end purpose and are therefore *not* recycled. However they all form part of a slick, interlinked, and co-ordinated set of activities that form the entirety of the cell.

By way of example, there are different types of compartment in Eukaryote cells and the purpose of one of these types is to generate energy. These are known as Mitochondria and they essentially charge tiny molecular batteries known as 'ADP' molecules, using energy rather than electricity. This is done by loosely attaching a phosphate molecule to the ADP, using an energy-rich chemical bond, which turns it into 'ATP'. If the bond is broken and the phosphate released, the energy is also released. ATP is cascaded to all parts of the body for use.

Unusually, mitochondria compartments have their own **circular** form of DNA, which is separate from the main linear DNA of the cell nucleus. It is nuclear DNA which generates of all of the other structures in a cell.

This section will focus on just one aspect of genetic operations, which will help us to make sense of the debate about Evolution that was explained in Chapter 6.

From earlier paragraphs you will recall that a **'coding gene'** is one section of a chromosome that defines how to make one component of a cell. There are approx. 21,000 of these in a 'typical' human cell. Each of the components is a polymer - either a protein, or a strand of RNA. Although each of these definitions is quite long, they collectively only represent $1^1/_2\%$ of the entire human DNA – a tiny proportion!

There are also 9,000 **non-coding** genes which help to configure and regulate the reproductive processes – so approx. 30,000 genes in total[12].

A full mapping of the human genome was published in 2004. It was a huge achievement, showing every nucleotide in the entire DNA chain, however it will take many decades for this to be analysed, to identify what each of the gene sequences does/achieves. What it already seems to show is that there are lots of repeated sequences within it, (perhaps as much as 50% of human DNA), either representing old redundant versions of many genes, or sections of code which have been replicated multiple times – for example, when certain genes have changed their position within a genome!

The same complex process of assembling polymer components is used by every living cell on the planet, (even if different types of cell deploy that process in slightly different ways).

We saw earlier that DNA defines two broad categories of end polymer: **Proteins** and **RNA**. Proteins are made from Amino Acids, while the different types of RNA are made from Nucleotides.

Cell walls, compartment membranes, and 'microtubules' are partly made from proteins but also require certain types of **Lipid/fat** to supplement them. These are formed from 'Monosaccharide' monomers, (sugars and fatty acids), but they are **not** defined within the DNA. They are products that emerge from components which DNA does describe.

We can summarise these relationships in the following table:

Small Organic Molecules	Official **Monomer** Names	**Polymers** Long Chains of Monomers	**Polymer Types**
Amino Acids (20 used in Life)	Amino Acids	Polypeptides	Proteins
Carbohydrates (Sugars & Fatty Acids)	Monosaccharides	Polysaccharides	Lipids, Starch, Cellulose, etc.
Nucleic Acids (4 used in life)	Nucleotides	Polynucleotides	DNA & RNA

RNA and Lipids are generally assembled by **Enzymes**, (in quite separate compartments/organelles within the cell), while Proteins are assembled by **Ribosomes** in the watery fluid, '**cytosol**', which surrounds the organelles.

It is believed that there are possibly a million distinct types of protein used in living things and probably many more versions of RNA, (which not only have to produce 'mRNA' copies of every protein, but also fulfil other functions of their own). The tricky point is that each of these useful chains/strings has to be constructed as a very long and *precise* sequence of monomers - a single error potentially being able to render it useless.

The monomers used have to be 'pure' versions, uncontaminated by rogue chemicals which may try to react with them. Once the chains of proteins or RNA have been assembled, they must also remain uncontaminated by unwanted reactions. The ways in which cells regulate their own activity to maintain this quality pose many fascinating questions.

Scientists distinguish different types of RNA by their end uses. 'rRNA', is a key part of a **Ribosome**; elaborate programmable machines mentioned earlier, (hence the 'r' designation). Others can act as simple labels, such as 'tRNA' (transfer RNA). Both of these are known as 'non-coding' RNAs.

Like many polymers all of these chains fold themselves into particular shapes, and it is the position of their reactive areas after folding that seems to determine their function, as much as the type of reaction they assist.

RNA and Proteins are produced 'to order', not as a continuous stream of all the 21,000 different types. The way in which these orders *arise* seem to come in three broad ways. The first comes from the "Cell Cycle" – which duplicates the existing cell entirely, and which follows a 'pre-programmed' routine coded into the DNA. Secondly, there are signals from outside the cell, (normally from other parts of a body), which request the cell to make more of a protein than the cell needs for itself, to be used elsewhere.

Thirdly, and possibly more contentiously, there are 'ad-hoc' requests which are needed when the cell needs to repair or maintain its operations. These seem to be the least-well understood, because their ways of 'placing their order' with the DNA are not so clearly identified.

This has suggested that such cases may not require an order. Where a need is identified within the cell, (eg. for maintenance), the associated process may simply grab a passing version of the necessary protein, that has been produced by the 'cell cycle', or on the instruction of an external signal. The difficulty with this is that different processes tend to require different proteins so there could be many situations where the desired protein isn't available, and we don't see cells regularly failing for this reason.

We can see that a series of chemical reactions is required to activate a gene so that it is ready to copy, (but we don't necessarily know what kicks this series into action). It is also unclear how these chemicals can jump to the correct place on the DNA strand, (as genes can seemingly be positioned anywhere along the DNA chain). This has been a real mystery, but the latest thinking is that the activating chemicals have evolved to recognise and bind to certain chemical signatures in the DNA – yet this implies that they drift around until they find a match, rather than any targeted response.

It is also unclear why some genes are copied from one of the chromosomes in a pair, (ie. from one parent), while other gene codes will be used from the chromosome of the other parent. Whichever strand is chosen, that version of the gene is always used in the body of that person.

DNA/RNA are topped & tailed with standard markers known as a '5-end' and a '3-end'. Regardless of which side of the DNA is being read/copied it is always done from the 5-end to the 3-end because the alignment of the nucleotides on each side gives it a polarity – ie. a sense of direction.

Interestingly the two sides of a DNA double helix point in *opposite* ways. Each side of the ladder has its '5' and '3' at the reverse ends, so although the nucleotide pairs only give one sequence in the middle of the DNA, one side will be replicated in the opposite direction to the other. This doesn't matter as long as the strands are marked for reading/use in a consistent way later – ie. they end up being topped and tailed to be read and folded in the same direction later.

The '5-end' is so called because it has 5 carbon atoms arranged in a ring, plus a phosphate molecule. Visually it resembles a knob. It is thought that replication processes start here because the enzymes which perform the copying process need the energy they can gain by breaking the phosphate bonds, to get them going.

The 3-end is named because the ribose ring which would normally be there, is terminated by a hydroxyl molecule (OH) after the third carbon atom. It appears like a small hole[12].

The 'capping' of newly copied strands of RNA is a complex but vital part of the process of replication. We can observe the different stages of what is happening but as with all chemistry, other unwanted reactions could potentially occur. The reasons why we only seem to get one outcome is largely due to

- the action of particular **enzymes** which control the activity, plus
- the limited range of chemicals which are available in that controlled environment, which only seem to permit certain reactions to occur when particular chemicals come close to each other.

However **why** these unthinking chemicals should create this highly tailored process is a complete mystery.

Onward Process

In eukaryote cells, as soon as they are generated, the three types of RNA move out of the Nucleus into the water-based fluid of the cell, known as the **cytosol**. It is here that a number of conceptual things have to happen.

In strategic terms, the precise template for producing a protein, (mRNA - which uses a *Nucleotide* code), has to be **translated** into a sequence of *Amino Acids* which form the protein, and they must also be assembled in the correct order. Each type of RNA plays a distinct role in this process.

Ribosomal RNA (rRNA) combines with some specific proteins to form a permanent Ribosome sub-unit. Each Ribosome has a large and a small sub-unit, however until they are used the two parts remain separate!

(How their 'coming together' is orchestrated remains unclear, even though we know that it happens once a strand of mRNA has been inserted into the small unit mechanism).

Ribosomes are one of the astonishing elements of physical life - true working programmable 'assembly line' machines, although they are made from proteins and rRNA rather than metals and plastics.

Elsewhere, tRNA is being used as a label to tag an appropriate Amino Acid. tRNA is quite a small polymer chain and it does resemble the tag on a parcel or Christmas present, with a thin string of nucleotides at one end, and a much broader 'label' section below it. The information it contains is actually an **anticodon** which sits at the very bottom of the label section.

The string is the bit which attaches to an Amino Acid, (shown in orange on the diagram below) – **but that Amino Acid has to match the anticodon at the bottom**.

This is the point of code translation and it is done by an enzyme although we don't fully understand how. Yet this is clearly a highly significant step in the overall process.

The final stage matches an mRNA codon to a tRNA anticodon. This is not a translation, but a gathering of correct Amino Acids in the correct sequence.

This stage is initiated when an mRNA strand is loaded into a small ribosome unit, thereby acting as an instruction - to begin assembly of the particular protein that's described in its code. In summary the full end-end process is:

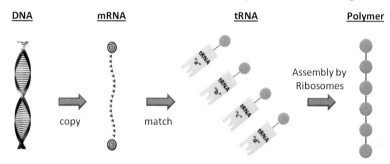

In bacteria, protein assembly by a ribosome can begin literally while the mRNA strand is still being generated from the DNA, but in Eukaryotes which have separate compartments, the mRNA has to be fully completed before later stages can commence.

The priming of the small ribosome unit, (generally portrayed in diagrams as being the lower part), also triggers it to join with a large unit to form a complete Ribosome. In one slick process, each codon in the mRNA strand is then matched to its nucleotide 'pairing'- a tRNA anticodon - and the attached Amino Acids are then strung together to build a protein.

It is useful to understand the way in which Ribosomes seem to work because their activities show the level of sophistication being achieved by these incredible machines, so please stay with it a little longer. (Remember, these are unthinking molecules which have somehow managed to assemble themselves to form a very intricate process).

Ribosomes have 3 main active sites where they interact with mRNA, and these are set out in a line. We can refer to them as the entry point 'A': a main production point 'P': and the exit point 'E'.

Each of these sites has active elements in both the large (top) section as well as the small (bottom) section of the ribosome. Per the diagram below, the top section will deal with tRNA & the assembly of proteins, while the bottom section will deal with the mRNA template.

The small ribosome unit will prime itself with the 'start sequences' of an mRNA strand at site 'A'. It uses the first few nucleotide molecules to position itself accurately to read the first codon, and also grabs a particular type of 'starter' tRNA label. This is the signal for the two parts of the ribosome to come together.

As those two units join, the starter tRNA is loaded into the large ribosome unit where it marks the beginning of the **protein** strand. This is done as the mRMA is moved along to the 2nd position 'P' and the first proper codon aligns with site 'A'.

Once the Ribosome is fully loaded in this way, the large unit selects the appropriate tRNA, (with its attached Amino Acid), to match the codon at position 'A'. The small unit then repeats the sequence by pulling the mRNA through the ribosome, 1 codon, (3 nucleotides) at a time – using it as a sort of conveyor belt. Each time a correct tRNA / Amino Acid is found at site 'A' it causes the shape of the Ribosome to flex slightly, generating the internal movement needed to move the mRNA forwards by 1 codon.

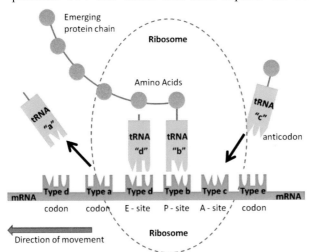

The selection of tRNA molecules is very rapid, suggesting that there is an element of pre-selection going on (rather than just a series of random attempts at a match), but this process isn't always accurate. There are numerous occasions where the match is 'close' but not quite right, leading to many rejections. The way in which a ribosome exercises 'quality control' at site 'A' partly seems to be one of timing.

Incorrect selections of tRNA will be ejected quite rapidly while correct selections, (matching codon and anticodon), will linger long enough for them to trigger a shape change in the Ribosome to clamp it to the mRNA, allowing the two to move forward to site 'P'.

Current theory suggests that errors which get past this selection process will lead to additional distortions in the Ribosome at site 'P' which will then affect the new match being attempted at site 'A'. Through the next few codons the degree of mismatch is thought to progressively increase until the entire process fails. However we don't really know. What we can say is that the emerging incorrect protein is rejected at that point, and its monomer components are recycled, along with the used & discarded tRNA.

We **can't** say that such rejections occur because of an incorrect chemistry between the Amino Acids in the emerging protein chain. All combinations of the 20 Amino Acids appear to be possible, (even if they don't necessarily prove to be useful), so something else has to distinguish a good protein chain from a bad one at the mRNA end of the process, and there **doesn't** seem to be a secondary 'check reading' by the Ribosome.

However there are also other controls later in the cell's processes that try to pick up errors which are not rejected at this point. Cells are truly remarkable in this respect - because those checks are done in very different areas of the cell that don't have access to a template. How is this done, and why unthinking chemicals would 'see the need' to develop such checks, is unclear – but they do. There are some clues, but again we don't know, and I ran through some of the thinking in Chapters 5 & 6.

While a very small number of incorrect proteins could slip through these various safety nets, this type of error is **not** generally thought to be a source of cell *mutation*, even if they were to happen in the early stages of foetal development. This is because the error **wouldn't** affect the genetic code and would almost certainly be a 'one-off', having minimal impact on the cell which needs millions of proteins in its operations.

So the prime areas of interest in the process of Evolution must lie in the mechanisms of the Nucleus.

Yet Ribosomes still pose a real dilemma for Evolution theory, because they are partly made of proteins and yet they are also the **only** things capable of manufacturing those proteins. So **how could the first ribosome come to exist**?

This is one of the many questions that has to be answered by Abiogenesis research. It is made even more significant by the fact that there is no apparent way for the different types of ribosome to have evolved from each other, (ie. between bacteria, archaea, and eukaryotes). They all seem to be individual developments. We might speculate about an earlier 'common ancestor' in the distant past, but if so, all trace of it has disappeared completely.

As you might imagine, Ribosomes have drawn a lot of interest from scientists but we are still far from an answer.

DNA Repair

Although I have emphasised the stability of DNA as a mechanism for preserving the genetic 'instruction manual', it is a fact that every piece of DNA in our bodies suffers tens of thousands of damaging effects each day.

This damage is caused by a variety of things such as: heat; mistakes in the mechanisms of the cell; and exposure to environmental factors such as radiation (sunlight or nuclear), or undesirable chemicals, (from excess alcohol to cigarette smoke, diesel fumes, and other toxins).

The integrity of DNA would quickly be lost if a series of mechanisms didn't correct such damage almost immediately, and with remarkable efficiency. Collectively these are known as 'DNA Repair'.

The different types of damage can be rationalised in the following ways:-

a) In many places along its enormous length, **one side** of the DNA ladder **can be broken**. At each of these points, mechanisms have to decide if this is a simple break that can just be re-connected, or whether an entire section of the ladder has been knocked out and needs rebuilding.

   If one side of the ladder remains complete then the other side can be rebuilt because the one-for-one pairing of nucleotides will clearly indicate which nucleotide has to sit on the opposite side of each rung.

b) **Both sides** of the DNA double helix ladder **may be broken** causing the ladder to split completely & separate. In this case the mechanisms have to determine whether the ladder has any missing sections, or can again be simply re-connected. Reconstruction has to follow the principles of Homologous Recombination below.

c) Individual **nucleotides can potentially be knocked-out,** even if the sides of the ladder remain intact. These 'missing teeth' are generally the result of chemical activity rather than a collision with something. For instance there are an estimated 18,000 instances each day, within every cell, of 'depurination' – where the bonds holding Adenine or Guanine nucleotides to the ladder are broken and they float away.

d) **Nucleotides** in the rungs of the ladder **can be chemically changed** so that they no longer represent a valid pairing. Some changes put a nucleotide beyond all recognition but others are more sinister, changing one nucleotide into another – for instance, one chemical change can transform a Cytosine nucleotide into a Uracil nucleotide, (an effect known as Cytosine Deamination). In that circumstance, a later check has to guess which of the nucleotides on either side of the ladder was the correct original.

e) Ultraviolet radiation can lead to **a Thymine nucleotide changing into a form that will no longer replicate**, even though it is still in place in the ladder. This will cause one or more of the nucleotide rungs to be missed, (effectively deleted), every time it was replicated, and as we know, that would cause every subsequent codon to be misread as something else – eg. a different type of Amino Acid.

f) **Other chemical changes** can also occur such as: oxidation, methylation, alkalination, opened carbon rings, and conversion of carbon double bonds to single bonds. Each of these will change the purpose or effectiveness of that part of the DNA.

Each cell appears to use a significant proportion of its DNA coding plus an equally large amount of its resources to build repair mechanisms. An array of protein enzymes constantly scan for different types of damage, and theory suggests that each enzyme is dedicated to just one type of problem, enabling it to know which solution to apply. They constantly test every section of DNA, and act when they find an error that matches their profile.

There is an obvious logic to repairing double helix DNA. If one side of the ladder still exists, any missing parts must have been the negatives of the nucleotides that remain. This is indeed the logic which seems to be applied by many repair mechanisms – except of course that chemicals don't think, so they should not be able to apply logic, just inevitable process.

Where single nucleotides are either shown to be damaged or missing, and the sides of the ladder still remain, processes can surgically cut a hole in the side, remove the nucleotide, and replace it. Alternately, where one side of the ladder is broken, a more complex set of processes is able to cut out a section of 30 nucleotides around the break, and rebuild that side again.

Yet we find numerous situations in DNA repair where the logic is not clear cut, if you pardon the pun. The examples we are about to run through are not hard to understand, but the detail required to describe plus some unfamiliar terms might make them seem more complex than they are. All I can suggest is that you try to keep the 'big Picture' in mind if you find yourself struggling – ie. is it a hole; a break; or a chemical change?

Our first example deals with a chemical change, (example 'd' above), where a process called 'Cytosine Deamination' changes one nucleotide into another – resulting in a mismatch on the rung. If left uncorrected any copy of the damaged side of the ladder would generate the wrong DNA or mRNA code that could ultimately result in an incorrect protein component.

In this situation the original nucleotide pairing would have been C-G, but chemical activity has changed the Cytosine to Uracil making it U-G. **This is an invalid combination**, but which part is incorrect?

The valid pairing with Uracil is Adenine, (U-A), so if the G is changed rather than the U we end up with a fully mutated nucleotide sequence U-A instead of a mismatch. However we also know that within DNA, (rather than RNA), Uracil is an invalid component, so it should always be the Uracil that is changed. There **is** an enzyme that seems to repair this situation, which deploys this extra logic, at least most of the time.

However we also know that the addition of a methyl group to Uracil will convert it to Thymine, which **is** a valid component of DNA, and there **are** situations where Cytosine will convert to Thymine[12]. There is still a mismatch with T-G, but which of the two nucleotides is correct? Both could be valid.

Without a clear course of action logic runs out, and in such situations many computer programs would just stop/crash. Yet it seems that the enzymes involved **have a guess** and quite a number of these guesses seem to result in errors which *mutate* the DNA code. How do chemicals guess? The implication is that they don't guess, but are pre-programmed to just use one side of the ladder as the default - yet this has not been fully proven.

Other major issues arise where **both** sides of the ladder are broken, causing the entire DNA strand to be completely severed. Here the difficulty is in knowing whether any of the code is missing in the gap. Of course, this may not be a clean break, so there could be additional sections of the code that are missing, either on one side of the break or even both. When an inspecting molecule finds a break there are many permutations, each with different potential solutions.

A crude repair would be to simply join the available ends together, (assuming that there was nothing missing in the gap). Yet the technique which does this also results in one of the remaining rungs being deleted at the join – so a mutation is inevitable. Yet, if there are complete sections of code missing, the situation could become very severe if the omission was formalised and then used to produce radically incorrect components.

To compensate for some of this the cell could combine some functions to rejoin the broken ends and fill-in any missing code on one side of the ladder that results from this, (ie. in situations where there has been an uneven break), but this still doesn't guarantee that no code is missing.

Sometimes the *way* in which a DNA strand is broken can point to a solution.

Quite a number of double breaks can occur when the entire chromosome is being copied, and in these situations the sections of code which have already been duplicated, (sister chromosome), can act as a template to rebuild the original DNA strand. This technique, referred-to as **Homologous Recombination**, can be very accurate even if it is highly complex. There are indications that the mere presence of the sister chromosome can somehow be detected leading to this procedure.

A final option is a risky twist on Homologous Recombination in those situations where the chromosome was **not** in the process of being copied. This uses the paired chromosome from the other parent to rebuild the DNA: however we should remember that this may **not** be the chosen form of gene that is being used by the body, so this technique could end up forcing different components into existing structures.

(It is this 2nd version of the process which is re-used in **Meiosis** to mix the genetic codes of parent chromosomes when generating eggs or sperm).

To give you an idea of the complexity of such processes, (which is not fully understood by scientists), let me share these outline steps:-

1. A preliminary step in the process seem to check that there is a good alignment between the two paired chromosomes – ie. that significant sections of the code seem to match on either side of the break.

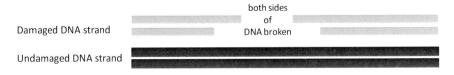

Damaged DNA strand

both sides
of
DNA broken

Undamaged DNA strand

266

2. If necessary, carefully positioned extra breaks can be engineered in the broken DNA, by introducing DNA damaging agents[22] or the Spo11 protein[23]. This <u>does</u> happen during the deliberate process of Meiosis where sections of code are to be exchanged; but in repair situations it might be used to establish 'clean' places where the codes match.

3. The ends of the strands are partly 'digested' by various types of enzyme, to provide a good join point for the rebuilding of the ladder.

4. Specialist proteins such as Rad51 coat the ends of the DNA strands with a nucleoprotein to form filaments, (thin strands), which are used to pull **one** end of **one** side of the damaged DNA, over to the complete chromosome at a position where the codes match.

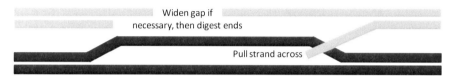

Widen gap if necessary, then digest ends

Pull strand across

5. The damaged section is then rebuilt using other special enzymes which replicate the code from the undamaged DNA: (normal copying processes would require enzymes to attach to the same strand).

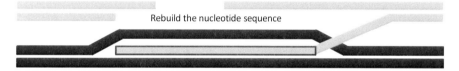

Rebuild the nucleotide sequence

6. Once the missing sections are reconstructed, (and somehow these processes seem to know where to stop), the repaired strand is dragged back to its broken counterpart and the two ends are reconnected, to form one complete side of the ladder on the damaged DNA.

Reconnect

7. The final process is then to duplicate the code on the other side of the damaged DNA to complete the double helix.

Replicate

Once again, that's not bad for a bunch of unthinking molecules... but the precise chemistry of how they do it is a mystery.

Overall, when we consider this process, we seem to see considerable logic and even a degree of awareness being applied: in deciding which repair function to undertake; and then in co-ordinating a series of enzyme components across quite separate strands of DNA. It's an aspect of cell operations that could point to other fundamental capabilities.

Of course, it could be argued that this is all part of the way the components were 'designed' to operate, and to throw the emphasis on an unexplained evolutionary process to achieve that design.

However any talk of pre-programming has to deal with the fact that every type of break represents a unique set of circumstances that has to be diagnosed and 'understood'. Even with certain 'inherited capabilities' from the DNA, (pre-programming), there would still be a need for an inevitable chemical mechanism to account for the decisions/actions at each logical stage, if the materialist perspective is correct.

Yet we don't know what applies that logic, or indeed have any idea what would give these unthinking molecules, (without a survival instinct), the impetus to develop such processes. We will have to see what emerges from future research.

As a final consideration, we should ask whether the original principle of one enzyme performing one discreet function is correct. This principle was incorporated into early theory to reinforce the point that chemicals can't make decisions and can only act in inevitable ways based on circumstances in their immediate locality, (things they can directly react with).

There is more and more evidence from this and other processes, (such as the controlling of the 'S' phase in the cell cycle – see Appendix B), that enzymes can do more than one thing.

Yet some of these processes are more versatile: seemingly able to look for different types of damage, and also exercising a broader and more proactive overview of what is happening – including the identification of other suitable strands of DNA that may be similar to the one they are working on. Finding similar code sequences in other parts of the matching chromosome, (while rejecting the other 22 paired chromosomes), is not straightforward in terms of logic. For chemicals that don't normally operate beyond the strand they are working on, that's a surprising move.

It is clear that with direct physical contact there is potential for chemicals to do a comparison with things that are directly linked, such as each side of a ladder, but it's hard to see how the detection of relevant things can occur when the chromosomes are not linked; the strands of DNA may not be sitting directly alongside each other; and genes may be held in a different sequence/position in chromosome strand. If there is some sort of chemical 'odour' being released into the fluid nearby, scientists haven't detected it.

RNA Editing

Why RNA Editing exists at all, is a mystery. All forms of this process do exactly what the name implies – they physically change the nucleotide code that has been so carefully copied from the DNA manual.

There is speculation that, within the process of evolution, it formed as a way of refining either mistakes or other experiments in the RNA code. Others suggest that it may have originated as a defence mechanism against viruses, etc. We simply don't know, yet it seems that when this technique is deployed it may have benefits.

These processes can be applied to all types of RNA that we have discussed, all-be-it in different circumstances. However to me it seems most bizarre when either used on strands of mRNA, or some of the regulatory activities that RNA has in the 'non-coding' sections of DNA.

By definition, these will either change the nature of the protein component that is to be built, (potentially in quite profound ways); or may alter the place to which it is transported, or the circumstances in which it is used.

In animals, two main forms of RNA Editing convert nucleotides from one type to another, and because there is **no pairing** on RNA strands, the change will proceed through the system, as no error checking is possible.

Altering an mRNA codon can result in the selection of a different Amino Acid during ribosome assembly of a protein, but it could also result in one of the codons in the middle of the sequence being turned into a premature 'stop' signal.

However one particular type of edit to a regulatory form of RNA is particularly prevalent in humans, and the indications are that it helps brain activity and may also prevent epilepsy. It is worth describing.

One of the editing enzymes changes Adenine into a different chemical called Inosine, and if this is done in particular places on some selected forms of RNA, it leads to the production of a 'transmitter–gated ion channel' in the brain that seems vital to normal brain development[12].

The characteristics which seem to prompt deliberate use of this technique partly seem to arise where an enzyme recognises that two sections of the same RNA strand can fold together, creating a nucleotide pairing that would normally feature only a DNA double strand. That same circumstance also seems to indicate precisely where the change should be made. This can be done in advance of the RNA folding making it difficult to see how the circumstances can be spotted. But even with such precision it's unclear why the DNA code wasn't specified correctly in the first place.

Whether this is to preserve alternate uses of the gene elsewhere in the body, or is it a partial indication of how evolutionary development may work, it seems to indicate that unthinking chemicals can somehow be looking to clarify a broader perspective of how the body operates.

Appendix B – Life's Amazing Metabolism

This appendix provides a fuller description of the Metabolic processes involved in the amazing day-to-day activities in which cells are engaged, for those who wish to gain a more complete understanding.

Cells represent the core of life and despite intense scrutiny the 'essence of Life' remains unexplained. However, scrutiny of different types of cell from bones, to organs, (including the brain and skin), have **narrowed the areas where such answers might be found**.

We see a lot of the mechanics and the chemistry, but we don't necessarily see **why** they are happening. The answers now seem to lie in the realms of atoms, where we cannot observe what is happening directly, and so we now have to deduce possible answers from intricate but indirect tests.

In their most basic form, the purpose of cells is to exist and to reproduce. These are easy things to say, but they are **not** easy things to achieve, as indicated by the complexity already presented in Appendix A. So this chapter looks at how cells maintain their existence.

If you recall, even the biochemical text books acknowledge that cells maintain their operations well above chemical equilibrium, and that requires special capabilities. Indeed, it seems to go against the basic principle that all chemical activity should naturally gravitate towards equilibrium.

To exist means that individual cells have to generate enough energy to sustain their operations. These activities are based on physical/chemical components whose complex structures also need raw materials. It is the purpose of a cell's metabolism to acquire the resources and then to use them to sustain the cell. Like a miniscule city, the 'acquisition' elements are the power stations and energy distribution networks. The areas which use the raw materials are factories which include assembly machines, quality control networks, storage, transport, and disposal mechanisms.

More specifically, 'Metabolism' represents a series of processes which :-

- **break down** food molecules - to release energy from them, and/or to salvage spare parts, (a process known as *Catabolism*), or
- **construct** larger molecules & cellular components such as proteins and nucleic acids, (a process known as *Anabolism*), and
- **transport** usable components or forms of energy to the areas which can make use of them, both within and between cells, and
- **dispose of/eliminate** waste products.
- **communicate** via **signalling mechanisms**, to control activities.

It is worth emphasising here that the term 'Reproduction' is *not* generally used to describe the way in which individual polymer molecules are built/duplicated, (which is 'Anabolism' above): as we have seen in Ch. 5 it refers to the broader process by which a new life begins, (either in sexual or asexual ways), ***plus*** the ways in which entire cells replicate themselves, modifying their 'daughter cells' to create the different parts of a body.

Anabolism therefore has two roles. The first is to support the day-to-day process of maintaining life, replacing parts that are used up. The second is a sub-step for the construction of an entirely new cell.

Both energy and raw materials are gained from the wider environment, as food or nutrient. These have to match the needs of each cell in terms of what it aims to construct, which is why each **'metabolic pathway'** represents a *fixed pairing* of catabolic and anabolic processes.

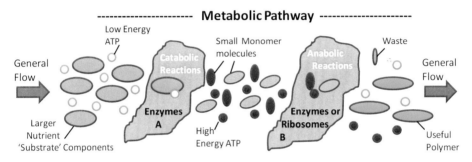

Chemicals that enter a **'metabolic pathway'** are transformed through a series of chemical reactions which use **enzymes** to assist and also regulate those processes. The pathways can be likened to a general flow of material that pass around various, near-stationary, enzymes positioned at different sections along the path. These enable specific reactions to take place.

In broad terms, the simpler Prokaryote cells will operate just one main pathway, while each internal compartment in Eukaryote cells will operate different metabolic pathways that digest and use different nutrients[12].

If you are unfamiliar with many of these terms you may be getting a little word-blind at this moment, so take a moment to make sure you've understood the outline of what we have covered so far.

At the most basic level, the working chemicals in all cells primarily consist of six types of atom:- carbon, hydrogen, oxygen, nitrogen, sulphur, and phosphorous. A body may also contain trace elements such as iron, which feature in some specialised cell components, (such as blood haemoglobin). The first 5 of these are also considered to be the dominant elements in the early environment of our planet, which gives materialists a basis for considering the origins of life. Using these chemicals, all cells are both constructed from & operate using water plus 3 main categories of polymer:-

Proteins, **RNA/DNA**, and **Carbohydrates/starch**.

As we know from Chapters 4 & 5, polymers are chains of 'standard' components known as monomers, however each of the 3 types of polymer use different forms of monomer building block. We can summarise these relationships in the following table:

Small Organic Molecules	Official **Monomer** Names	**Polymers** Long Chains of Monomers	**Polymer Types**
Amino Acids (20 used in Life)	Amino Acids	Polypeptides	Proteins
Sugars	Monosaccharides	Polysaccharides	Carbohydrates Starch, Cellulose
Nucleic Acids (4 used in life)	Nucleotides	Polynucleotides	DNA & RNA

So Proteins are made from Amino Acids, while DNA and the different types of RNA are made from other types of monomer building block: Nucleotides. Finally, Carbohydrates are assembled from Monosaccharide monomers such as sugars, (but **not** within the nucleus of a cell).

Within each of the three polymer types are an enormous variety of different molecules, which have allowed different types of cell, (such as Prokarya and Eukarya), to do very different things in very different environments across the globe. Proteins in particular are the dominant workhorses of living cells.

Generating and Distributing Energy

In order to obtain the different materials and energy that they need for their particular types of protein, some organisms (Organotrophic) will feed off organic material such as fats and proteins, while others (Lithotrophic) feed off rocks & inorganic chemicals.

However not all catabolic processes digest nutrients to gain energy. 'Phototrophic' organisms, (typically plants), obtain their energy from sunlight using a process known as photosynthesis. They do this by using a specific ring of molecules in their key chemical, chlorophyll, whose shape helps to position the collective energy of those molecules at a tipping point.

Even a small amount of sunlight is enough for the ring of molecules to absorb enough energy to take them to the next energy level. The extra energy causes an electron to be lost, which is used to bind carbon dioxide to water, creating sugars. Yet the missing electron in the chlorophyll then has to be replaced from a lower energy source, which is taken from other water in the plant's system. The end result of that process is the production of free oxygen from the water - which is how the oxygen in the atmosphere is believed to have originated, and is still being replenished to this day.

Don't worry about these details, it is sufficient to realise that while this is all very mechanical & inevitable, it is still remarkable that the ring and other mechanisms not only emerged but also became associated with each other in a complex and purposeful way, enabling the process to happen. It is another example of 'Strategic Arrangements' that either had to evolve or be established by other means.

So are there any remarkable features in those other catabolic processes which do 'digest' nutrients?

We should first realise that in larger animals, digestion begins in the stomach and intestines where sizeable chunks of organic matter, including proteins, are initially disassembled. This results in the smaller monomers such as Amino Acids, sugars, and fatty acids, entering the blood stream, which in turn cascades them to cells throughout the body.

This mechanism delivers those partly processed nutrients to each cell where the catabolic mechanisms then continue the sequence which either generates energy or prepares components for re-use.

It's interesting to note that while bacteria and plants can generate all of the 20 Amino Acids they require to make proteins, mammals can only make 11 **non**-essential Amino Acids. The other 9 essential ones can only be obtained/salvaged from the food they eat[12].

One type of internal compartment, common to almost all Eukaryotes, is known as Mitochondria, whose normal function is to extract *energy* from nutrients & store it in an easily transportable/usable form known as **ATP**.

Mitochondria are unique in having a double membrane boundary and also having their own DNA! Interestingly, mitochondrial DNA closely resembles that of bacteria, being circular, not linear.

There can be several Mitochondrial compartments in each cell, and they can also move around the cell to a degree.

> In terms of explaining how Eukaryotes may have originated, the linking of these basic facts about compartments to the idea of predatory cells, has led to the notion that Mitochondria first arose in the distant past when one cell absorbed another. Rather than one digesting the other, the rationale is that they both survived and flourished together – finding the arrangement mutually beneficial.
>
> As an interesting side note, you may recall that Mitochondrial DNA is passed down exclusively from the mother, and people may be aware that it was this genetic trait that allowed the skeleton of King Richard III of England to be identified after being discovered in 2012 under a car park in Leicester.

Returning to our main theme, mitochondria are a main element of the first metabolic process I listed above, 'Catabolism'. The energy released by breaking down nutrients in mitochondria is captured & stored primarily in the chemical 'ATP' through its loose but energy-rich chemical bonds. For this reason ATP has been described either as a battery or as a '*Universal Energy Currency*' within individual cells and the wider body.

That energy is used when ATP bonds are later 'hydrolysed', ie. broken –
either: - as part of the Anabolic processes; or
- the processes of Reproduction; or
- in functions that have a broader purpose, such as flexing muscles or powering brain activity.

Yet there's a deeper question – what makes each stage in a process only use ATP energy at an appropriate moment? It isn't just a case that energy is released when different molecules happen to bump into each other. There does appear to be targeted use, so we have to ask why?

At a superficial level, one part of the reason is because ATP molecules are attracted to certain chemicals which act as connection points on motors and other cell machinery; however the ATP doesn't necessarily get used as soon as it connects. There are occasions where it is held until needed and that type of evolutionary development is also a strange one to rationalise.

Strategically, while we do know that signals from the brain can cause activity within a cell to 'ramp up' or 'scale back' through a complex series of steps, (using ATP), it's less clear how such regulation is achieved when cells live in isolation, with no outside signals being received.

An Overview of Cell Structures and Movement

At a strategic level, a cell is defined by its outer wall or 'membrane'. This globular sack is a porous barrier, but it can be quite selective about what it lets through into its middle.

The internal area is dominated by a watery fluid known as the 'cytosol' which enables things to move about, and it also holds tiny particles in suspension, (meaning that these tiny bits don't 'sink to the bottom' in an unusable sludge).

In a line 'down the middle of the cell' are a series of main compartments (organelles) which perform the main functions of Metabolism. In terms of the general flow of activity the first of these is the **Nucleus**, followed by a 'huge' and strangely shaped organelle known as the **Endoplasmic Reticulum** (or ER), and finally there is the **Golgi Apparatus**.

Around this central core, squeezed into odd places, are various other organelles such as Mitochondria, a Lysosome, Centrosome, and Endosomes.

Each of their functions will become apparent as we step through the partially circular processes which these components perform.

General Movement

While there are some larger objects floating inside the cytosol, most particles are tiny molecules such as ATP, Amino Acid monomers, nutrients, or other basic materials. These are the things which are needed throughout the cell and require general distribution, but they first emerge at various points in the cell's system.

The first and most obvious entry point is the cell wall/membrane. This means that fresh material has to spread from the outer areas of the cell towards the middle.

Other sources of tiny particles are the peripheral compartments/organelles within a cell such as: Mitochondria which produce ATP; and the Lysosome, (a cell's main recycling unit) which releases monomers – such as nucleotides which are salvaged from used RNA.

The trouble is that, (for the most part), the cytosol fluid inside a cell doesn't flow. It just sits there, and yet the small particles do move around within it - cascading to all parts of a cell relatively quickly. The way they do this is through an effect called 'Brownian Motion'.

This causes all **small** particles to bounce around in a 'random' pattern, due to the vibrations of atoms and molecules. This type of movement resembles the action of a ball inside a pinball machine – except that *everything* is being pushed around in a similar way.

These small jerky movements can push one molecule past another before hitting a third one behind it, yet this **does** result in small particles being spread around quite effectively.

However, large objects such as proteins are too big to be moved in this way, as they are being hit from all sides continuously. So these items are transported by very different processes which we will come across shortly.

The Assembly Processes

This section and the next will involve some detail, and because the terms may still not be familiar to you I will begin with a partial recap of the processes described in Appendix A to ease us into the later stages.

In Appendix A we saw that in Eukaryotes all of the different types of RNA polymer are produced in the **Nucleus**, by biological assembly devices known as 'protein enzymes', using nucleotide monomer building blocks.

Scientists distinguish the different types of RNA by their end uses. 'rRNA', forms part of elaborate machinery known as Ribosomes, (hence the 'r' designation). Others can act as labels, such as 'tRNA'. Both of these are known as 'non-coding' RNAs.

The other forms of RNA are coding RNAs – primarily 'mRNA' which describes how to build one or other of the many **proteins** that a cell needs in order to function. There is growing evidence that one of the early sections of the mRNA strand is also a 'destination code' which indicates where a finished protein must be delivered to, for use.

All three types of RNA are then transferred outwards, through the nucleus membrane, to the cytosol fluid which also holds the machines, building blocks, and power packs needed to make a protein.

tRNA is used to label Amino Acids, so that each of the 20 different types can be recognised by a Ribosome assembly machine when needed.

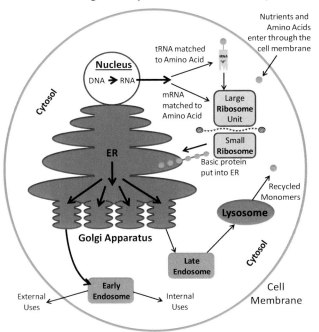

Ribosomes[60] come in two separate parts which float about in the cytosol. It is the smaller section, (which is normally depicted at the bottom of the assembled machine), that initiates the protein production process when it loads a new strand of mRNA.

Through the priming and matching mechanisms that we saw in Appendix A, the two parts of the Ribosome come together to form a complete unit and then feed the strand of mRNA through it – using it both as a conveyor belt, and a template that defines the precise **sequence** of Amino Acids needed to build a particular protein.

When a protein is destined to remain in the cytosol, per the mRNA destination code, the Ribosome finishes the production of the protein immediately, but if it is destined for use anywhere else, the Ribosome pauses because it first has to attach to the next compartment in the assembly cycle, at a point where it can directly insert the emerging protein into that compartment. This 'next' organelle is known as the **Endoplasmic Reticulum**, commonly referred-to as the ER.

While paused, a Ribosome will seek out an unoccupied connection point on the outside of the ER membrane, known as a 'Translocon'. It is believed that intermediary chemicals between a Translocon and the Ribosome will enable the two to both find each other and bind, but we don't know how those chemicals manage to only act with a paused Ribosome, or how the Ribosomes make their way over to the ER.

Once attached to the ER, the Ribosome continues its manufacture of the protein, feeding it directly **into** the ER through its membrane, via the Translocon. After the protein has been finished, the ribosome detaches and returns as two detached parts to the midst of the cytosol.

However in a remarkable display of efficiency, ribosomes often seem to daisy-chain their use of a single long mRNA template. As this strand emerges from the first ribosome, it enters the next. Quite extensive chains of ribosomes can end up producing many copies of the same protein at the same time, while adopting a spiral or rosette formation[12]!

Once the tRNA and mRNA have served their purposes and are released by the ribosome, it is believed that they are recycled. tRNA might be returned to the start of the metabolic pathway, to be attached to another appropriate Amino Acid. Alternately both tRNA and mRNA can be transported to the Lysosome for disassembly and recycling of the nucleotide components.

As the basic strands of protein are formed *outside* the ER by ribosomes, we have to ask what that huge ER structure does on the inside?

Well, quite a number of things, but I should first give you a bit more background information.

With the principal exceptions of red blood cells and spermatozoa, all Eukaryotic cells have an ER, although they can vary in size and emphasis depending on the purpose of a cell within the body.

ERs are positioned between the nucleus and another large organelle called the '**Golgi Apparatus**', and this positional sequence marks a general line of travel in the manufacture and distribution of polymers. Both the ER and the Golgi Apparatus contain a number of surprises.

In terms of shape, the ER resembles a stack of many sizeable, flattened discs pointing towards the Golgi Apparatus. These discs instinctively suggest that they must represent different stages of a process.

Yet the discs are all enclosed by a **single** membrane, and on the inside, we find that they are not individually sealed, but are interconnected by numerous tubes plus a central channel. They are effectively a single operating space.

Indeed the same membrane wraps around the nucleus as well, forming what is known as the 'outer nuclear membrane'.

Some sections of the ER will be designated as 'Rough', because their outer membrane will be covered in ribosomes, making it easy to see that this is where the majority of proteins will initially be generated. Other sections of the ER will be designated 'Smooth' because of the absence of ribosomes. This is where Lipids/fats etc. are generated most commonly via enzymes.

Typically the ER will be a patchwork of rough and smooth areas but the relative size of those rough and smooth zones will reflect the different functions that different cells may perform, (for instance, smooth areas are much bigger in liver cells, or ones that produce steroid hormones).

Returning then to the main flow of activity, we can now consider what the ER does. Firstly, in biochemistry text books, you will see that this organelle 'sequesters' chemicals such as Ca^{2+}.

You may feel rather unmoved by this revelation, but if I translate this into saying that it **stores** such chemicals for re-use later, its meaning will probably have much greater significance to you.

Why should any unthinking chemical process choose to store things?

It isn't just that they float about waiting to be used, they are actually stored in the discs and then returned to the cytosol when required. (Ca^{2+} is an important factor in cell signalling).

Secondly, the ER contains a number of 'quality checking' mechanisms for the proteins being inserted into it. *How* the proteins are checked is only partly understood, but this process does include testing the **shape** being achieved by each polymer.

If the proteins and fats do not fold in the correct way, (and therefore do not adopt the correct shape), they become useless. Yet the ER also tries to fix errant molecules by applying 'chaperone' chemicals which latch onto them and then assist, check, and adjust the folding process.

I use the word checking because at some point proteins can be rejected as beyond repair, and will also be sent to the **Lysosome** for disassembly and recycling. But what is it that makes the assessment?

At face value it seems that a judgement is being made, because although it is relatively easy to see whether a protein is 'incorrect', (eg. if certain bits don't line up as they should), a failure of that test doesn't say whether a strand is fixable.

A number of different checking mechanisms are applied in different sections of the ER and none of these are well understood, however there is no indication that it is based on information exchanges with the nucleus DNA, or indeed by reference to any other sort of 'look up' mechanism.

So how could such 'decisions' on suitability be made?

One suggestion, which matches some of the observed activity, is that, no decision is being taken at all - the process is simply a 'race against the clock'. What is meant by this is that there are mechanisms which 'roam around' the ER and grab anything that isn't correct - carting them off for recycling. This would imply that many fixable proteins would also be destroyed in this way. If correct then the process may not be very efficient.

Part of the rationale behind this, in terms of shape checking, is that the very presence of chaperones on a protein, may indicate whether a protein is correct or not, (as chaperones only drop off when the shape is correct).

While the 'race against the clock' notion **is** potentially a good way to avoid suggestions of decision-making, I gather that the latest evidence isn't clear cut about what passes and what fails, so we can't be sure that this is indeed the way they operate.

Even so, it is still remarkable that chaperones and sweeper mechanisms should exist at all if chemicals have no sense of purpose.

The third set of ER activities is to 'finish' the proteins by removing bits left over from the formation process, and generally 'topping and tailing' them - which may help to refine the destination codes on the proteins.

The fourth set of activities relates to the smooth areas of the ER which hold enzymes that construct fats, carbohydrates and other lipid polymers. Their purposes are broadly for energy storage, signalling, and the construction of cell structures such as membranes and tubes.

A fifth function, **and one of the most significant**, is that the lipids/fats making up the smooth ER walls, can form 'bubbles' which act as containers to transport proteins, and these may occasionally help some of the proteins to fold correctly as well[12].

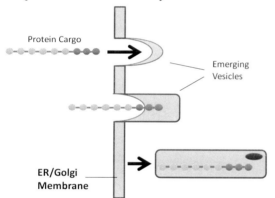

When the bubbles break off the ER wall, as a container, they become known as a '**vesicle**', and there are so many vesicles being transported that the **entire** membrane is replenished[12] every 30mins - and that's a lot of fatty material which has to be produced by the smooth sections of ER.

The formation of one of these bubbles is generally encouraged & assisted by a lattice of small proteins that form at a point on the surface of the ER membrane. These seem to determine the shape of the eventual vesicle, (which could be circular, cylindrical , oval, or irregularly shaped). This lattice may also help to set markers on the outside of the container to determine an end destination: whether the cargo is for internal use in another organelle, or for use outside the cell by the wider body.

These containers can carry more than one protein – generally of the same type: but they are not just for convenience. Conceptually at least, they protect the cargo from heavy buffeting by the myriad of smaller molecules in the cytosol, (Brownian motion), and also prevent unwanted chemical reactions from occurring.

Despite this simple logic, vesicles appear to be a remarkable development even in terms of evolution. Why would unthinking chemicals recognise any need for them when they don't care about the end outcome?

Once the vesicle containers are completed, the different types of polymer (typically protein or fat), need to be taken to the place where they can be used or recycled. The Golgi Apparatus is the next main stage in that process.

Astonishing Transportation within a Cell

In terms of aiding route planning to a destination there are two basic categories of road network in a cell:

- Secretory pathways mark the main assembly & distribution flows, while
- Endocrytic pathways – (for our purposes), can be thought of as routes for recycling and waste disposal.

However in terms of construction these routes follow two types of 'road':

- Microtubules – tubes which run out from the centre of the cell
- Filaments – twisted stands that run outwards and also across the microtubules to form a loose grid.

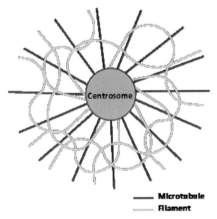

— Microtubule
····· Filament

The vesicles have to find their way to the correct set of roads before they set off to their end destination – being **pulled by chemicals that walk**[42]!

Part of the strategic routing of vesicles to different destinations is achieved by the different types of *coating* which these containers have, of which there are 3 main types which seem to designate the main pathway options.

The second part of this routing process is the 'end destination marker' on a vesicle which is done using a 'Rab Protein', (one out of a set of approx. 60, which seem to point to different locations in some way).

How this guides the transporters is unknown, but final docking at the destination is partly achieved when 'Rab Effectors' (effectively sensors), recognise the destination label[12] at the target organelle.

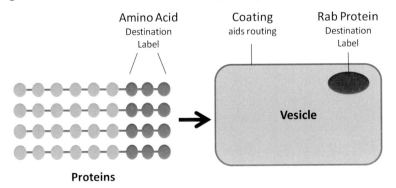

It is also unclear precisely how the protein cargo & container end up having the same destination, but it is suspected that in some way the destination code built into the polymer cargo is either used to label the vesicle, or is used to put the cargo in the vesicle which *already* has the desired address.

The Golgi Apparatus has two main functions:

- to assemble various types of fats/lipids, (in addition to the ER).
- to distribute polymers and vesicles to other parts of the cell, either for use, or for recycling, based on the different pathways.

What we *can* observe is that the Golgi Apparatus gets its main 'assembly' flow from the ER, yet there are also lesser flows which are 'retrieval' paths

- **back to the ER** for some polymers which have accidentally 'escaped' from their normal operational areas within the ER, and also some components which may need to be corrected or reused, and
- **into** the Golgi as a return from later destinations.

Both of these 'retrieval' processes require additional mechanisms that identify, collect, and package the relevant components. Where they are intended for reuse, the proteins etc. must not be damaged in that process.

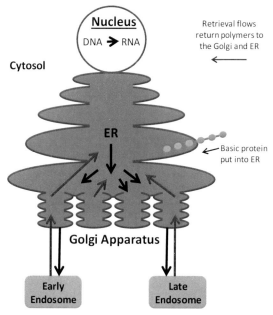

How the Golgi determines pathways and destinations is **not** well understood. The Golgi is an ordered series of compartments that resemble a series of stacked pitta breads, (typically 4-6 tall), each with internal networks of tubes and channels. We also know that each Golgi stack has surfaces and networks that can attract different types of vesicle, and these do indicate a filtering process.

In a similar manner it is also suspected that escaped proteins which need to be returned to the ER may be chemically attracted to those vesicles whose coating will route them back to the ER.

Scientists have observed a large number of enzymes within the Golgi stacks which modify and possibly label different components and vesicles.

However as they emerge from the Golgi the vesicles will be sent out on one of the main routes, (which all have **many** possible end destinations).

Some will lead to other routing mechanisms known as Endosomes, while others may be directed straight out of the cell to the wider body.

<u>Roads with Walking Transport Molecules</u>

At this stage we have completed proteins sitting in cargo vesicles, with some indication of an end destination. What we need is a means of getting them there, and as indicated earlier, there is an elaborate network of structures, vehicles, and behaviours to achieve this. If the target organelle/compartment is nearby, vesicles can effectively attach themselves to strings and be reeled-in, but the majority are picked up and *carried* some distance by a range of 'walking molecules'!

When I first heard rumours about protein molecules that could walk and carry things I thought that it had to be ridiculous nonsense, but the biochemistry text books tell us that they are indeed real.

As a category, these walking chemicals are generally referred-to as '**motor proteins**' because they have moving parts which can exert a force on other things, causing one or both of them to move. There are 3 main 'families' of these proteins, each having a number of different versions/types:-

- Myosins – which either walk along thread-like 'filaments' carrying other molecules as cargo, (such as Myosin V), or which cause muscles to contract rapidly when they stay still by pulling muscle filaments past each other, working together in large numbers[43], (per Myosin II).

- Kinesins – which can walk along 'microtubules', (thin rigid tubes made of 13 strands laying side by side like a sheet which is then bent round to form a cylinder). Other types of Kinesin can feature in cell reproduction, causing the formation of 'spindles', and helping chromosome separation when a cell divides.

- Dyneins - which can also walk along microtubules, (as above), carrying other cargo such as mRNA[12,40], but in other forms they can also cause minute flaps on a cell, (such as cilia or flagella), to beat – allowing some cells to move.

Another potential family is 'Harp', one of which has been found to rewind DNA after it has been unwound/used[41]. However in our current topic, it is the three bulleted families of motor protein which catch the eye because of their ability to carry things along their preferred type of strand. It's worth spending a few moments describing how they manage to walk.

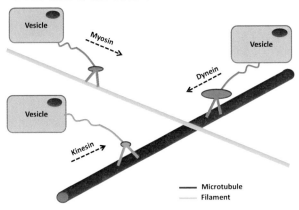

Vesicle

Myosin

Vesicle

Dynein

Vesicle

Kinesin

—— Microtubule
—— Filament

282

Essentially, these long motor polymer molecules attach at one end to a cargo vesicle, while at the other end there are two legs, resembling a 'V' shape. The central connection point of this 'V' is where the motor is situated, which either twists/flips the 'V', (as done by Kinesin/Myosin), or which flexes the angle in the 'V' in an alternating 'in-out' manner, (deployed by Dynein). These alternating actions generate the walking movement, but that is not the full story.

If the legs just 'waggle' back and forth, the protein won't go anywhere. One leg must grab and push, while the other moves – which requires intricacy and co-ordination in these mechanisms. They also need an energy source for their actions, and it seems that the ATP power packs which they use for this purpose also explain part of the movement.

If you recall, ATP acts as a universal energy currency and these tiny molecules are spread throughout a cell. Each time an ATP molecule attaches to one of the legs, it causes that leg to grab hold of the filament or microtubule it is following, and then powers the motor to twitch, (either one way or the other). This exhausts the power in the ATP battery, causing the leg to let go of the strand and the battery to detach.

While this has been happening the other leg, without power, has been moved forward by the first twitch, where it then gets another ATP molecule that causes it to grab the strand and twitch the motor again. It is this process which moves the molecule along the 'road' but it requires precise timing while walking, plus the unfailing presence of charged ATP molecules when needed, (otherwise it might detach completely from the strand).

However these motor protein molecules also need a 'sense of direction' and it's believed that this may come from the filament and microtubule roadways themselves, whose components all seem to align in the same way, creating a 'polarity' which can effectively point in one direction.

Kinesins, (with the exception of K14), only follow microtubules towards the 'positive' end, (moving from the centre towards the outer wall of the cell), while Dyneins take the opposite direction towards the 'negative' end (inwards to the centre)[43]. *How* the motor proteins are so direction specific, in a way that matches their cargo, is not entirely clear – other than suggesting that it is another 'miracle of evolution', etc.

It is also remarkable that the microtubules are mainly laid out as roadways in consistent outward pattern as well. They all extend like spokes on a 3D wheel from another compartment/organelle known as the 'Centrosome'. In this way the roads are partly structural: forming part of the 'Cytoskeleton' of the cell which helps to give it its shape.

Filaments can run sideways across the spokes as well as to the outer cell membrane – helping to form a navigable network... except that there's no known map to follow. (Short 'intermediate' filaments are also used to tension the network while holding organelles in a relatively fixed position).

As a basic concept, a vesicle being transported may need a kinesin plus a dynein, plus a myosin to run along the network in different directions, and there are indications that all three forms accompany the vesicle in order to complete a journey, with the inactive motor proteins hitching a ride until they are needed. It is certainly true that at points of intersection the motor proteins have to choose which direction to go in, and if necessary exchange cargo with other motor proteins[42]!

Although the different types of motor protein only travel in one direction along one type of strand, remarkable findings from 2014 show that biochemists have now engineered new forms of motor-protein which will cause them to change direction when blue lights are switched-on[44] – a really interesting finding but **not** one that I feel we should incorporate into our cells!

Despite the fact that Myosin motors are twice as big as Kinesin motors, and they walk along different types of fibre, they actually seem to use the same type of motor 'technology'[43]. This has suggested that they evolved from a common ancestor - unlike Dyneins, (which are 4 times as big again), and are thought to have evolved from another type of ATP user molecules, (AAA-ATPases). Indeed, Dyneins seem to incorporate 6 types of these 'AAA' molecule[43].

It also remains unclear why these proteins only set off on their journey once they have cargo on board, and why they don't accumulate in huge numbers at their end point, (as they generally seem unable to go in the reverse direction). It could be that they are swept away with the vesicles for recycling, rather than them being returned to their starting position in some unknown way, but the question is strangely absent from the text books I have consulted and also on the web.

Across all families of motor protein there is only mention of one which travels in the 'wrong' direction, (Kinesin 14), seemingly because its motor components are positioned at the opposite end of the molecule to normal. But it **is** the only one known to do this[12] and it is **not** described as the vehicle by which other motor proteins are returned to their start point.

Even if such movement was identified it would raise further questions on how these unthinking molecules could identify an end destination and plan a route to get there... while matching the use of the cargo.... although that is an important question even for the bits that we know.

The Centrosome is thought to control the building of the transport network, but there is nothing to indicate that it controls movement along it. During cell replication, (where an entire cell is being formed inside an 'adult' cell), parallel transport networks have to be constructed and then be adjusted as the cell divides into two. Yet the motor proteins still seem to know which ones to use, despite them being in the same cell, (as it hasn't divided yet).

So both microtubules and filaments can be extended and reduced in response to the changing circumstances of a cell, and the position of its organelles. How, this is planned and controlled is a complete mystery.

The motor proteins show traits that are both structural (evolutionary), and dynamic (showing properties that challenge perceptions of Matter/Energy).

Such is the importance of these transport mechanisms that several severe, and sometimes fatal, conditions have been linked to motor protein mutations. On a positive note, however, scientists have found ways to increase the power in these motors to improve the performance of weakened heart tissues[43].

Although we have known about Dyneins for some 20 years more than Kinesins we know a lot less about them because they are so large and complex – which has undermined some of the normal analytical processes for proteins such as X-Ray crystallography. As a reminder, Dyneins have motors that are 8 times larger than Kinesin motors.

Endosomes & Lysosomes

Endosomes are another type of routing compartment. 'Early Endosomes' can be thought of as directing finished components from within the cell, to areas which can use them, but they can also direct nutrients entering the cell to places where they are needed – the start of the main pathways.

Once again it is unclear how this routing takes place.

'Late Endosomes' set the paths which lead to recycling – primarily to the organelle known as the Lysosome. This essentially salvages amino acids & nucleotides from used or malformed components, and then either returns them for use within the cell, or disposes of waste materials out of the cell.

As we have seen, both Early and Late Endosomes have retrieval mechanisms which can return things to the Golgi.

The Effectiveness of Enzymes

Returning to the base metabolic functions of assembly, disassembly, and distribution, the vast majority of reactions depend entirely on the successful use of enzymes. In general terms these are large protein machines which do three main conceptual things: they

- catalyse reactions – enabling them to happen in conditions where they wouldn't normally occur.
- enable reactions to occur very quickly making the cell far more efficient than equivalent processes outside the cell.
- prevent other unwanted reactions from occurring – thereby maintaining an element of quality control.

To enable these things to happen enzymes must position themselves in *exactly* the right place on their much smaller target 'substrate' molecules in order to align their active areas and produce just one precise effect/chemical reaction. As mentioned earlier both enzymes and substrate are polymer chains that look like bundles of chemical spaghetti, yet they fold themselves in precise ways to position their active areas in certain locations on their outer surfaces.

The reactions they produce are used to either assemble or disassemble substrate molecules as part of the anabolic or catabolic process.

Assembly generally means forming strong **covalent** bonds between atoms and molecules that create long-term components, while disassembly involves breaking such bonds and replacing them with weaker, temporary, **hydrogen** bonds that stabilise something in readiness for its re-use, later.

In broad terms the formation of a covalent bond will require additional energy which gives it strength, while its replacement with a hydrogen bond would release energy. So part of the sophistication of enzymes lies in energy management and the use of ATP power packs, but some of the energy can be drawn from or returned to the background environment.

If a weaker hydrogen bond has been put in place, there will be a much greater chance of it being undone in other types of unwanted reaction – especially if there has been a net release of energy into the fluid nearby.

Indeed, many biological reactions are 'reversible' in this way and in test tubes or the wider environment scientists see as many desirable reactions being undone as are being created - a state known as 'chemical equilibrium' where reactions normally tend to stabilise. This is **not** a very good position for biological processes, because our bodies wouldn't be able to harvest many 'good outcomes' if they were constantly being undone.

However cells are remarkable for maintaining their operations well above equilibrium[12]. Put another way, they operate at a high level of efficiency, producing **only** the desirable outputs in **large numbers**. This is clearly an indication that there's something special happening in a cell's environment.

Part of this lies in the fact that the **background** level of energy/heat in a cell **wouldn't** normally be sufficient to allow many of these reactions to take place at all, either good or bad.

It is the enzymes' use of energy that enables reactions to occur, but they also ensure that only the desired reactions happen because they bring the right molecules with them so they are the only ones available when a reaction is possible.

Another part of the remarkable efficiency of cells is their control of the broader environment, via their outer wall/membrane, which only allows certain types of chemical to be present. (Yet this doesn't remove all unwanted chemicals from the cell, as it produces its own waste products).

The final element of an enzyme's efficiency & quality control relates to the shape of the molecules and how they position themselves with such speed.

The active areas of an enzyme must be placed exactly over the bonds they wish to influence. High energy atoms on the enzyme will 'tug at' the target chemical bonds on the substrate, weakening them so that a <u>lower level of energy</u> is required to break them. This is the factor which allows reactions to occur when they wouldn't normally do so.

Different 'sensors' on an enzyme can also tell if the correct effects are being achieved, through the changing shape of the substrate as reactions happen. This means that sensors in other locations on the outside of an enzyme have to line up too, (and may require the enzyme to change shape during the reactions as well).

So the positioning of enzyme and substrate is highly precise, and is often described as being a 'lock and key' arrangement, because the shapes are so unique to each reaction. Yet it is estimated that each enzyme **reacts** with substrates thousands of times a second[12]! How can that happen?

It has been a matter of some debate precisely how this is done.

We cannot see what is happening directly because key stages of these activities occur at the level of individual atoms, but as a first step, spectroscopic analysis indicates that four types of movement may bring substrate and enzyme together very rapidly:-

- Gentle flows that may be likened to **currents,** (possibly flowing down tubes within a cell), could bring the smaller substrates close to the enzymes, (which effectively stand still).

- **Rotation** in enzymes can be as much as a ***million*** times per second – although that is an extreme which doesn't occur in most enzymes.

- **Brownian motion** from vibration in atoms causes small movements.

- Short range **attractions** between different types of molecule could bring the active areas into line.

It is argued that this alignment happens 'inevitably' because the four types of movement cause the substrate molecules to bounce off the enzymes continually until they find the right place.

That may not sound very efficient, but some estimates suggest that where the substrates are in quite high concentrations, (still only one part per 100,000 water molecules), a single ***enzyme*** could be struck over half a million times per second, (but not all in the right place). Yet if the concentrations drop, the number of collisions will drop proportionately. So if the nutrients are diluted to say one tenth of this, (one in a million water molecules), then there would be only 50,000 collisions per second[12].

In short, it is argued that with enough random collisions, the enzymes and substrates will move together often enough to eventually be guided by their shapes into a position where they can quickly bind and react – yet still at a rate of thousands per second!

The only alternative to such thinking is that enzymes and/or substrates can somehow sense each other and guide themselves in a more purposeful manner, but without anything to actively demonstrate a specific 'sense' mechanism scientists are inevitably reluctant to pursue this thinking.

This mainstream theory does seem to have a reasonable logic and it is also supported by different findings such as spectral analysis, but it **is** dependent on the accuracy of the claimed collision and reaction rates.

While this is accepted by most scientists, I gather that there are still a few unresolved issues with enzyme reaction rates. Yet it is hard for laymen to get their minds around this – for instance *it is difficult to imagine how something spinning a million times per second could bind with anything*.

Yet scientists argue that we can't equate our perception of how things work at our level of existence with how atoms and molecules operate.

Setting aside these doubts, we <u>can</u> be sure that virtually every stage of every paired metabolic process (catabolic and anabolic stages), requires a series of such reactions that must be conducted in a precise sequence. That suggests a **lot** of distinct enzymes working in their correct place on the 'assembly line', but *how* they are positioned there is not fully understood.

Signalling

Our bodies are filled with sensors that monitor almost every conceivable aspect of their operations, and that is equally true within cells.

Whether the signal is chemical or electrical, the information which is generated is processed and the body or cell responds in some way.

To this extent we can argue that the core of our operations is information processing, and yet we have to be cautious about such thinking because, as tempting as our instincts might be about what is happening, we need to remind ourselves that the core biological components are just chemicals which don't compute or think. They can only form bonds in pre-set ways.

For materialism to work it has to establish a clear set of causes for every outcome: an inevitable path – even if we can't *predict* what may occur because we can't see all the interlinking influences at any point in time.

The main focus of research to date has been on communications between individual Eukaryote cells, ('intercellular' – on the outside of cells), but some of the signals have been followed into the core of cells revealing their effects there as well, (intracellular). The impression at this stage is that very similar processes seem to be in operation in both environments.

Yet Bacteria are also capable of sensing their neighbours through a process known as 'Quorum Sensing', and even yeast cells appear to communicate with each other prior to mating[12]. Another remarkable effect is that many Eukaryote cells need a continuous series of signals in order to survive, without which the cells activate an 'auto-suicide' process – "Apoptosis".

It seems that a body can also detect the difference between a suicide, and a death from infection or damage, because the former will effectively cause the cell to shrivel while the others might burst it - spilling its contents. A body is therefore able to detect different types of chemical 'signature'.

Biochemists have identified 4 main ways in which cells communicate[12]:-

a) Direct contact between cell walls/membranes, ("contact dependent")

b) Physical 'cables' between cells using electrical signals, ("synaptic")

c) Small 'local' molecules generated by a cell can act as intermediaries with other cells which are close, ("paracrine")

d) Cells which produce hormones and then secrete them into the bloodstream as a general alert throughout the body, ("endocrine")

Synaptic signalling is most obviously used in the brain, but interestingly, although we can liken it to electrical circuitry, the ends of each cable do not directly feed into the next cell's circuit. They actually end just before the target cell, at a 'chemical synapse' which generates a 'neurotransmitter' chemical that crosses the tiny gap to the other cell. So in detailed terms *all* cell communications ultimately seem to operate on a chemical basis.

Yet, as mentioned earlier, the absence of many suspected signals or other feedback loops, have led to speculation about short distance electrical signals or electromagnetic fields amidst the ion-filled waters of the cytosol.

That said, synaptic communications do offer a means of targeted long range signalling between specific cells, in contrast with endocrine signalling which is very 'broad brush'.

Almost all types of external chemical signal are **unable** to cross the outer membrane of a cell, so these chemicals are all detected by binding to specific receptors on the outside of a cell. Each receptor is tailored to receive one specific chemical signal, so there are hundreds of different types, although they basically operate in 3 ways: forming the main basis of their classification. We don't need to delve into the precise mechanics.

Suffice it to say that the challenge for scientists has been to understand how cells interpret the signals. Is there any intelligence being applied?

In line with materialist thinking, it is currently believed that there **isn't**. What is suggested instead is basically a series of on/off switches which, if used in combination, can produce a series of graded responses. However that basically suggests that they act like a programmed computer chip. The 'intelligence' has already been set out in the program – but the origin of that programming is unknown.

To give every greater subtlety, various cell communication methods can be used in combination, so for instance an external chemical signal can be detected by a cell receptor which then issues a different type of 'secondary signal' within the cell. Yet with hundreds of types of signal there are a true myriad of possible combinations, so it is **not** clear that this **is** simple one-for-one programming... in which case we return to the question of whether a more sophisticated interpretation mechanism is being used.

Such ideas are reinforced by three factors[12]:

1) receptors can be triggered by the wrong signal, and cells have also found ways to try and distinguish a good trigger from a bad trigger;

2) different types of cell can respond to exactly the same chemical signal in different ways. For instance, the neurotransmitter 'Acetlycholine' can decrease heart rate, or stimulate a salivary gland, or cause muscle to contract.

3) Some cells, most easily demonstrated in the brain, but also elsewhere, can produce **different** responses to the **same** situations.

One way that a cell manages to avoid responding to false signals seems to be through a need for more than one type of signal before activation. This can either be through a combination of direct chemical signals at the same moment, or possibly a 'delayed' scenario when the first signal primes something for action, but it doesn't get triggered until other signals, from elsewhere in a pathway, show a readiness for it, (as in a feedback loop).

In short, there is huge complexity in cell signalling, and only a small part of this is understood. Those parts inevitably conform to the principles of 'single cause single effect' because that is the only basis on which they are declared to be 'understood', but the others may not conform, and we also have to distinguish the **how** from the **why**. There needs to be a complete path from initiation to end result.

So the choice we face is in deciding whether all aspects are likely to be traced to precise 'switch mechanisms' alone, or whether something else is indeed needed – and there are people arguing from both perspectives.

Even if the strict materialist perspective is correct, there is still a lot of pre-programming which needs to be explained.

Of course, this becomes much more dynamic when the processes of the brain seem to be creative, not just responsive. There is a lot more work to do relating to Thought and intelligence. As we saw in Chapter 4 hard causal logic isn't enough for our normal decision-making, and Chapter 12 pursued this in more detail.

An Outline of Cell Reproduction

The only way to make a new cell is to duplicate one that already exists[12], and even to this day, the only mechanisms available to do this lie within cells themselves.

In this section I will **not** be repeating the mechanics of DNA replication or the processes which assemble polymers, (although these will be elements of the overall activity).

We will be looking at the ordered sequence of events which cause a cell to produce an entire second cell like a baby within it, before all of the duplicated components are separated by the cell splitting in half.

During replication of a cell's contents, (both internal compartments & machinery), everything has to move around to make space for the newly created items, and indeed, the entire cell membrane has to expand. Yet the original components have to seamlessly continue their operations and the internal road networks that supply them have to be constantly adapted to take account of moving locations and increased size.

These activities are broadly known as 'The Cell Cycle'.

One of the most important parts of the cycle is the 'S' phase (synthesis), in which the DNA chromosomes are copied, and organelles, ribosomes, enzymes etc. are also duplicated. This produces the components necessary for the new cell to operate. As just mentioned, through this activity the cell has to grow, and as it does so it tends to stretch outwards in one direction, thereby losing its original round shape. The shape of a cell is an easy way for scientists to tell which stage of the cycle it has reached.

During this growth a second cytoskeleton/road network must also be developed to serve the new cell when it splits. A new Centrosome will start to form a large central microtubule spindle in the elongating cell as well as the beginnings of the normal cytoskeleton spokes.

In the 2nd 'M' phase of the cycle, (Mitosis), the spindle is used to separate the duplicated copy of the DNA from the original, and pulls the new set of 23 paired chromosomes to the elongating end of the cell.

The pulling apart of the two sets of DNA is thought to be achieved because of the sense of direction given by the two sets of microtubules, (original cell and new cell), and the motor proteins which are deployed to push them past each other. (The strands of both cytoskeletons point outwards from their Centrosome, but in the direction where the Centrosomes face each other, the strands point in opposite directions).

A number of Kinesin and Dynein motor proteins, working in their preferred directions, are believed to grab hold of the microtubules and slide them past each other, (instead of them carrying cargo). However this can only succeed if the two sets of microtubules are attached to different copies of the duplicated chromosomes – not the same copy.

It's not clear how the different cytoskeletons know how to organise themselves to attach to different copies of each Chromosome, but it seems that mistakes do occur – possibly quite a lot.

Suggestions have been offered that because the different cytoskeletons approach the chromosomes from opposite sides they will each see just one of the duplicates to attach to – but this presumes that the different chromosomes are perfectly aligned at right angles to the spindle in order to do this.

Another rationale is that where motor proteins try to pull a chromosome to one side or the other, they will fail because the different sets of motor proteins will be working against each other, if they are attached to the same chromosome. A correction mechanism would therefore be needed to change the connections on a 'trial and error' basis, but even this presumes that there is some feedback from the motor proteins to some controlling mechanism, and also something to ensure that only one copy of each chromosome ends up on each side of the cell. Neither have been observed.

By whatever means, we see that there **is** a mechanism to separate components which have been duplicated, but this is not the case in relation to the ER and Golgi apparatus, which are essentially too large to be duplicated. It's believed that both of these are torn in two when the cell divides during the later stage of 'Cytokinesis', giving half to each entity – and requiring the other halves to be re-grown. (Despite the fragmentation it is believed that enough functions survive in the ER and Golgi to complete the rebuild).

Once separation has fully occurred, each cytoskeleton reorganises its internal operations and forms a new nucleus membrane around its set of chromosomes. The Centrosome in each cell is suspected of controlling aspects of these reorganisations but we don't know how.

As already indicated, once there are two functioning sets of cell mechanisms, the original engorged cell splits in two in a phase known as Cytokinesis. This is done by the outer cell membrane folding-in, between the two units, from all sides until it touches at a point in the middle. This effectively seals the two entities which then split apart. Although we can think of Cytokinesis as a distinct phase it is normally considered to be the last stage of Mitosis. However there are two other stages.

If we imagine a continuing cycle between the S and M phases, where one begins as the other ends, there are actually 'gap periods' between the start and end of each. These are regarded as phases in their own right – labelled G_1 and G_2, but they are not without purpose.

G_1 can be thought of as a pause before a new cell cycle begins, but it isn't quite that. It is a period when the cell finalises its reorganisations and prepares for the next cycle. As part of this it seems that the cell checks its environment to see if it has the right conditions to enable it to complete the cycle, (as an interruption part way through could be disastrous). We do observe cells that stay fixed in the G_1 state when conditions are *not* right, and this suspended activity is referred-to as G_0. However this checking is a remarkable feature that is not fully understood[12].

G_2 somehow checks whether all chromosomes have been correctly copied and other processes are ready to progress to Mitosis. Part of this relates to the DNA repair mechanisms which constantly check for damage, these can trigger some signalling through chemicals known as ATM and ATR. If errors are detected then it seems that the processes will try to undertake various types of repair, but if these are deemed unsuccessful most multi-celled organisms will cause the cell to commit suicide. (Some single-celled organisms actually resume the cell cycle anyway, even if incorrect).

The control mechanisms behind the complexities of the Cell Cycle, ('Cyclins'), are different chemicals to those used in DNA replication and the manufacture of individual proteins.

The way in which they exercise control is partly explained by the fact that cyclins work in partnership with specific enzymes (CDKs): activating them in particular ways and even directing them to work on particular target molecules (substrates). However they show remarkable sophistication – being able to control several process not just one.

At one level, the same cyclin-Cdk complexes can be used in different phases of the cell cycle because in later stages the old substrates will no longer be present and new ones will have taken their place[12] – so they are still able to precisely target the molecules they need to change.

However M-Cdk controls **all** of the complex stages in Mitosis, not just one or two. It is believed that this is done in part by M-Cdk 'phosphorylating' different proteins but we don't know which, or why this is achieved in a particular sequence. **It breaks the normal model of a single enzyme with a single purpose.**

Another aspect of control is that when certain tasks are completed, a regulatory chemical known as 'Cyclosome' (or APC/C) can switch-off certain activities by removing both the substrate molecules and the cyclins at that point – flagging them for destruction.

So we know how some control processes work but not all, and even those where we see the mechanisms involved plus what they seem to do, we may not necessarily understand **why**, (ie. what causes those controls to be exercised). The presumption is that various feedback loops will be in operation, but that is a presumption.

Notes

1	Although the term 'atomism' is derived from Greek, the first known instances of the theory arise from ancient India and particularly the Ajivika and Carvaka schools of philosophy (c. 600-500BCE). This was later developed in the Nyaya and Vaisheshika schools of Hinduism, and also in Jainism. It is unclear whether the Greeks developed the idea separately or were influenced by Indian culture. The term was coined by the ancient Greek philosopher Democritus (460BCE) and later adopted by the Roman philosopher Lucretius.
	'Indian Atomism: History and Sources' M.Gangopadhyaya (1981) Atlantic Highlands, New Jersey: Humanities Press. ISBN 0-391-02177-X
	Re:disputed origins – 'Lost Discoveries: The Ancient Roots of Modern Science R.Teresi. (2003) Simon & Schuster. ISBN 0-7432-4379-X.
2	The theory of Evolution by Natural Selection was first proposed by Alfred Russel Wallace in 1858 in a series of papers published jointly with some writings by Charles Robert Darwin (b.1809–d.1882). Both had independently formed similar ideas at the same time but while Darwin was writing a book, Wallace completed his essay first – prompting a joint publication. However it was Darwin's book "*On the Origin of Species by Means of Natural Selection, or the Preservation of Favoured Races in the Struggle for Life*" (1859) that really persuaded the scientific establishment and the general public.
	Darwin was an English naturalist and geologist who formulated his theories from evidence he gathered on a 5 year voyage on HMS Beagle across the pacific ocean between 1831 and 1836. Wallace was also British (born in Wales to Scottish/English parents) but had travelled the Amazon and Malay Peninsula to form his views.
	The theory now has several permutations which elaborate on key themes using modern scientific knowledge of the genetic processes and mechanisms used by living cells, (based on later scientific discoveries).
3	Physics has identified just 4 forces in nature and they are all believed to operate by using distinct 'messenger' particles. This is proven in relation to the 3 'functional' forces which hold atoms together and account for chemical reactions, (the 'Strong' and 'Weak' nuclear forces, plus Electromagnetism), yet no messenger particle has been discovered for Gravity. It remains a mystery how it works.
	The nature of Life is also not known, but there are theories which argue that it is just an effect from some of the other functional forces. For this reason it is not formally regarded as a force in nature even though many people **will** view it in this way.

4	French philosopher & mathematician Rene Descartes (1596 – 1650) is generally attributed with the phrase 'I think therefore I am' although similar ideas had already been proposed by Plato and Aristotle. As an aside, Descartes spent 20 years of his adult life in the more liberal Dutch Republic, but died in Stockholm.
5	Erwin Schrödinger, (1887 – 1961), Austrian physicist, won the Nobel Prize for his work on quantum physics in 1933. Amongst many notable achievements he is also famous for the logical paradox known as Schrödinger's Cat.
	The search for a modern definition of life is often thought to have begun with his small book entitled "What is Life" (1943).
	Although a declared atheist I understand that Schrödinger still seemed to hold pantheist views and had a lifelong interest in the Vedanta beliefs of Hinduism which advocate that individual consciousness is part of a single consciousness which permeates the universe.
6	This definition was never an official public statement/position by NASA. It was simply a working concept for use by the "Exobiology Discipline Working Group" in the early 1990s.
	Although the definition is often attributed to Gerald Joyce of the Scripps Research Institute, (because he mentioned it in the foreword he wrote for a book), he claims it was a group effort which he contributed to, (per interview "Forming a Definition for Life : Interview with Gerald Joyce" with Leslie Mullen – 25 July 2013 – Astrobiology Magazine).
	References to this definition may be found in both Bruce Jakosky's book, 'The Search for Life on Other Planets' and to G.F.Joyce's work "The RNA World: Life Before DNA and Protein"
	Wikipedia reports that in 2009, Joyce's lab was the first to produce a self-replicating test-tube based system, capable of growth & continuing evolution, composed entirely of RNA enzymes.
7	The definition has been re-stated as "Life is a self-sustained chemical system capable of undergoing Darwinian evolution" The change suggests that Life is only a chemical process.
8	There are various sources for this timeline but I first came across it in "Origins of Existence" Fred Adams. The Free Press (2002)
9	"Hints of life on what was thought to be desolate early Earth". S.Borenstein (19 October 2015). Excite. Yonkers, NY: Mindspark Interactive Network. Associated Press. Retrieved 2015-10-20.

10	"Potentially biogenic carbon preserved in a 4.1 billion-year-old zircon" EA Bell; P.Boehnike, T.M.Harrison (19 October 2015) Proc. Natl. Acad. Sci. U.S.A. Washington, D.C.: National Academy of Sciences. 112 (47): *14518–21.* Bibcode:2015PNAS..11214518B. ISSN 1091-6490. PMC 4664351 PMID 26483481. doi:10.1073/pnas.1517557112. Retrieved 2015-10-20.
11	The Blue Brain project was formed in 2005 by the Brain and Mind Institute of EPFL (École Poytechnique Fédérale de Lausanne) in Switzerland. It aims to create a synthetic brain, (digital simulation of a human brain), by reconstruction/reverse engineering of real brain circuitry/neural networks, including biologically realistic models of neurons, the neocortex etc.. It began by generating a model of a rat's 'neocortical column' a sophisticated component of the brain which is believed to generate conscious thought. It then sought to extrapolate these findings, in combination with scans of human tissues, to generate an equivalent human 'neocortical column' which is much more complex. Building up from such components and the known structures of 'neural networks' it seeks to develop a full model of a human brain by 2023. Whatever level of success is achieved the model is believed to be useful in advancing our understanding of healthy vs diseased brains.
12	"Molecular Biology of the Cell" 6th edition B.Alberts et al. Garland Science (2015) ISBN 978-0-8153-4464-3
13	Brain water content is described in many web articles such as http://www.ncbi.nlm.nih.gov/pmc/articles/PMC3413327/ or http://articles.mercola.com/sites/articles/archive/2009/01/22/fascinating-facts-you-never-knew-about-the-human-brain.aspx download 23.11.15
14	"A Short History of Nearly Everything" Bill Bryson. Transworld Publishers (2003) ISBN 978-0-55299-704-1
15	In a 2015/16 TV series about "The Brain" written and presented by Dr. David Eagleman (b.1971 – American Neuroscientist), it was shown that both emotional and logical areas of the brain are **always** normally used in decision-making. A patient (Tammy Myers) who was formally a successful engineer, lost her ability to make decisions after an accident, because it was thought that she could no longer make emotional assessments about the options available to choose from. This was illustrated in a supermarket where she felt unable to choose from the selection of potatoes available when doing her weekly shop.

16	"Comparative spermatogenesis, spermatocytogenesis, and spermatozeugmata formation in males of viviparous species of clinid fishes (Teleostei: Clinidae, Blennioidei)" L.Fishelson; O.Gon; V.Holdengreber; Y.Delarea *The Anatomical Record: Advances in Integrative Anatomy and Evolutionary Biology* (2007).
17	"When does consciousness arise in human babies?" C.Koch Scientific American (Oct 2009)
18	"The universal nature of biochemistry". N.R.Pace (January 2001). Proc. Natl. Acad. Sci. U.S.A. **98** (3): 805–8. "Which fertilized eggs will become healthy human fetuses?" by Stanford University Medical Center (4.10.2010) Science Daily. download 25.11.2017 (lead authors R.Reijo Pera; C.Wong; K.Loewke)
19	Richard Dawkins is a prominent biologist and philosopher with strong atheistic views. He has written many successful books and produced TV documentaries. A passionate advocate of Evolution theory in such books as the 'Blind Watchmaker', he also wrote the popular book 'The God Delusion' in 2006 (now Transworld Publishers 2007).
20	The theory of Evolution by Natural Selection was first proposed by Alfred Russel Wallace in 1858 in a series of papers published jointly with some writings by Charles Robert Darwin (b.1809–d.1882). Both had independently formed similar ideas at the same time, but while Darwin was writing a book, Wallace completed his essay first – prompting a joint publication. However it was Darwin's book *"On the Origin of Species by Means of Natural Selection, or the Preservation of Favoured Races in the Struggle for Life"* (1859) that really persuaded the scientific establishment and the general public. Darwin was an English naturalist and geologist who formulated his theories from evidence he gathered on a 5 year voyage on HMS Beagle across the pacific ocean between 1831 and 1836. Wallace was also British (born in Wales to Scottish/English parents) but had travelled the Amazon and Malay Peninsula to form his views. The theory now has several permutations which elaborate on their key themes using modern scientific knowledge of the genetic mechanisms in use, (based on late scientific discoveries).
21	US Government National Human Geneome Research Institute factsheet on Chromosomes – 16 June 2015.
22	"DNA Repair" I. Kruman ch19 "Meiosis as an Evolutionary Adaptation for DNA Repair" H.Berstein, C.Bernstein, E.Michod (2011) InTech Open Publisher

23	"Meiosis-Specific DNA Double-Strand Breaks Are Catalyzed by Spo11, a Member of a Widely Conserved Protein Family". S.Keeney, C.Giroux, N.Kleckner (1997) Cell
24	In 1973 the first 'Transgenic' organism was created (a bacterium) followed in 1974 by the first Transgenic animal – a mouse produced by Rudolph Jaenisch, however the inserted gene was **not** passed on to its offspring. The first 3 transgenic animals which could pass on their genetic code to their offspring were achieved in 1981 by 3 distinct teams working in collaboration. The mice which showed a green fluorescent glow (from eGFP) under UV light were reported in a research article "Gene expression in tumor cells and stroma in dsRed 4T1 tumors in eGFP-expressing mice with and without enhanced oxygenation" I.Moen et al (2012) in BMC Cancer (https://bmccancer.biomedcentral.com/track/pdf/10.1186/1471-2407-12-21?site=bmccancer.biomedcentral.com) latest download 27/12/2017
25	Attributed to W. R. Rice (University of New Mexico) and G.W. Salt (University of California, Davis).
26	*"Fossil Record of the Monotremata" Ucmp.berkeley.edu. Retrieved 2011-06-09* "Monotreme nature of the Australian Early Cretaceous mammal Teinolophos". T. H. Rich., *et al.* Acta Palaeontologica Polonica **46(1)**. 2001 Pages 113–118.
27	"Platypus Genome Reveals Secrets of Mammal Evolution" Scott Norris for National Geographic News. May 7, 2008. (reprinted Thursday, October 28, 2010) "Platypus genome unravels mysteries of mammalian evolution" Genome Research ('Tip Sheet' printed 25 Oct 2015) CSH Press.
28	"Mitochondrial DNA and human evolution" R.L.Cann, M.Stoneking, A.C.Wilson (1987), Nature, **325** (6099)
29	"Sequencing Y chromosomes resolves discrepancy in time to common ancestor of males versus females". G.D.Poznik, B.M.Henn, M.C.Yee, E.Sliwerska, G.M.Euskirchen, A.A.Lin, M.Snyder, L.Quintana-Murci, J.M.Kidd, P.A.Underhill, C.D.Bustamante (2013) Science. **341** (6145):
30	"A Revised Root for the Human Y Chromosomal Phylogenetic Tree: The Origin of Patrilineal Diversity in Africa". F.Cruciani; B.Trombetta; A.Massaia; G.Destro-Bisol; D.Sellitto; R.Scozzari (2011) The American Journal of Human Genetics. **88** (6):
31	"A recent bottleneck of Y chromosome diversity coincides with a global change in culture". Karmin; et al. (2015). Genome Research. **25** (4)

32	"A recent common ancestry for human Y chromosomes" M.F.Hammer (1995). Nature. **378** (6555)
33	"New binary polymorphisms reshape and increase resolution of the human Y chromosomal haplogroup tree" T.M.Karafet; F.L.Mendez, M.B.Meilerman, P.A.Underhill, S.L.Zegura, M.F.Hammer (2008) Genome Research. **18** (5)
34	"Menopause and treatments". V.Ringa. (2000). Quality of Life Research.
35	"Predictive factors of age at menopause in a large Australian twin study" K.A,Do; S.A.Treloar; N.Pandeya; D.Purdie; A.C.Green; A.C.Heath; N.G.Martin (1998). Hum Biol. **70** (6
36	"What is menopause?" E.Kennedy Shriver National Institute of Child Health and Human Development. 28 June 2013. Retrieved 8 March 2015 "The menopausal transition : interface between gynecology and psychiatry" Warren, volume editors, N.Claudio N; M.Soares (2009)
37	"Effect of Age on Male Fertility Seminars" S.J.Sherman (1991) Reproductive Endocrinology. Volume, Number 3, August 1991.
38	"Menopause in nonhuman primates?". M.L.Walker J.G.Herndon, (2008) Biology of Reproduction.
39	"Globicephala macrorhynchus" Whales and Dolphins.
40	"Neuronal Tracing" E.Oztas (2003). Neuroanatomy. **2**: 2–5.
41	"Biologists Discover Motor Protein That Rewinds DNA" University of California - San Diego (2 Nov 2008) Science Daily The HEPA family of motor proteins stand for 'HepA-related proteins' and were discovered by Jim Kadonaga and his team.
42	"Cargo Transport: Molecular Motors Navigate a Complex Cytoskeleton" J.L.Ross, M.Y.Ali, D.M.Warshaw (15 Jan 2008) Curr Opin Cell Biol
43	Three excellent videos by Ron Vale, (recorded in Oct 2015), that can tell you a lot about the different motor proteins can be found at https://www.ibiology.org/cell-biology/motor-proteins/
44	"Light Sensitive LOV2 Domain attached to Kinesin14" Nakamura et al (2014) Nature Nanotech 9:693
45	"New Naturally Occurring Amino Acids" I.Wagner, H.Musso (November 1983). *Angew. Chem. Int. Ed. Engl.* **22** (22): 816–828.

46	"A semi-synthetic organism with an expanded genetic alphabet". F.E.Romesberg, D.A.Malyshev, K.Dhami, T.Lavergne, T.Chen, N.Dai, J.M.Foster, I.R.Corrêa, (May 7, 2014). Nature. **509** (7500)
	"Scientists Create First Living Organism With 'Artificial' DNA". E.Callaway (May 7, 2014). Nature News. Huffington Post.
	"Life engineered with expanded genetic code" B.J.Fikes, (May 8, 2014). San Diego Union Tribune
47	"NASA Researchers: DNA Building Blocks Can Be Made in Space". Steigerwald, John (8 August 2011). NASA.
48	Stanley Lloyd Miller – Jewish-American chemist (b.1930 – d.2007).
	His famous experiment to see if the building blocks of life could emerge spontaneously from a primordial soup of chemicals, was documented in "Production of amino acids under possible primitive earth conditions" SL Miller *Science* 1953.
49	Additional mixes include Hydrogen sulphide and other gasses from volcanoes such as Hydrogen Cyanide - "Amino-acid synthesis from hydrogen cyanide under possible primitive earth conditions". J. Oró & S.Kamat (*Nature* **190** (4774): April 1961.
	Use of UV light Co & CO^2 – "Synthesis of organic compounds from carbon monoxide and water by UV photolysis" H.Hartman & A.Bar-nun
	Decreasing amounts of hydrogen in the atmosphere - "Early Earth atmosphere favorable to life: study". University of Waterloo. Retrieved 2005-12-17.
50	"Oxford dictionary of biochemistry and molecular biology" AL.Smith (Ed) (1997). Oxford University Press. ISBN 0-19-854768-4.
51	"Examples of Transcription Regulation in Eukaryotes: DNA Regulatory Regions" K.Klucevsek http://study.com/academy/lesson/eukaryotic-transcription-regulation.html downloaded 27.10.2017
52	Epigenetics is a science which recognises that while the DNA code can remain unchanged in the sequence of nucleotides, other add-ons to the genetic code can affect the way in which a protein can perform.
	In some cases the chemical add-ons can switch on or switch off a gene so that the protein may or may not be manufactured. In other cases it is believed that the *nature* of the protein is affected so that it produces different effects.
	Epigenetics is therefore central to the study of how newly fertilised cells (which could become any other type of cell) transform into cells dedicated to one part of the body or another.

	Epigenetic changes can be passed-on by one cell to its 'offspring' however these changes have to be initiated by something, as we don't see uncontrolled development of a baby in the womb. Epigenetic processes are also seen as potential messengers between cells which may contribute to the overall control mechanisms in the body.
53	"Secrets of Quantum Physics" Jim Al Khalili. Channel 4 documentary.
54	James Lovelock (B. 1919 in Letchworth, England) formulated the scientific Gaian hypothesis with the microbiologist Lynn Margulis in the 1960/70s after he had worked for NASA on developing equipment to remotely analyse the atmosphere and surface of Mars, and also to investigate the factors in determining the presence of life.
	"Atmospheric homeostasis by and for the biosphere – The Gaia hypothesis". J.E.Lovelock; L.Margulis (1974). Tellus.
	In later years he produced the first evidence for the widespread presence of CFCs in the atmosphere which ultimately led to the realization that they were having an adverse effect on the Ozone layer.
55	Tectonic plates are the cracked solid crust or surface of the Earth that floats on the hot liquid magma that lies below. As the tectonic plates move around on the surface, the vibrations caused as they rub past each other are known as earthquakes, and where gaps open up between them volcanoes erupt. Movement is driven by the underlying temperature of the liquid magma and the strength of the currents that it generates.
56	Pantheism - (not Panentheism) - is a belief that the totality of nature and the physical universe is equivalent to God and some forms of Pantheism take a very similar view to the beliefs about primordial deities in ancient Greece – where the gods were themselves, literally, the stuff of the sea, the rocks, air, and the heavens. There are several ways in which Pantheist beliefs can be categorized and sadly I have found that the terminology has changed over the years, however all believe in an eternal substance – ie. none of them believe in pure creation.
57	"Richard III: The King in the Car Park" Darlow Smithson Productions MMXIII and Dazzler Media Ltd 2013 for Channel 4.
58	Dr. Ian Stevenson (1918 – 2007) Canadian born psychiatrist who worked as a professor at the University of Virginia for some 50 years. His international fame comes from his 40 years of research into reincarnation and his extensive travels around the world in that time.
	He believed that certain phobias and other types of mental illness could **not** be put down to heredity or environmental factors so he looked elsewhere. The evidence which he accumulated suggested that images, facts, memories and even some physical features such as birth marks could be transferred between lives.

59	Tom Schroder (b.1954) award winning investigative journalist on Washington Post covering such topics as the Gulf Oil Disaster, and the Hunt for Bin Laden. Pullitzer Prize 2010. His book, 'Old Souls' (1999) describes an expedition and follow-up investigations by Ian Stevenson.
60	The Nobel Prize in Chemistry 2009 was awarded to V.Ramakrishnan, T.A. Steitz, and Ada E. Yonath for determining the detailed structure and mechanism of the Ribosome.
61	A 1978 survey by Hornsby-Smith and Lee into the beliefs of Roman Catholics in England & Wales found that 27% believed in reincarnation. A succession of European surveys have shown that such beliefs are held by 25% in West Germany and 23% France (eg. Harding, Phillips, & Fogarty – 1986), reported by I.Stevenson in his book of European Cases. "A very private belief: Reincarnation in contemporary England". T.Walter, H.Waterhouse. (1999) Sociology of Religion. Archived from the original on 2005-06-27. Retrieved 2009-06-25. This survey was conducted among communities that did not belong to a religion which advocated reincarnation – finding that 20-25% of people did hold some belief in it, claiming that similar levels of belief were also held in USA.
62	*"20 cases Suggestive of Reincarnation"* I.Stevenson. University of Virginia Press (1974)
63	*"Old Souls"* T. Shroder. Simon & Schuster Paperbacks. (1999)
64	5 year old Suzanne Ghanem's case was also reported at the time in the Lebanese weekly journal 'Monday Morning' July 1977.
65	*"European Cases of the Reincarnation Type"* I.Stevenson. McFarland & Company (2003) This reported 22 European Children cases vs 668 elsewhere in the world (admittedly a much large area)
66	*"30 Most Convincing Cases of Reincarnation"* T.Hardo. Jaico Publishing House (2008)
67	Mrs Virginia Tighe of Puebulo Colorado described a previous life as 'Bridey Murphy' who lived in 19th Century Ireland. Her descriptions were remarkably detailed in terms of dates re: Bridey's birth/death, locations where she lived, names of family etc, yet she could not be traced in official records. There were rare problems with her testimony in that she described going to a church that was not constructed until after her supposed death. Researchers finally came to believe that she had learnt the details of the previous life from an Irish immigrant who in reality had lived across the road from Mrs Tighe in her childhood, one Bridie Murphy Corkell.

	Cryptomnesia suggests that various memories, whose origins may be lost, can be combined by a mind to formulate a new dreamlike identity during hypnosis.
68	This is the case of Carl Edon who was born in Middlesbrough, England on 29 December 1972. As early as age 2 or 3 he said "I crashed a plane through a window" and he began drawing planes and insignias. A few years later he made very specific claims about the type of plane in which he flew. *"European Cases of the Reincarnation Type"* I.Stevenson. McFarland & Company (2003)
69	Raymond Moody (b.1944) US medical doctor and psychologist. His book *'Life after Life'* was first published in 1975.
70	The Horizon Research Foundation – Near Death Experiences – download 22 June 2014.
71	Widely reported in the press, but as a sample – Mail Online – 19 Sept 2008. Studies co-ordinated by Dr.Sam Parnia of Southampton University and the Weill Cornell Medical Centre in New York.
	"AWARE-AWAreness during REsuscitation-a prospective study". S.Parnia, K.Spearpoint, G.de Vos, P.Fenwick, D.Goldberg, J.Yang, J.Zhu, K.Baker, H.Killingback (2014-12-01). Resuscitation.
72	*"Multiple Identities & False Memories: A Sociocognitive Perspective"* N.Spanos (1996) American Psychological Association
	Nicholas Peter Spanos (b.1942, d.1994) Canadian born. Professor of Psychology and Director of the Laboratory for Experimental Hypnosis at Carleton University. Across 30 years of research he concluded that Hypnosis wasn't an altered state of mind but a type of role play where suggested behaviour may or may not be taken up by a participant.
73	*"Across Time and Death: A Mother's Search for her Past Life Children"* Jenney Cockell Piatkus, 1994 (ISBN 0-671-88986-9) This was adapted into a TV movie by CBS, called "Yesterday's Children" (2000) where the character was Jenny Cole - American not British
74	The 'Biography Channel' ran a series of TV programmes called Psychic Investigators. In one episode which was later held out to be a 'gold standard' in such examples, psychic Nancy Weber claimed to have helped the New Jersey police solve the serial murders of Amie Hoffman and Dierdre O'Brien in 1982. James Koedatich was arrested in 1983 and later found guilty of murder. The two police detectives she worked with, Hughes and Moore, verified that Weber had given them information she could not have known.

75	"*An Experimental Test of Psychic Detection*" R.Wiseman, D.West, R.Stemman in *"Journal of the Society for Psychical Research"* 1996 Wikipedia also references further tests conducted at the University of Hertfordshire in 1997.
76	*"Improving Human Performance: What About Paraspychology?"* within *"The Hundredth Monkey and Other Paradigms of the Paranormal"* K.Frazier. Prometheus Books. pp. 149–161. ISBN 978-0-87975-655-0.
77	*"Examining psychokinesis: The interaction of human intention with random number generators--A meta-analysis"* H.Bösch, F.Steinkamp, E.Boller (July 2006). *Psychological Bulletin* **132** (4): 497–523.
78	"Consciousness: A very Short Introduction" - Susan Blackmore - 2005
79	"Consciousness Explained" - Daniel Dennett - 1991 (page 29)
80	"Philosophy and the Mirror of Nature" - Richard Rorty - 1980
81	*"Survey on physicians' religious beliefs shows majority faithful"* J.Easton 14 July 2005 U of C Chronicle Medical Center Public Affairs. (accessed:1-February-09) http://chronicle.uchicago.edu/050714/doctorsfaith--.shtml
82	There are many reported surveys conducted in the USA about the beliefs of scientists across different disciplines. Wikipedia references surveys conducted in 1914, 1933, 1997, and 2007 via reports in the magazines Science and Nature in 1997 eg - Nature 386, 435 - 436 (3 April 1997) Scientists are still keeping the faith, Edward J. Larson & Larry Witham – University of Georgia; and Science vs. Religion : What Scientists Really Think (2010)- Elaine Howard Ecklund, University at Buffalo, The State University of New York Although percentages vary slightly between surveys there is a broadly consistent pattern of $^1/_3$ Atheist, $^1/_3$ Agnostic, $^1/_3$ with a belief in some form of God.
83	The observation that the corpus callosum is the main connector between brain hemispheres was discovered by Roger Sperry who won the Nobel Prize for this work in 1981. "*Two brain halves, one perception: How communication between brain hemispheres determines individual's subjective experience.*" Max-Planck-Gesellschaft ScienceDaily. ScienceDaily, 1 September 2011. "*Interhemispheric Connections Shape Subjective Experience of Bistable Motion*" E. Genç, J. Bergmann, W. Singer, and A.Kohler. *Current Biology*, 2011.

84	When an unseen object is held in the right hand of CD individuals or people with severed corpus callosum connections (callosotomized), it will be recognized by the left hemisphere of the brain, and both groups can easily name that object verbally, because it is the left hemisphere that most often dominates verbal language.
	Yet, when an object is held in the left hand and thus recognized by the right hemisphere, callosotomized patients fail to verbally name the object because the missing corpus callosum prevents the right hemisphere from communicating with the left hemisphere. However, CD patients have no difficulties in naming an unseen object regardless of the hand holding it.
	"*Alternative pathways let right and left communicate in early split brains.*" Publicase Comunicação Científica. ScienceDaily, 12 May 2014.
	"*Structural and functional brain rewiring clarifies preserved interhemispheric transfer in humans born without the corpus callosum*" F.Tovar-Moll, M.Monteiro, J.Andrade, I.E.Bramati, R.Vianna-Barbosa, T.Marins, E.Rodrigues, N.Dantas, T.E.J.Behrens, R. de Oliveira-Souza, J.Moll, and R.Lent. Proceedings of the National Academy of Sciences (PNAS), May 12, 2014
85	"The brain... it makes you think. Doesn't it?"conversation between David Eagleman & Raymond Tallis The Guardian (29 April 2012) https://www.theguardian.com/science/2012/apr/29/neuroscience-david-eagleman-raymond-tallis
86	The theoretical physicist Sir Roger Penrose and the anaesthesiologist Stuart Hameroff collaborated in the 1990s to formulate what has become known as the Orch-OR model of consciousness, (Orchestrated Objective Reduction). In essence this argues that the brain partly works through Quantum Mechanical principles which do not require direct physical connections and which may utilise space to hold data.
	The theory remains credible in many respects by using observed effects but without explaining how they work. Inevitably it has been challenged by various people such as Litt, Eliasmith, Kroon, Weinstein and Thagard
	(in their 2006 article "Is the Brain a Quantum Computer") arguing that neurocomputation (essentially 'hard wiring') is sufficient to account for brain activity. The main debating ground seems to be that :
	• While the Quantum effects which Penrose and Hameroff have described may occur, people cannot see how they would last long enough to affect the physical neurons.
	• The chemicals which have been argued to be part of brain activity can indeed bind to physical channels and receptors in the brain but they do not always produce effects, (eg anesthesic chemicals not always generating anesthesia)

	- Some brain functions such as the process for bird flight is understood to operate on a purely neurochemical basis and does not require Quantum processes, however bird flight is not regarded as consciousness. (Bird navigation is different).
	- Some measurable electrical brain activity related to conscious perceptions seems to occur **after** subjects have responded to circumstances. People such as Dennett, Kinsbourne, Koch and Crick have therefore argued that we react unconsciously before we **then** form a conscious impression of what has happened, after the event. Quantum Entanglement can get around this problem/issue.
	Neurocomputation cannot explain how brain activity in non-linked parts of the brain can be synchronised (referred-to as Global Brain Gamma Synchrony EEGs).
	In addition to the roles described above, Stuart Hameroff and Roger Penrose have proposed that microtubules function in consciousness.
	[S.Hameroff, R.Penrose Physics of Life Reviews 2014, 11, 39-78]
87	*"The Emperor's New Mind: Concerning Computers, Minds and The Laws of Physics"* R.Penrose (1989) Oxford University Press. p. 480.
88	"The Soul Hypothesis" - Mark Baker and Stuart Goetz - 2011 A collection of writings by different authors into the possible scientific reality of the Soul.
89	Karl Pribham (b1919) is a Professor of psychology & psychiatry at Georgetown University. David Bohm (1917 – 1992) was a theoretical physicist. They promoted their ideas in the mid 1960s, based on the general notions that holograms could store information and the vehicles for this could lie in certain fibres and fields in the brain.
90	"The Soul Hypothesis" M.Baker, S,Goetz (2011) Continuum Books
	Mark C. Baker was Professor of Linguistics and Cognitive Science, Rutgers University NJ. Stewart Goetz was Professor of Philosophy at Ursinus College, Collegeville, PA
91	"Cartesian Linguistics" – Noam Chomsky 1966
92	"Speaking: from Intention to Articulation" - Willem Levelt 1989
93	A Chimpanzee call Lana was brought up in this way and taught to use a set of symbols in a basic artificial language known as Yerkish (after Robert Yerkes who developed it and also the Yerkes National Primate Centre in Atlanta USA, which worked with Georgia State University to produce the findings). The symbols representing the words (lexigrams) were mounded on boards with 3 panels containing up to 340 keys. Communication went both ways, from ape to researcher and vica versa.

94	Global Language Monitor – 1 January 2014 http://www.languagemonitor.com/number-of-words/number-of-words-in-the-english-language-1008879/ downloaded 4 Nov 2015
95	"New plant species gives insights into evolution" D.Torrent (17.3.2011) University of Florida. https://phys.org/news/2011-03-species-insights-evolution.html
96	An example is Olefactory genes in human beings, and among such non-functioning genes we have strong indications that, for instance, our ancestors may have has a far better sense of smell – on a par with most other animals.
97	A very good animation of how one type of virus self-assembles is shown at https://www.youtube.com/watch?v=Ofd_lgEymto&feature=related Made by P.Lieman, V.Kostyuchenko, and M.Rossman of Seyetllc It shows how a multitude of distinct particles come together a very intricate and precise series of steps to form 4 very different sections of one particular virus – Bacteriophage T4. This is also a multi-layered entity so it is very clear that chemical reactions mustn't happen as the reactants find something to react with. If done too early or too late things would be in the wrong place (eg outside instead of in), or forming completely the wrong thing.
98	The Radical Pair Mechanism was first proposed by a team at the University of California Irvine "A model for Photoreceptor-Based Magnetoreception in Birds" Ritz, Adem, and Schulten Biophysical Journal 78 (2000) 707
99	Professor Jim Al-Khalili, OBE – "Quantum Life: How physics can revolutionise biology " - Lecture to the Royal Institution, London 2013 http://richannel.org/jim-al-khalili--quantum-life-how-physics-can-revolutionise-biology Jameel Al-Khalili is Professor of Theoretical Physics and Chair in the Public Engagement in Science at the University of Surrey. British theoretical physicist, author & broadcaster. Born 1962 in Baghdad, Iraq.
100	The only company to have successfully produced spider silk from transgenic goats was Nexia Biotechnologies (which went bankrupt in 2009). It sold the product under the trade name of 'BioSteel' Since then research has continued under Randy Lewis of Utah State University which now operates a farm of over 30 goats. See *"MATERIALS SCIENCE: Mammalian Cells Spin a Spidery New Yarn"*. Service, R. F. (2002). Science *295 (5554): 419b–4421.* doi:10.1126/science.295.5554.419b. PMID 11799209. Also *"Bridges made of spider silk? You can thank goats for that."* Boatman, Liz. Berkeley Science Review. Retrieved 18 October 2012.

101	"Chemical Synthesis of Proteins" B.L.Nilsson, M.B.Soeller, R.T.Raines (Oct .2010) HHS Public Access https://www.ncbi.nlm.nih.gov/pmc/articles/PMC2845543/
102	"The ribosome as a missing link in the evolution of life" M.Root-Bernstein, R.Root-Bernstein (21 Feb 2015) Journal of Theoretical Biology vol.367, p130-158
103	"Minimal cue perception of the regard of others: The feeling of being stared at" L.Williams (1983) Journal of Parapsychology 47: 59–60.
104	Rupert Sheldrake, British biochemist & parapsychologist who published a controversial work in 2003 entitled 'The Sense of Being Stared At' in which he claimed that over thousands of trials, blindfold people would accurately report when they were being stared-at 60% of the time. In a later experiment with the BBC, an audience which didn't know about the tests being conducted, were videotaped during the performance and independent reviewers concluded that people did glance sideways more often when researchers at the back of the hall were scrutinising them.
105	"*A Book for Burning*" Editorial by J.Maddox Sept.1981
106	Steven Peter Russell Rose (b.1938) – emeritus professor of Biology and Neurobiology at Gresham College , London and the Open University. Aside from his challenges to Rupert Sheldrake, he has joined others in opposing the idea of 'sociobiology' – suggesting that human social behaviour has emerged from the processes of evolution.
107	http://www.open.edu/openlearn/whats-on/ou-on-the-bbc-blue-sky-staring *23rd February 2009*
108	https://psi-encyclopedia.spr.ac.uk/articles/sense-being-stared-experimental-evidence (updated 3 July 2017)
109	"The Sense of Being Stared At, and open peer commentary" R. Sheldrake (2005) *Journal of Consciousness Studies*
110	Daryl J. Bem (b.1938) Professor Emeritus Cornell University "Study suggests precognition may be possible" L.Edwards (18 November 2010) also Journal of Personality and Social Psychology
111	Other people who have followed Ian Stevenson's lead to investigate further cases of reincarnation include: Antonia Mills, Professor in First Nation studies at the University of Northern British Colombia, who has studied cases amongst the Inuit peoples and the Beaver Indians. Erlendur Haraldsson, Professor emeritus in Psychology at University of Iceland who has co-authored books investigating children claiming

	memories of past lives in Sri Lanka and contrasting them with paired children who did not claim such memories. His 2006 work "Popular psychology, belief in life after death and reincarnation in the Nordic countries, Western and Eastern Europe" provides many statistics. Satwant Pasricha, Head of Clinical Psychology, National Institute of Mental Health and Neurosciences at Bangalore. Has written a book on reincarnation, "Claims of Reincarnation: An Empirical Study of Cases in India" (1990) New Delhi: Harman Publishing House and whose work "Making sense of near-death experiences: A handbook for clinicians" S Pasricha; DJ Wilde; M Perera; K Jagadheesan (2011) was highly commended in the Psychiatry category of the 2012 British Medical Association Book Awards.
112	Paul Edwards editor-in-chief of the Encyclopedia of Philosophy was one of Stevenson's main critics from 1986. In a series of works he criticised Stevenson as having nothing to counterbalance the 'presumption against reincarnation', and cited a number of stats about Stevenson's cases that were firmly rebutted by other academics such as Robert Almeder – Professor emeritus of Philosophy at Georgia State University.
113	Journal of the American Medical Association (1975) Journal of Nervous and Mental Disease (1977)
114	Various studies by neuroscientists have strongly indicated that Out of Body Experiences have genuine effects in an area of the brain known as the hippocampus, which are recorded in MRI scans. The prominent articles that I have seen relate to tests conducted in Sweden by Dr.A.Guterstam of the Karolinska Institute the main report being published in the journal 'Current Biology' "Posterior Cingulate Cortex Integrates the Senses of Self-Location and Body Ownership" A.Guterstam, M.Bjornsdotter, G.Gentile, H.Ehrsson Current Biology vol.25 1 June 2015 https://www.sciencedirect.com/science/article/pii/S0960982215004121 Also preliminary news reports at : "Out-of-Body Experience Is Traced in the Brain" Live Science 30 April 2015 - https://www.livescience.com/50683-out-of-body-illusion.html "Brain scans reveal what happens during an out-of-body experience: Event causes 'place cells' to trigger a person's built-in GPS" Daily Mail (UK) 1 May 2015 - www.dailymail.co.uk/sciencetech/article-3064103
115	"Out-of-body experiences: Neuroscience or the paranormal?" Medical News Today 19 July 2017 https://www.medicalnewstoday.com/articles/318464.php

116	An example of a paramedic's report of an OBE can be found at http://www.emergencymedicalparamedic.com/out-of-body/
	Dr. Susan Blackmore has also written extensively on this and has many examples which can be found at: https://www.susanblackmore.co.uk/articles/near-death-experiences-in-or-out-of-the-body-2/#
117	In relation to the Motor Cortex, there has been a long-standing debate about whether this part of the brain operates on a 'one- for- one' basis between an area of the brain and a single muscle, or whether a single area of the brain controlled many muscles. The prime paper suggesting 'one-for-one' was made by Asanuma in 1975, (see below), but the encyclopaedias I have seen suggest that virtually all other papers have taken the opposite view, (both prior, and with 7+ papers since then up to 2008), also showing that different areas of the brain have overlapping control over muscles.
	"The Intelligent Movement Machine" M.Graziano (2008). Oxford University Press - also "Complex movements evoked by microstimulation of precentral cortex". M.Graziano, C.Taylor, T.Moore (2002). Neuron
	"Complex organization of human primary motor cortex: A high-resolution fMRI study". J.D.Meier, T.N Aflalo, S. Kastner, M.Graziano (2008) Neurophysiol.
	"Recent developments in the study of the columnar arrangement of neurons within the motor cortex". H.Asanuma (1975) Physiol. Rev. 55
	"Somatic motor and sensory representation in the cerebral cortex of man as studied by electrical stimulation". W.Penfield, E.Boldrey (1937) Brain. **60** (4): 389–443.
	"Experiments on the brain of monkeys - No. 1" D.Ferrier (1874). Proc. R. Soc. Lond. **23** (156–163): 409–430.
118	"Why would an animal lose its brain?" http://www.bbc.com/earth/story/20150424-animals-that-lost-their-brains
119	Jack Szostak (b.1952) Professor of Genetics at Harvard Medical School and became a Nobel Laureate in 2009. His work was instrumental in helping scientists to track and manipulate genes; techniques that greatly contributed to the Human Genome Project.
	He went on to demonstrate that some basic forms of RNA could replicate and evolve in the test tube and his team has pursued the origin of life and the dream of creating the first artificial forms of living cell.
	His joint paper with K.Adamala "Nonenzymatic Template-Directed RNA Synthesis Inside Model Protocells" *Science* 29 Nov 2013, describes how multi-layered fatty 'protocells' can divide allow their short RNA strands to continue replicating, with magnesium and citrate.

Index

315